THE STORY OF CHEMISTRY

Dr. William H. Nichols
A foremost pioneer of chemical industry in America

THE STORY
OF CHEMISTRY

By
FLOYD L. DARROW
Author of Through Science to God

"Science is the soul of prosperity of nations and
the living source of all progress."—PASTEUR

ILLUSTRATED

THE BOBBS-MERRILL COMPANY
Publishers : : : : Indianapolis

INTRODUCTION

The Story of Chemistry begins with the alchemist and moves forward through two centuries and more of scientific discovery until the accomplishments of to-day foreshadow the actual realization of the dreams of that mystic groper after the "unattainable." This narrative endeavors to sketch the historic background of the science and to trace its development from the discoveries of that brilliant group of pioneers of the modern era to the dominating position of chemistry in the industrial and political world of the twentieth century. This historic unfoldment has been adopted as the readiest and least difficult approach for the lay reader. Enough of the underlying principles and facts of chemical science have been set forth to enable one not familiar with the subject to understand past and present achievements. It will be noted that the emphasis is upon recent developments. Much that appears in the following pages has never before been assembled in popular book form. It has been gathered largely from the current literature of the most authoritative publications in the field of science. In particular is the story of the atom and its constitution brought down to date. The highly significant disclosures of such important gatherings as the 1926 Institute of Politics, at Williamstown, Massachusetts, and the International Conference on Bituminous Coal, held at the Carnegie Institute in the autumn of this same year, are here presented, it is hoped, in simple, understandable language. The chapter on American Progress in Chemistry should enable the citizen, not only to take just pride in the achievements of his country's chemists, but also to reach a more adequate appreciation of what chemistry means to the economic and political future of the nation. Especially should the reader ponder the rôle of research in the growth of industry and civilization. If this book carries one message more important than another, it is this need for fundamental research. Out of it will issue the material and to a large extent the spiritual progress of the decades and centuries to come.

The Story of Chemistry does not claim to be an encyclopedia of chemical information. Many phases of chemical industry have had to be omitted. It could not be otherwise. From the vast mass of material available as general and broad a treatment as possible has been made. The newer developments and applications of chemistry have been stressed. In these pages, we stand somewhere near the "firing line" of chemical investigation. Still, much that is comparatively recent is of necessity absent. However, if this very fact shall stimulate the reader to pursue further this fascinating field of inquiry, a chief purpose of the book will have been accomplished.

In the hope that *The Story of Chemistry* presents in thoroughly popular form the salient features of a science fundamental to the highest welfare of all nations both in peace and war, this book is offered to the public.

FLOYD L. DARROW

CONTENTS

CONTENTS—*Continued*

CONTENTS—*Continued*

CONTENTS—*Concluded*

LIST OF ILLUSTRATIONS

LIST OF ILLUSTRATIONS—*Concluded*

THE STORY OF CHEMISTRY

THE STORY OF CHEMISTRY

CHAPTER I

THE ALCHEMIST

CHEMIST HAS BECOME THE ALCHEMIST—PHILOSOPHER'S
STONE—KING AND PRINCE—PARACELSUS—ALCHEMIST'S LAB-
ORATORY—MYSTIC SYMBOLISM—APPARENT EVIDENCE OF AL-
CHEMY—INHERITANCE FROM ARISTOTLE—THREEFOLD NATURE
OF THE METALS—WHAT ALCHEMISTS ACCOMPLISHED—
ALCHEMY AND MEDICINE—DEATH OF ALCHEMY.

WHY do we begin a book on modern chemistry with
the alchemist? Did he not pass off the stage a century
and a half ago? What is there in any way modern about
this old mystic whose art was born of superstition, fos-
tered by fraud and imposture, and in the natural
sequence of events came to an inglorious end? Why
bother with a character as obsolete as the cave man and
as misguided as any one of a half-dozen types of modern
enthusiasts?

For the simple reason that the chemist has become
the alchemist. Is not chemistry to-day pursuing the
same will-o'-the-wisp that lured the alchemist on and on
for so many centuries? Did I say "will-o'-the-wisp"?
Yes, but we must now say it under our breath, for has not

Sir Ernest Rutherford been battering atoms to pieces for nearly a decade and thereby producing lighter elements from heavier ones? In principle the dream of the alchemist has already come true.

To be sure neither the claim of Dr. Adolph Miethe of Berlin nor that of Dr. H. Nagaoka of the Institute of Physical and Chemical Research, Tokio, to having changed mercury vapor into gold seems to have been substantiated by other workers. But suppose it has not been, before this book is off the press the achievement may be a commonplace of the current news. It already looms big on the scientific horizon. Theoretically, as we shall see, this transmutation is as simple as that two and two are four. It is bound to come. Still there is no cause for excitement. This planet will be vastly older and millenniums may come and go before the manufacture of gold will have reached the investment stage. The monetary systems of the world are in no danger of being undermined by an overabundance of the yellow metal.

But let us return to the alchemist. Superstitious, often dishonest, always mistaken though he was, without this blind groper after the hidden mysteries of energy and matter, modern chemistry would never have been born. I can see him now, working over his pots and retorts in crude laboratories and dark caves, shrouding in deepest mysticism his secret activities, his imagination often fired with a lofty zeal, exercising an almost infinite patience, as with the passionate purpose of a religious fanatic, he sought to find or make the Philosopher's Stone.

Yes, it was the Philosopher's Stone that this medieval mystic worshiped. And who would not? The fortunate possessor of this magic "Essence" might at once obtain those two highest goods,—health and wealth,—and, with its continued presence, elevation of character and spiritual refinement. Many a knave arose to lay claim to the mighty discovery.

One such rogue was one day giving a dinner to some friends. In the midst of it he related a personal incident which he said had occurred eight hundred years before. Noting the looks of incredulity and astonishment on the faces of his guests, he turned to his valet, saying, "John, is not that true?" Whereupon, John, faithful servant that he was, answered, "Master, you forget that I have been in your service but five hundred years."

Many of these alchemists were simply rascals, who had the sense to realize the futility of their quest, but utilized their ingenuity to dupe credulous kings and subjects, thereby separating them from their fortunes. We have them to-day in the persons of our glib-tongued oil stock promoters and gold mine experts. With the craftiness of the alchemist who fooled his victims by secreting a nugget of real gold in the crucible in which the "transmutation" was being effected, these modern gentry, upon whom the alchemistic mantle seems to have fallen, accomplish their purposes with equal facility. Possibly it is unfortunate that some of them can not meet the fate of the alchemists who failed their kings, for it is asserted that they were often hanged on a gibbet, gilded, in accordance with the grim humor of the times, with golden tinsel.

Every king and prince of the Middle Ages provided himself with an able alchemist. Even to this day one may see near Hardshin, the beautiful castle of Prague, a half-dozen small houses with their huge fireplaces, built by Emperor Rudolph II close to his own palace for the use of his "gold-cooks." Henry VI of England recommended to all noblemen, theologians and scholars the study of alchemy. A company upon whom he conferred the right to make gold produced a metal which had the appearance of gold and from which coins were stamped. It is related that the cautious Scotch were skeptical and that the Scotch Parliament passed a law forbidding entry of the English "gold" to their State. Lulli, an alchemist of the thirteenth century, is said to have changed fifty thousand pounds of base metal into the purest gold.

Paracelsus, who in the sixteenth century turned the course of alchemy from the making of gold to the preparation of medicines, has left this picture of the overworked alchemists of his day: "They diligently follow their labors, sweating whole days and nights by their furnaces. They do not spend their time abroad for recreation but take delight in their laboratory. They wear leather garments with a pouch, and an apron wherewith they wipe their hands. They put their fingers amongst coals, into clay and filth, not into gold rings. They are sooty and black like smiths and colliers and do not pride themselves upon clean and beautiful faces."

The "Father of Medical Chemistry" thus sketched the interior of an alchemist's laboratory: "A gloomy, dimly lighted place, full of strange vessels and furnaces, melting pots, spheres, and portions of skeletons hanging from the ceiling, the floor littered with stone bottles, alembics, great parchment books covered with hieroglyphics; the bellows with its motto, spira spera (breathe and hope); the hour glass, the astrolabe, and over all cobwebs, dust and ashes. The walls are covered with various aphorisms of the brotherhood, legends and memorials in many tongues.''

The dismal interior of the alchemist's workshop was a true reflection of his distraught brain. Unguided by fundamental principles and sound experimental facts, he cluttered his mental and physical environments with the ''chaff which the wind driveth away.''

But how this old mystic did labor! His experiments were fully as elaborate as are those of modern scientists. His methods of procedure fell into twelve groups: calcination, dissolution, separation, conjunction, putrefaction, congelation, cibation, sublimation, fermentation, exaltation, multiplication and projection. A false step at any point of the transformation meant complete defeat and the necessity of renewing the process from the beginning. But work, what was that to him? Simply dust in the balance as compared with the goal of his endeavors. Here, in spirit, was the forerunner of the modern research scientist.

In the interest of secrecy, the alchemist recorded his results in a mass of mystic symbols, usually meaningless and often nonsensical. For instance, Paracelsus gave utterance to the following: ''The life of metals is a secret fatness; . . . of salts, the spirit of aqua fortis; . . . of pearls, their splendor. . . . The life of all men is nothing else but an astral balsam, a balsamic impression, and a celestial invisible fire, an included air and a tinging spirit of salt.''

The magic power of the alchemist extended not only to the making of gold and the preparation of medicines. Albertus Magnus claimed command of the weather. Instantaneously, he was able to transform a winter's day into that of balmy spring or genial summer. To this he testified by many witnesses. His pupil, Thomas Aquinas, breathed the breath of life into a statue and then in desperation at the wisdom it displayed broke it in pieces. That was still in the day of miracles. Anything could happen. Nothing was impossible. Belief in the transmutation of the metals was a perfectly logical outcome of the philosophy of the time.

True, actual proof of success was never forthcoming. Still, in that day of easy credulity, the atmosphere was rife with marvelous tales of miraculous accomplishments. Some "unknown stranger" had provided a powder which exhibited the properties of the Philosopher's Stone. As evidence a nugget of gold would be produced. Even to-day in the museums of Europe, may be seen gold of the alchemists with detailed accounts of the methods of production. Belief in alchemy was a part of the religion of the time. Following is a quotation from an alchemical treatise:

Everybody must try to get two things, eternal bliss and earthly happiness: the former is granted by the Kingdom of God, which is taught by the theologian, while the latter is granted by the Philosopher's Stone of the alchemist.

Thoroughly imbued with the implicit faith in the ancient proverb, "As above, so below," the alchemist applied to the inorganic kingdom of the metallic ores the same laws of growth and decay which he observed in the organic world above. Animals and plants were seen to grow. Why should not the metals? Why should they

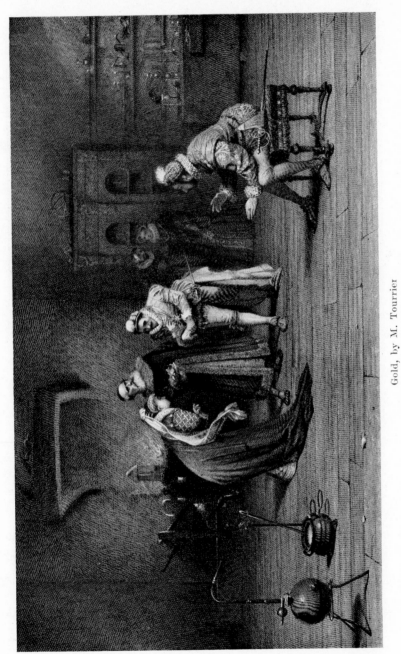

Gold, by M. Tourrier

The **alchemist** boldly defies his visitors to detect any lack of genuineness in the product of his transmutation

Antoine Laurent Lavoisier
(1743–1794)

Sir Humphry Davy
(1778–1829)

John Dalton
(1766–1844)

Sir Henry Cavendish
(1731–1810)

not constantly progress toward the perfect state of the noblest of them all,—gold? That they actually did, the alchemist believed.

But let none of us smile or frown. The chemist in this twentieth century of enlightenment takes much the same view. Somewhere in the cosmic crucibles of the celestial spaces, probably at innumerable points, he believes in an evolution of the elements from hydrogen, the simplest of them all, to uranium, the most complex. This has come, not as an outgrowth of religious mysticism, but as a result of the cold logic of the irresistible facts of scientific experiment. The alchemist sought the Philosopher's Stone. The modern chemist seeks the key whereby he may change another metal into gold or unlock for man's use the vast reservoirs of energy stored within the electronic systems of the atoms in infinite quantity. The alchemist groped in the dark. The chemist of to-day works in the sunlight of rapidly growing knowledge. Yes, it is surely true, the chemist is becoming the alchemist.

The alchemist found much in support of his great faith. Near Herrngrund, a little town in Hungary, is a spring of "water pure and clear." Into it the alchemist thrust an iron vessel. Upon withdrawing the vessel after several hours, he found that it had apparently changed into copper. His methods of analysis could not tell him that the "water pure and clear" contained copper in solution, and he did not know that iron, a more active but less "noble" metal, will deposit copper from its solutions. To his simple understanding, iron had actually been transmuted into copper.

And again, did not the alchemist actually find gold

and silver in lead ore? Had he not heard time and again of worked-out mines which, after long periods, exhibited new "crops" of these precious metals? Crude lead when heated in an open crucible of bone slowly changed to a powder, leaving a button of silver. What is more natural than to suppose that lead is transmuted into the nobler metals? Would it not take more scientific keenness than the average individual of to-day possesses to detect the fallacy?

Iron rusted, and a new substance formed. Mercury falling in rain upon melted sulfur was transformed into a black substance which, when heated, yielded a beautiful red solid. Copper and mercury combined to form what seemed to be a new metal having the appearance of gold. Bronze had been known for centuries. In an age of superstition and complete ignorance of the fundamental principles of chemical action, does it seem at all surprising that the alchemist should have had implicit faith in the possibility of making gold?

Was not this transmutation, too, in strict accord with the philosophy of matter inherited from Aristotle? This versatile Greek had taught the existence of a "primordial matter," a fundamental substance from which all other substances were formed. And Aristotle ruled the world of science. When this original matter became associated with the properties *cold* and *wet,* water was the product. The properties *warm* and *wet* gave the element air. The element earth was derived from the properties *cold* and *dry,* while the fourth element, fire, originated in the properties *warm* and *dry.* Simplicity itself was this system. The four elements were only modifications of the primordial matter. To transmute one into another, it was only necessary to change the properties. Alchemy was the logical outcome.

In time, however, Aristotle's system became greatly modified, just as scientific theories now are in a state of perpetual flux. The meaning of each element was broadened to include many substances. *Fire* embraced all forms of light; *air,* smoke, steam and gases; *water,* all liquids and later acids; while *earth* came to mean all solids. But why should we smile upon such an imperfect state of chemical knowledge? It was not until a century and a half ago that this view of the elements was disproved. To-day, we are at best only kindergarteners in our understanding of the ultimate realities of energy and matter.

The mysticism of the alchemist is revealed in his conception of a threefold nature of the metals. These three aspects corresponded to body, soul and spirit of man. Symbolic of them were: Principles, peculiar to each substance; Elements, characteristic of many substances; and the Essence, common to all. Three principles were recognized,—Sulfur, Mercury and Salt. All substances were produced from the four elements through the mediation of the three principles. The essence was the common spirit which must be obtained in order to effect transmutation. The metals possessed this spirit in largest quantity, and gold, the noblest of them all, was thought to be nearly pure essence. Still it was so masked as to be almost impossible of separation. To change a baser metal into gold, it was necessary to purge away its body, the dross, by many processes of purification. A very small quantity of the Philosopher's Stone made unnecessary these laborious processes and magic-like instantaneously changed all matter into finer gold than that of the mines.

What did belief in this system of Nature accomplish? Much. These alchemists were prodigious workers. Their faith was that of fanaticism, their goal the redemption of mankind from pain and drudgery. We are talking now about the real alchemists, not the impostors. They had inherited from the ancients an empirical, that is an experimental, rule-of-thumb knowledge of certain chemical processes. The metallurgy of the common ores had become a highly perfected art. The "bronze age" had written a knowledge of simple alloys into the imperishable record of man's progress. The working of glass and its artificial coloring give glimpses of the high degree of skill attained by early workers and passed on, in part at least, to their successors. The preparation of soaps, dyes and pigments, many medicines, oils and perfumes dates from prehistoric times. A knowledge of fermentation, a fundamental process of the alchemist, was one of the earliest possessions.

The alchemist did not add much to this inherited knowledge. He made little progress in explaining the processes which he used. He still pottered around in the same old way, in the midst of ashes, soot and cobwebs. Through a mellow haze of fact and fancy, we see him to-day, silhouetted against the background of his time, the most picturesque figure of an age of mingled romance and distressful reality. Though scientist he was not, in one important respect he carried the world a long way forward. He turned the current of pseudo-scientific thinking away from pure speculation and gave a tremendous impulse to the actual working with substances.

The deductive philosophy of Aristotle in part gave way to the methods of experimental investigation. This work, too, brought to the alchemist a high degree of skill in manipulation and a superficial knowledge of fundamental chemical processes. Without this heritage, born of superstition and much labor, the beginnings of modern chemistry might even yet be in the future.

With the coming of Paracelsus, curious mixture of medieval mystic and modern scientist, alchemy took a new bent. The preparation of medicines and the curing of disease became its goals. The Philosopher's Stone was sought with no less zeal than formerly, for its possession would confer upon mankind the priceless boon of health, but the transmutation of the baser metals into gold was crowded somewhat into the background. The apothecary shops of Europe now became veritable research laboratories, in which, under the stimulus of preparing new medicines, many important discoveries were made. That was the heroic age of medical progress. Many was the poor victim who sacrificed his life, a martyr to the cause of science, because some alchemist in his eagerness to try out a new remedy dosed his patient with a deadly poison. Indeed, the poisonous properties of many drugs were discovered in this way. First aid to the afflicted in those times often meant death.

Gradually alchemy was swept away by the irresistible tide of new knowledge, left as a relic stranded upon the sands of time, only to be rescued a century and a half later by the hand of the modern scientist. For, though the incentive is vastly different, the goal of him who to-day seeks to compass the inmost secrets of energy and matter has much in common with that of the alchemist.

So hats off to this crude embryo scientist of the yester-centuries! Without his coming, much of our boasted progress would still be but a mirage above the shimmering sands of desert speculations

But before we leave him, we must pause to shed a tear over his bier. Among the scientific men of England, alchemy came to an end with a tragedy. It happened in this way. James Price, a Fellow of the Royal Society and an amateur chemist of some note, deluded himself into thinking that he had succeeded in preparing a powder capable of converting any of the baser metals into gold. Because of his high standing among men of science, the discussion provoked by Mr. Price's announcement of his discovery made it necessary for him at once to demonstrate the truth of his claim. Accordingly, in the presence of a select group of men of rank, this man who had thus precipitately brought himself into the spot-light of the scientific world undertook a series of experiments. These were seven in number, covering a period of nearly three weeks in the spring of 1782, and in all of them Mr. Price seemed to produce gold and silver. King George III was pleased to receive a sample of the gold so made. Price was the recipient of a degree from the University of Oxford, and his wonderful achievement became the topic of the hour. But many were skeptical, and so furious became the controversy which followed that the Royal Society felt itself in honor called upon to ask Price to prove to his associates that he could really make gold.

In vain did Price plead that the cost of making gold by his method rendered it prohibitive; that the expense for making a single ounce of gold would be seventeen pounds sterling. Excuse, however, availed him nothing. Price was told by Sir Joseph Banks, president of the Royal Society, that his own honor as well as that of the Society was involved. At length Price consented to make the test. Preparatory to doing so, he asked permission to repair to his laboratory at Guildford for a few days. Six months passed, during which public sentiment had turned strongly against him, before he invited the members of the Society to meet him. Only three accepted the invitation. Price expressed keen regret that so few had come, but apparently prepared for the test. When the time arrived, he stepped quickly to one side, raised a flask of laurel-water to his lips, bowed to his friends and swallowed the contents. A distressing change immediately swept over the man, and in a few moments he was dead. With the laurel water had been mixed a violent poison.

No one has ever been able to say whether Price actually believed he had discovered the secret of the ages. In any case, it sounded the death knell of alchemy.

And now with the historic background of chemistry thus sketched, we shall turn to other fields.

CHAPTER II

AFTER THE ALCHEMIST

DAWN OF A NEW DAY—COMBUSTION—PHLOGISTON THEORY—
LAVOISIER—SOME FOUNDERS OF THE SCIENCE—DISCOVERY OF
OXYGEN—LAW OF DEFINITE PROPORTIONS—SIR HUMPHREY
DAVY—ATOMS AND MOLECULES—ATOMIC THEORY—ATOMIC
WEIGHTS—WÖHLER AND LIEBIG—ANALYZING THE STARS—
SPECTROSCOPE—PRINCIPLES OF SPECTROSCOPIC ANALYSIS—DIS-
COVERY OF ANILINE COLORS—KEKULÉ AND BENZENE RING—
PASTEUR AND POLARIZED LIGHT—VAN'T HOFF AND MOLECULAR
ARCHITECTURE—ELECTRICITY AND CHEMICAL ACTION—DIS-
COVERIES OF FARADAY—THEORY OF ELECTROLYTIC DISSOCIA-
TION—ARRHENIUS—EVIDENCE FOR THEORY—EXPLANATION OF
ACIDS, BASES AND SALTS—IONS AND HUMAN BODY—STORAGE
BATTERY—OSTWALD—FISCHER AND GIBBS

AFTER the alchemist came the dawn of a new day.
Yes, and it was a glorious dawn. How I envy the early
workers in that bright morning of chemical discovery!
Slowly, painfully, blunderingly had the infant science
of chemistry emerged into the sunlight of modern
triumphs. After the dark night of medieval ignorance
and superstition, the golden age of science seemed at
hand. Innumerable secrets were ready to yield their
meanings. New paths opened on every side. Vast
realms of unexplored truth beckoned the investigator.
Untrod fields stretched away beyond the farthest vision
of the boldest dreamer.

Passing through the chrysalis stage, the alchemistic caterpillar assumed the wings of the chemical butterfly and flew away to a new world of light and freedom. Such alchemists as Geber the Arabian, Basil Valentine, Albertus Magnus, Roger Bacon, Raymond Lully, Thomas Aquinas and many more had become but dim, silent figures moving through the mists of an age that had gone forever. A new spirit was abroad in the land, as fresh and invigorating as the breath of mountain air. The newly discovered force of galvanism, or voltaic electricity, had taken the popular imagination by storm and other wonders were eagerly anticipated. Such was the atmosphere in which the Sir Launfal of modern chemistry girded on his armor and rode forth in search of the secret meanings of energy and matter.

Still, alchemy did not vanish in a moment. One damaging legacy lingered on for many years to becloud the thinking even of the most brilliant of the early workers. It was the famous *Phlogiston Theory* of combustion.

COMBUSTION

The mastery of fire marked the first great turning-point in the evolution of the race. But fire had always remained a deep and impenetrable mystery. Everybody used it, primitive peoples worshiped it, but no one was able to explain it. And yet combustion is the most fundamental of chemical processes. No real progress was possible until it was understood. John Mayow, an English scientist who died in 1679, came very close to unraveling the mystery. He clearly recognized in the air a substance which causes burning, unites with metals and changes venous to arterial blood. Although he anticipated the discovery of oxygen by a hundred years, he did not solve the problem.

Explanation of some sort the mind will always have. Determined to provide one, Georg Ernst Stahl, physician to the King of Prussia, put forth the idea that all combustible substances, that is, substances which will burn, possess a common principle, which escapes during the burning process. This imaginary substance, as intangible as the scientist's ether and as elusive as the Philosopher's Stone, he called *phlogiston*. Every one had observed that some substances like coal almost entirely burn up. These were nearly pure phlogiston. It was perfectly clear that something escaped in the burning process. How else could fire nearly annihilate such a host of substances? True, many metals when heated in the air lost their luster and actually increased in weight. This, it was believed, was due to the escape of phlogiston, for, when heated again with charcoal, nearly pure phlogiston, the product was restored to its metallic state. It was well known, too, that air is necessary as a supporter of combustion. But these ingenious theorists asserted that there must be something to absorb the phlogiston. Again, they knew that a lighted candle, placed under a bell jar, is soon extinguished. Yet that was easily explained. The candle went out because the air under the bell jar had become saturated with phlogiston.

Although a false one, this was the first general principle put forth in the history of chemistry. It was an honest attempt to explain things as they are, and it did seem to explain a large number of facts. Somewhere there should be a monument to the memory of Stahl, for, though alchemistic still, he headed the young science in the right direction.

But this beautiful theory ran against a snag. It could not explain satisfactorily why a metal, when heated in the air, should gain in weight. In vain, it was asserted that this hypothetical phlogiston possessed the property of *levity,* or negative weight, and therefore with the loss of its buoyant effect a body should weigh more. The ashes from coal did not weigh more.

Still, the world did not have long to wait for the coming of the man who could make facts and theory agree. He was Lavoisier, brilliant French scientist who lost his head in the Revolution because its leaders had "no need for chemists." Joseph Priestley's discovery of oxygen in 1774 gave him the key to the solution of the problem. He repeated Priestley's experiments and learned first-hand how brilliantly substances burn in this new gas, called "dephlogisticated air." In a series of epoch-making experiments, he proved that it is this newly discovered substance which supports combustion and causes metals heated in the air to increase in weight. One of his classic experiments had to do with tin, an easily oxidized metal. In a sealed glass vessel, he heated a quantity of tin for a considerable period, thus changing a portion of the metal to oxide. He weighed the vessel both before and after the change, and found it to be the same in each case. Then, he opened the vessel, and, as he did so, he heard an inward rush of air. This showed him that the tin had united with something in the air originally contained inside the vessel. The vessel, then, weighed more than before, and Lavoisier showed that this increase was exactly equal to the increase in the weight of the tin itself. Air from which he had removed the newly found gas, named by him *oxygen,* would no longer support combustion. The phlogiston theory had received its death blow. Although its devotees, and they were many, clung to it for nearly or quite half a century, it could not survive the light of the new knowledge.

Before we leave this Frenchman, let us note that, balance in hand, he proved that in the economy of this universe nothing is lost,—all is saved. In any chemical change, the substances taking part in the change are exactly equal in weight to the products formed. This generalization is known as the *Law of the Conservation of Matter.* To Lavoisier we owe the establishment of the first two fundamental principles in the development of chemical fact and theory.

SOME FOUNDERS OF THE SCIENCE

But we are ahead of the story. We have jumped right over a number of the most important of those early workers who blazed the trails leading from alchemy to chemistry. Let us go back to Robert Boyle, seventh son of the Earl of Cork. All of you who once studied Boyle's Law of Gas Pressures in high school physics are already acquainted with this nobleman of science. First among eminent investigators of Nature to break away from the fetters of alchemy, he may rightly be called the "Father of Modern Chemistry." To him we owe the first scientific conceptions of elements and compounds. He recognized that certain substances seem to be elementary, that is, they can not be changed into simpler forms, and that, when two or more of them combine, compound substances result. He fixed the meaning of the expression *chemical reaction,* a chemical change such as burning or fermentation, and was the first to make use of the term *analysis* as we understand it to-day. A hundred years before the time of Lavoisier, he urged that chemistry should be studied for its own sake.

Up in Scotland, at the Universities of Glasgow and Edinburgh, lived Joseph Black, who in a long life devoted to quiet research advanced the cause of chemistry to an exceptional degree. His classic work on the gas carbon dioxide, which he called "fixed air," did much to overthrow the phlogiston theory. Prepared by his own discoveries, unlike many of his contemporaries, he readily accepted Lavoisier's explanation of combustion as soon as it was announced.

Of all the picturesque figures in that transition period from alchemy to modern chemistry, none was more eccentric than that crabbed old bachelor and gifted recluse, Sir Henry Cavendish, who loved truth for truth's sake more passionately than any other scientist of his time. His thirst for knowledge was never satisfied, but it was always a selfish thirst. He did not even want the public to know of his discoveries. He cared not a fig for their practical value, and their theoretical interest was a private matter. Invited to a banquet in recognition of some of his work, he precipitately fled when he learned that he was to be the guest of honor. One of the wealthiest men in England, money had no attractions for this man who had dedicated his life to science. Throughout his life, he lived with the severest simplicity. Even in the hour of death, he wished to be alone and savagely ordered his servant to leave him and not to return until the end had come.

Judged even by the high standards of to-day, a remarkably accurate investigator was this scientific discoverer of great wealth and few friends. In 1766, he discovered the elementary gas *hydrogen*, an element which has proved to be of vast significance both for practical and theoretical chemistry. Discovering that the new gas, which he called "inflammable air," burned with intense heat to form water, he was led to determine the composition of water with great accuracy. No longer could the old alchemistic notion that water is an element be maintained. And this old curmudgeon laid the ghost of another of Aristotle's elements in his marvelously accurate analysis of air, showing it to be a mixture of several elements and not a single substance. He came remarkably close to anticipating by a century Sir William Ramsey's discovery of the rare gases of the atmosphere. Still, although Cavendish did not die until 1810, he stubbornly refused to recognize the validity of the mass of evidence in support of Lavoisier's theory of combustion and remained to the end of his days a staunch phlogistonist.

Now the scene shifts to Sweden. We are in a little apothecary shop of Gothenburg. Before us we see an original investigator in whose eyes shines the light of new knowledge and whose mind is fired with the genius of discovery. Beset with poverty, afflicted with ill-health, snatching from the necessity of making a living precious hours for experimental research, Karl Wilhelm Scheele, who died at the early age of forty-three, enriched the growing science of chemistry with a wealth of important discoveries. Independently of Priestley and at least two years earlier, he discovered oxygen, preparing it in a variety of ways, but unfortunately failed to publish his results until a later date. He prepared chlorine and was acquainted with its bleaching and poisonous properties. He experimented with the compounds of tungsten and molybdenum, metals of vast importance in the manufacture of steel, and the former constituting the ideal material for the filament of the incandescent lamp. He worked with many important gases, divising, himself, the apparatus for his experiments. He became the first master of qualitative analysis and was the founder of organic chemistry. Although familiar with oxygen and its properties, he failed to recognize the relation of this gas to the process of combustion, clinging to the phlogiston theory to the end. The following extract from one of his letters expresses the keynote of his life, *"It is the truth alone that we desire to know, and, oh, what joy there is in discovering it!"*

I think I hear some of you asking, "Why in a book whose chief purpose is to set forth the progress of modern chemistry do we need to spend time with men who lived and worked a century and more ago?" For the simple reason that we can not interpret the present without understanding the past. Present accomplishments strike their roots deep into the subsoil of earlier discoveries. Recent triumphs must be viewed against the historic background of fact and theory out of which they grew, just as they in turn will become the stepping stones to future achievement.

We have already mentioned Priestley, who in his turbulent threescore years and ten mixed theology, politics and science in the queerest fashion. To escape persecution in his own country, this English clergyman fled to

America. His last resting place is in the beautiful ceme-
tery at Northumberland, Pennsylvania, and it was there
at the commemoration of the centennial of his discovery
of oxygen in the summer of 1874 that the idea of the
American Chemical Society took root and two years later
flowered into an organization which to-day is the largest
and strongest of its kind in the world. In Dickinson
College, we may even now see much of his original
apparatus, a large part of which was fashioned with his
own hands. It is interesting to know that, though his life
was often a stormy one, Priestley was a man of means,
leaving at his death a substantial fortune. We shall
always remember him as an independent discoverer of
oxygen and the first to make its properties known to the
world. The invigorating effects of inhaling pure oxygen,
discovered by personal tests and by placing mice in an
atmosphere of the gas, were investigations of great
moment in their time. Without the researches of Priestley, Lavoisier's brilliant explanation of combustion
would have been long deferred. And yet Priestley could
not see the light. He remained a phlogistonist to the
last.

Now we turn to two Frenchmen, Louis Berthollet and
Joseph Proust. In the early years of the last century, a
heated contest was waged between these men. This controversy resulted in the establishment of the fundamental Law of Definite Proportions. That law spells the
difference between a haphazard world of utter chaos and
one of dependable stability. Berthollet contended that
when elements unite to form compounds they may do so
in any number of proportions. For instance, water may
be the result of the combination of hydrogen and oxygen

in all sorts of ways. In any given chemical change the
chemist could never be certain in advance of just what
would be produced. A chemical edifice reared upon such
a base would have been in sorrier plight than the house
placed upon the proverbial foundation of sand.
Proust attacked this position, not with logic but with a
series of the most brilliant experiments in the early history of chemistry. He showed that carbonate of copper
from whatever source, whether artificially prepared or
obtained from mineral sources, always contains the same
elements in the same invariable proportions by weight.
Furthermore, he proved that, when two elements, such as
iron and sulfur, unite to form more than one compound,
any given amount of one will always unite with varying
amounts of the other which are definite multiples of each
other. Let me illustrate. In one compound of iron and
sulfur, fifty-six grams of iron unite with thirty-two grams
of sulfur, while in another compound fifty-six grams of
iron unite with sixty-four grams of sulfur. The amount
of iron in each case is the same, but the amount of sulfur
in the second compound is just twice as great as it is in
the first. Although Proust did not formulate it, here was
another law, the Law of Multiple Proportions, which was
of vast significance in shaping chemical theory.

Let me give another illustration of the Law of Definite
Proportions. Suppose we take water obtained from all
sorts of sources. I have driven it from the mineral gyp-
sum, crystallized in combination with other elements in
the earth's crust many thousands of years ago. It may
be prepared from the burning of hydrogen and oxygen.
We may distil it from artesian water coming from great
depths or from sea water. We may catch it as it de-

scends in rain from the clouds. But from whatever source water may come, the chemist always finds it to be a combination of the elements hydrogen and oxygen in the same unalterable proportions by weight. Here was the rock upon which modern chemistry built its structure. In establishing it, the youthful science had traveled a long way from the mystic gropings of alchemy.

We must not forget Sir Humphry Davy, youthful pioneer in many fields. I can see him now in the laboratory of the Royal Institution in London. He is bending over a platinum disk from which two wires lead to a battery of electric cells. Upon the disk rests a small quantity of whitish powder. Presently, he begins to dance about the room like a madman. He has seen shining globules of molten metal appear upon the disk. From sheer joy, the supreme joy of discovery, he is unable to complete the experiment and leaves it to his assistant. A new element, potassium, takes its place in the limited number then known. Davy quickly follows this event with the discovery of five more,—glory enough for half a dozen lifetimes. And this is the first chemical discovery to be made with the electric current.

Going back a few years, we see Davy, as head of the Pneumatic Institute at Bristol, discover the anesthetic properties of nitrous oxide, or laughing gas. Later in the Royal Institution, assisted by his pupil, the immortal Faraday, he does the pioneer work on the liquefaction of gases. He experiments with the poisonous gas *chlorine* and shows it to be an element and not a compound. In agricultural chemistry we find him the first investigator before Liebig. Many-sided genius of the heyday of initial triumphs, how he would glory in the host of elec-

Justus Von Liebig
(1803–1873)

Robert Wilhelm Bunsen
(1811–1899)

Jöns Jakob Berzelius
(1779–1848)

Michael Faraday
(1791–1867)

Courtesy, Scientific American

Electronic orbits within the atom of mercury

Mercury possesses 80 negative electrons revolving about the positive nucleus. (Discussed in following chapter)

trochemical industries established about the brow of Niagara, industries in which his own researches blazed the way!

ATOMS AND MOLECULES

Possibly some of you have been wondering why nothing has yet been said about *atoms*. Well, up to this point no one had bothered himself very much about these imaginary entities. I presume people spoke of "smashing things to atoms," but this was only a figurative expression. True, Democritus, a speculative Greek, more than two thousand years ago had invented a theory of atoms surprisingly similar to the present view. But it was based upon no experimental facts. A host of scientists of the Greek type would never have put a foundation under the creative imagining of Democritus.

In the first decade of the last century, along came John Dalton, Quaker schoolmaster of Manchester, however, and the world of the unseen has "looked" different ever since. With him atoms took their rightful place of vast significance in the chemical edifice. This significance has grown with every decade. To-day, as we shall see, the atom and the subatomic worlds within it seem to afford the key to the ultimate unfolding of many ages-old secrets of the universe.

For nearly a century, atoms and the molecules which they build were supposed to be the ultimate units of matter. They proved to be only stepping stones to glimpses of subordinate miniature worlds of bewildering complexity and apparently marvelous perfection. But of these worlds, more later.

For some time it was uncertain whether Dalton's

name would be associated in posterity with the theory of atoms which he formulated or with the phenomenon of color-blindness, with which he was afflicted and which his investigations did so much to clarify that this eye defect has been known as *Daltonism* ever since. But this uncertainty vanished long ago. Dalton's monumental work consisted in his experiments with gases and the conclusions which his genius prompted him to draw from those experiments. Before Dalton, no one had thought it interesting or important to do much work in the percentage analysis of gases. We call this work quantitative analysis now. Let it be emphasized, too, that Dalton's investigations were carried on as a matter of pure research. That is, he had no idea that any results of theoretical or practical value would come from them. This is the kind of research, however, which from the beginning of time has proved to be the most practical of all. Without such research, world progress ceases and civilization stagnates. All of those early workers were pure researchers. The hosts of applied developments and the mass production of to-day are based upon their discoveries. Let us not forget the debt we owe to them.

Dalton experimented with a number of different groups of gases. In the first were two compounds of hydrogen and carbon known as ethylene and methane. His analysis showed him that the latter of these compounds always contained just twice as much hydrogen combined with any given quantity of carbon as the former did. That is, ethylene was found to contain two grams of hydrogen united with twelve grams of carbon, while four grams of hydrogen combined with twelve grams of carbon in the case of methane. When he turned to the gases carbon monoxide and carbon dioxide, he found a similar situation. In the former, sixteen grams of oxygen combined with twelve grams of carbon, and in the latter, thirty-two grams of oxygen with twelve grams of carbon. He found similar relationships existing among the oxides of sulfur and those of nitrogen respectively. That is, in any group, if a given amount of one of the two combining elements is considered, the varying amounts of the other which combine with that fixed amount are in the ratio of small whole numbers to each other. Here was the Law of Multiple Proportions, foreshadowed by Proust and now definitely established by Dalton. Upon it, Dalton proceeded to establish his theory of atoms.

This now famous theory may be stated substantially as follows: *"Elements are made up of smallest particles called atoms, and chemical compounds of the elements are formed by the union of these atoms in simple numerical proportions."* It seemed perfectly clear to Dalton and to several generations of his successors that, if we were to divide and to subdivide a piece of iron, for example, and to continue to do so, we should eventually reach a point where physical division could go no further. We should have produced multitudes of tiny pellets, probably spherical, and utterly beyond the reach of the most powerful microscope. These were the atoms. The atoms of one element differed in properties, such as color, density and weight, from those of every other element. When the elements united to form compounds, it was the atoms which combined. Let us illustrate with ethylene and methane. In the former, two atoms of carbon united with four atoms of hydrogen to form a molecule, while in the latter, one atom of carbon united with four atoms of hydrogen. In some instances, several atoms of one element might unite with several atoms of another to form molecules. More than two elements might also combine to form molecules of compounds through the union of their respective atoms.

Such a theory fitted the facts as Dalton found them, precisely. With it he could explain the experimental facts of his analyses and his Law of Multiple Proportions. Likewise, it was seen that, if these atoms never vary in weight or in any other respect, their existence and powers of combination afforded a simple explanation of the Law of Definite Proportions, which states that the composition of a chemical compound never varies. Here was a generalization of more significance to practical and theoretical chemistry than the explanation of combustion. As put forth by Dalton, however, this view of the atoms was only an hypothesis. It was to require an immense amount of experimental research from many workers before it could rise to the status of an accepted explanation of the facts of Nature. But it has long since received that support. For nearly or quite a century it has constituted a bulwark of theoretical and applied chemistry. Despite the flood tide of new knowledge regarding the atom, of which we shall learn in the next chapter, so far as chemical combination is concerned, the Atomic Theory of John Dalton remains to this day the working guide of the practical chemist. Of the existence of atoms, there can be no shadow of doubt. They are the ultimate units of chemical reaction. That they enter into chemical union to form compounds in simple numerical relations, has been established by a wealth of evidence.

Something has been said about *molecules*. What are they? Suppose we consider the chemical compound known as sodium chloride, or common salt. If we were to continue the division of a grain of salt into constantly smaller and smaller particles, going far beyond the range of the microscope, we should eventually reach a point beyond which we could not go without, through chemical means, breaking up these tiny particles into atoms of their constituent elements, sodium and chlorine. These smallest particles, which will still retain the properties of salt and beyond which division can not go without chemical decomposition, are molecules. And so we might illustrate with other compounds. The smallest droplet of water which can exist and still be water is a molecule. If we break down the molecule, we obtain two atoms of hydrogen and one atom of oxygen. The droplets which paint the rainbow and those which make the vastness of the sea are composed of innumerable trillions of inconceivably small molecules of hydrogen and oxygen. In general, we may say that molecules are the building blocks from which chemical compounds are constructed. Vibrating, combining, dissolving,—these molecules may lie in the soil or speed through the atmosphere to-day and to-morrow blossom in the rose. Every object, both animate and inanimate, is but an aggregation of these universal units.

How large are these molecules? We are told that a cubic inch of any gas at normal temperature and pressure will contain four hundred and forty-one quintillion of these physical units and still leave oceans and oceans of space for billions and billions more to be packed between them. F. W. Aston, an eminent English scientist, says that, if an ordinary evacuated electric light bulb were to be pierced with an opening such that one million molecules of air could enter per second, it would require a hundred million years to fill the bulb. The molecules in the smallest drop of water, if enlarged to the size of average grains of sand, would form a roadway from New York to San Francisco one-half mile wide and one foot thick. A billion billion could rest comfortably on the point of a pin. It is asserted that, if a tumbler of water were mixed with all the water in the "seven seas" and refilled from the mixture, it would contain two thousand of the original molecules. Suppose the temperature about our planet were suddenly to fall to two hundred degrees below zero on the Centigrade scale. The atmosphere, which extends outward to a distance of possibly fifty miles, would form an ocean of liquid air covering the earth to a depth of only thirty-five feet. And even the molecules in liquid air do not touch.

Sugar dissolves in water, which simply means that the molecules of sugar find their way with perfect ease between the huge spaces which separate the molecules of water from one another. Gold dissolves in liquid mercury. If we could look within the densest solid, we should see billions and billions of these infinitesimal units moving with tremendous velocities in hit-and-miss fashion, forever colliding, rebounding, jostling in a mad phantasmagoric dance of perpetual motion.

We may beat a piece of gold into a leaf but one four-hundred-thousandth of an inch in thickness, and still the gold leaf will contain many layers of molecules. A soap bubble may be blown to a thickness of one three-millionths of an inch, but even here it is estimated that the molecules lie, tier on tier, twenty or thirty deep. A film of oil spreads on the surface of water to the exceedingly minute thinness of a fifty-millionth of an inch, but still the scientist tells us that we have a double layer of molecules. When we stop to reflect that the thickness of this film comprises the diameters of two molecules together with the much larger space between them, we can begin to understand how past all comprehension is the smallness of a molecule.

One who has passed time in a chemical laboratory knows how a tiny bubble of chlorine gas will scent every particle of air in a large room. The trillions and trillions of molecules which it pours forth must find their way to the remotest portions of the confined space. The molecules in a single grain of indigo will distinctly dye a ton of water, and a grain of musk will scent a room for years.

Is the scientist who thus talks in such a matter-of-fact way about physical units which he has never seen and may never hope to see merely a visionary enthusiast? Is there any real basis for such seemingly incredible statements? No one would presume to call Millikan a visionary, and yet listen as he states that "we can now count the exact number of molecules in any given volume or in any known weight of any homogeneous substance with even more certainty than we can count the population of a city or a state." Consider the extraordinary precision with which this distinguished physicist places the molecular population of a cubic centimeter of air (a small thimbleful) at "exactly 27.05 billions of billions." No, these statements are not fiction. They are the most reliable of scientific facts.

If it appears that molecules are small, what shall we say when we consider atoms? Dr. Paul D. Foote, of the Bureau of Standards, asserts that a pound of copper contains forty-three million million million million atoms. It is possible by indirect means to weigh an individual atom with far greater accuracy than a grocer weighs his merchandise. It would require on an average four hundred million atoms side by side to measure an inch. A quintillion atoms of gold would be required to weigh a gram, a very small quantity. (There are 28.35 grams in an ounce.) Sir Oliver Lodge puts the absolute weight of an atom of hydrogen, the lightest element, at twenty-five ten-thousandths of a grain divided by *one* followed by twenty-one ciphers. An avoirdupois pound contains seven thousand grains. Or, we may say that an atom of hydrogen weighs a million million million times less than a tiny grain of lycopodium powder. But why tangle our thoughts and tie our brains into hard knots by attempting to grasp mentally units so infinitesimally small, much less to visualize them? We shall simply have to take their existence on faith, believing that the scientist knows what he is talking about and that he has a wealth of the most reliable evidence upon which to base his conceptions.

ATOMIC WEIGHTS

Something has been said about the weights of atoms. I have heard Professor Theodore W. Richards of Harvard say that the atomic weights, that is the comparative weights of the atoms of the elements referred to the weight of an atom of hydrogen* taken as the standard,

---

*Hydrogen was the early standard. Oxygen is the present one.

are the most significant set of constants in the universe. They are the relative weights in which the atoms of the elements enter into chemical combinations with each other. This universe might be resolved into primeval chaos, but it would be strictly in proportion to these weights that the atoms would recombine to form new compounds. Of course, we can not directly measure the absolute weight of an atom. But the chemist does not need to know this. He only requires the relative weights of the atoms with respect to each other, and these it is not at all difficult to determine with great accuracy.

It will be to the everlasting credit of John Dalton that he had the boldness to undertake this task, a much more formidable one than it is to-day. Considering that he was a novice in an untrod field, with no established methods to guide him, compelled to devise the apparatus employed, urged on only by a sublime faith in the existence of ultimate units which many contemporaries regarded as wholly imaginary, this English schoolmaster did remarkably accurate work. It was in the magnitude of the task he essayed and the very audacity of the man that he revealed his genius.

Soon, however, another able master turned to this important field of investigation in the person of Jöns Jakob Berzelius, great Swedish chemist and for half a century the "Czar of Chemistry." The unsurpassed zeal for accuracy and thoroughness which he brought to this work have made every subsequent chemist his debtor. He determined the atomic weights of more than fifty of the elements, obtaining in many cases values almost identical with those resulting from the most precise of modern methods. Berzelius was the first great quantitative chemist. As did Lavoisier before him, he approached chemistry with a balance.

Not only was Berzelius an investigator of the first rank. He was also a master teacher. In that time no laboratory instruction was given in any of the universities of Europe. To Berzelius, whose fame rapidly spread abroad, came students who were later to enroll themselves among the most distinguished chemists of the century. There, in those simple rooms in Stockholm, the great German chemist Wöhler studied as a young man. From my *Masters of Science and Invention*, I take the following: "Arriving at night he [Wöhler] knocked at the door of Berzelius' residence. He tells us that his heart beat fast as the door was opened by a large man with a florid complexion, who proved to be Berzelius himself. Entering the laboratory, Wöhler could scarcely believe that he was in the place where so many important discoveries had been made. And he was amazed to find that this laboratory contained no water, no gas, no draft-places, no ovens. There were two plain tables, a blow-pipe, a few shelves of bottles, a little simple apparatus, and a couple of balances. We should hardly call it a good home laboratory outfit for a grammar-school boy now. Yet in it many new compounds had been discovered, atomic weights had been determined and the whole groundwork of theoretical chemistry rebuilt. When a genius sets to work, his material requirements are few."

To Berzelius chemistry owes its symbols for the elements and the present system of chemical formulæ.

TURNING POINTS IN CHEMICAL PROGRESS

I have just mentioned Wöhler. His name is associated with one of the most important discoveries in the history of chemistry. Before his time, organic chemistry had meant the chemistry of those compounds supposed to be formed through the agency of vital force. Inorganic chemistry had to do with mineral substances and elements and compounds wholly unrelated to life forces. But in 1828 this German chemist succeeded in preparing, synthesizing the chemist calls it, urea, an organic compound, artificially, without the assistance of vital energy. Wöhler himself was so astonished that he did not publish the result for three years, fearing that it would not be believed. This was a revolutionary discovery. Many would have preferred that it had not been made. It upset ages-old ideas. It introduced a new conception of vast significance into the growing science of chemistry. Henceforth, there could be no hard and fast line between the two divisions of chemistry. Organic chemistry came to mean simply the chemistry of the carbon compounds. Since that time literally thousands and thousands of such compounds have been artificially synthesized in laboratories all over the world, and thousands more remain to be prepared.

Inseparably linked with the name of Wöhler is that of Justus von Liebig. One of the most beautiful memories in the history of science is the life-long friendship between these two men, who in many respects were the direct opposites of each other in character. Impetuous, passionate, bitter in his denunciations, sometimes wrong in his conclusions, with a keen sense of justice, loving truth for truth's sake as vehemently as did that other tartar of the science, Sir Henry Cavendish, Liebig was the most forceful and energetic figure in the field of chemistry in his day and generation. We remember him now chiefly as the "Father of Agricultural Chemistry" and as one of the most remarkable teachers that the science of chemistry has produced. In Paris, under the renowned French chemist Gay-Lussac, he had received his training. Returning to his native land, he became professor of chemistry at the University of Giessen and there inaugurated the first systematic laboratory instruction to be given in any institution of learning in the world. Students flocked to his laboratories from every country. He infused these searchers after truth with his own fiery and impetuous spirit. He stimulated them with the charm of his vigorous personality and inspired them with his own enthusiasm. He spared no pains in giving individual instruction, but he made his students think for themselves. He threw them upon their own resources and expected and received much from them. One who had the privilege of sitting at his feet has said, "What a boon it was to drink the pure breath of science, as it flowed from Liebig's lips! Each word of his carried instruction. Every intonation of his voice bespoke regard. His approval was a mark of honor."

After Scheele, Liebig was the first great organic chemist, devising methods of analysis and laboratory technique which have remained standard to the present day.

BRINGING THE STARS WITHIN THE LABORATORY

Yes, we may bring the stars within the laboratory. We may determine with the utmost accuracy the elements of which they are composed and obtain precise knowledge of their physical states and motions. And this, notwithstanding the fact that Dr. Edwin Hubble of the Mount Wilson Observatory has quite recently determined the radius of *observable* space as being one hundred and forty million light years. That is, the light which bears the indelible impress of these messages in some instances left its source one hundred and forty million years ago and has been traveling earthward ever since at the seemingly stupendous speed of one hundred eighty-six thousand miles a second. In other words, the stellar pictures obtainable from the most remote regions of observable space present the conditions prevailing there when our planet was vastly younger than it is now,—many millions of years before man appeared upon its surface. Even the "news" coming from our nearest star neighbor is four and one-third years old when we receive it. In the case of the pole star, the message has been more than forty years on the way.

The explanation of the analysis of the stars goes back to Sir Isaac Newton. Two and one-half centuries ago, he showed that white light, such as sunlight, in being passed through a three-cornered glass prism, is broken up into the colors of the rainbow; dispersion, we call this phenomenon. Upon recombining the separated colors, white light was again produced. No one would have imagined at that time that this discovery of the composition of light was to lead in the nineteenth century to the invention of the most marvelous instrument for revealing the secrets of the heavens and the mysteries of the atoms and the molecules which science has thus far produced. But that is precisely what it did. In the early part of the last century, Wollaston, Fraunhofer and

others devised the spectroscope, of which we shall hear
much in succeeding pages. Shortly after the turn of the
century, in the hands of Bunsen and Kirchoff, two distinguished chemists of the University of Heidelberg, this
instrument was greatly improved and adapted to the
work of chemical analysis. In fact it became a more
amazingly accurate device for the detection of exceedingly minute quantities of elements than the boldest
scientist had dreamed possible. With it, so small a
quantity as one two-hundred-thousandth of a grain of
sodium may be detected with perfect certainty. And it
makes no difference whether the substance being examined is in the laboratory or in a distant star.

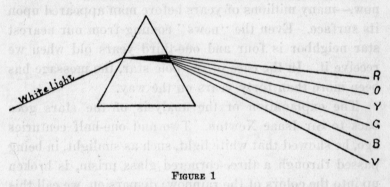

FIGURE 1

The dispersion by a triangular glass prism of a beam of white light
into the colors of the rainbow.

It will be worth our while at this point to study
briefly the construction of the spectroscope and its way
of operation. In the first crude devices, sunlight was
allowed to pass through a narrow slit and fell upon one
of the faces of a triangular glass prism. Now light, in
spite of certain disconcerting facts recently disclosed,
seems to be an electromagnetic wave motion in the all-

pervading ether of space, the hypothetical medium which the scientists invented to account for the transmission of light and heat energy from the distant stars to our earth. Light differs from the vibrations which produce heating, wireless and chemical effects only in its wave length. Radio waves may be several miles in length, while light and heat waves are measured in millionths of an inch, and chemical and X-ray waves are shorter still. It is simply a matter of pitch, entirely analogous to the pitch of musical tones. The waves which produce red are of a lower pitch than those which produce violet or X-rays, but of vastly higher pitch than those of heating or radio waves. When light waves are

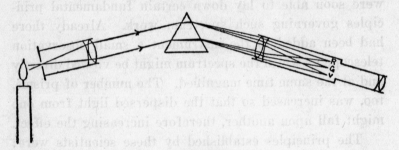

FIGURE 2

The spectroscope. Rays of light from a candle are thrown upon one of the faces of a triangular glass prism, through which they pass. In doing so, they are dispersed into their component colors, after which they are brought to focus by the small observation telescope at the right.

allowed to fall obliquely upon one of the faces of a glass prism, those which enter the glass are retarded in velocity, the shortest waves being retarded most. Therefore, it is clear that when white light passes through a prism the red waves are retarded least and the violet waves most, with the colors of the other wave lengths lying between. This unequal retardation is called dispersion, and, as can readily be seen, it results in the separation of the light into its component colors, thus producing what is known as a spectrum.

Wollaston and Fraunhofer caught the spectrum of sunlight and sometimes that of a star on a screen. In studying the spectrum of sunlight, the former of these scientists discovered that this band of color was crossed by a few dark lines. Fraunhofer had soon counted as many as four hundred, and their number has since been multiplied to many thousands. Known ever since as the "Fraunhofer Lines," their explanation was a mystery until the coming of Kirchoff. Together with Bunsen he adapted the spectroscope to chemical analysis, and they were soon able to lay down certain fundamental principles governing such spectrum work. Already there had been added to the instrument a small observation telescope by which the spectrum might be viewed directly and at the same time magnified. The number of prisms, too, was increased so that the dispersed light from one might fall upon another, therefore increasing the effect.

The principles established by these scientists were: (1) *Incandescent solids and liquids and also gases under high pressure give a solid band of color;* (2) *incandescent gases under low pressure give a series of bright lines, the number and position of which depend upon the elements present;* (3) *when white light passes through a gas of lower temperature than its source, this gas will absorb, or neutralize, in the white light those colors which it would produce, if viewed by itself in the incandescent state.*

If I turn a spectroscope upon a glowing mass of iron, I see a solid band of color. Likewise an incandescent gas

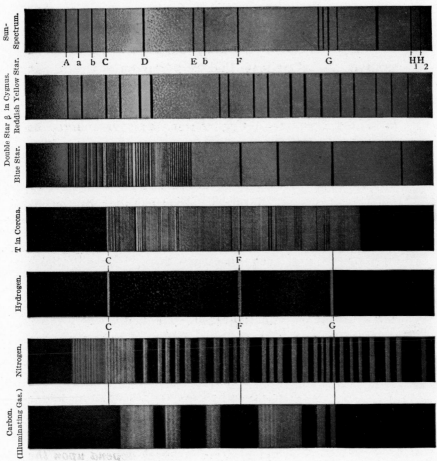

From Dull's Essentials of Physics, Courtesy of Henry Holt & Company.

SPECTRA OF DOUBLE STAR AND CORONA COMPARED WITH SUN'S SPECTRUM AND THE SPECTRA OF THREE ELEMENTS

under great pressure, such as obtains in some stars, will produce a continuous color scale, gradually shading from one color to another. But if I hold a platinum wire which has been dipped into a solution of ordinary salt in the colorless flame of a Bunsen burner, I obtain two bright yellow lines very close together, superposed upon the continuous spectrum of the hot platinum wire. These are due to the incandescent vapor of sodium produced by the action of the hot flame on the salt. They constitute a bright-line spectrum. Now let us repeat this experiment with the sodium vapor, but between the Bunsen flame and the spectroscope introduce an iron pan in which we heat a little metallic sodium until it vaporizes. The yellow light from the sodium flame of the Bunsen burner must pass through an atmosphere of non-luminous sodium vapor before it enters the spectroscope. The result is two dark lines where the bright yellow lines appeared before. That is, the sodium vapor of lower temperature has neutralized or absorbed the colors which the incandescent vapor produces.

The last of these principles at once gave the clue to the mystery associated with the Fraunhofer lines. A spectrum thus produced would be crossed by a series of dark lines, the number and position of which would depend upon the elements present in the cooler absorption gas through which the light had passed. It was perfectly clear that the dark lines in the sun's spectrum were due to elements in the state of incandescent vapor in the sun's atmosphere, through which the light was compelled to pass.

The next step was the identification of these elements. The second of the foregoing principles pointed the way so plainly that the path could not be missed. Each element in the state of incandescent vapor gives a characteristic bright-line spectrum. In other words, the wave lengths emitted by this vapor paint against a dark background a perfectly definite set of bright lines unduplicated by those from any other element. The colors and positions of these lines in the case of any particular element are absolutely fixed. Now, by comparing the dark lines crossing the sun's spectrum with the various sets of bright lines produced by the known elements, it at once became possible to determine the kinds of elements in the sun's atmosphere. For instance, it was found that the sun's spectrum possesses a set of dark lines corresponding precisely in position with the bright lines produced by incandescent hydrogen. There could be no question but that hydrogen is a solar element. Likewise with many of the other elements.

Spectroscope attachments were soon adapted to the astronomical telescope and for the eye-piece of the instrument a photographic plate was substituted. The latter is a vastly more sensitive detector of these tell-tale spectral lines than is the human eye. Thus it became possible to know what elements may be present in any of the stars or nebulæ whose light will reach our telescopes. Though this light may have been on its way thousands and even millions of years, it never tells a lie. Furthermore, it is perfectly evident that the character of the spectrum discloses the physical state of the star or nebula from which it originated. An incandescent solid or liquid will give a continuous band of color. A heavenly object in the gaseous state produces a bright-line spectrum. Although it does not come within the realm of chemistry, it may be noted that the spectroscope also reveals the motion of a star. If the star is coming toward us, its spectrum will be shifted toward the violet. If it is moving from us, the spectrum will be shifted toward the red. The amount of the shifting gives the velocity of the body with a remarkable degree of accuracy.

In the laboratory, the spectroscope is an indispensable aid to chemical analysis. It will detect an element even in the presence of other elements. With the coming of radioactivity, the old definition of an element, namely, that it is a substance which can not be changed into anything different from itself by any known means, has broken down, as we shall see. But the characteristic spectrum still remains. That is the one certain means of identifying a new element. Though radium spontaneously decomposes into other elements, it has a spectrum all its own.

Bunsen had scarcely perfected this magic-like diviner of imprisoned secrets when he discovered with it two new elements,—rubidium and cæsium. But even with this marvelously sensitive instrument it required the evaporation of forty tons of spring water to obtain enough material for the test.

In 1868, Sir Norman Lockyer was exploring the heavens with the spectroscope when he discovered *helium* in the atmosphere of the sun in prodigious quantities. The practical utilization of that discovery was farthest from his thought. But to-day we are filling our airships with the gas. Nearly a generation later, Sir William Ramsay in one of the classic researches in the whole history of chemistry discovered this element issuing from certain minerals and as one of the rare gases of the atmosphere. I count it one of the great privileges of my life once to have heard Sir William give a series of lectures in which he described this work and exhibited spectra of the first samples of this gas ever to have been isolated. As a by-product of this research, too, the rare gas *argon* was discovered. Once thought to be utterly useless, it is now important in the filling of incandescent lamp bulbs. Of helium, we shall learn more in the next chapter. It is an element of vast significance in arriving at an understanding of the structure of the atom.

Once more out of the darkness of the unknown had come the search-light of truth. A new key had been placed in the hand of the chemist of far more import than would the Philosopher's Stone have been to the alchemist. For has it not told us of the unity that pervades all space? The clay beneath our feet, we ourselves and all that we may see are kin to the dog star, the fire mist of the Milky Way and every other particle of matter in the universe. The same elements are everywhere present. From farthest sun to farthest sun throughout this infinity of time and space, one grand harmony prevails. For aught we know these elemental building blocks of the Great Architect evolve through nebulæ, stars and solar systems, eventually flowering into organic life, dotted here and there with civilizations, only to be resolved once more into the primordial stuff of primeval chaos. Surely an instrument which enables ephemeral creatures of but the tiniest fraction of a cosmic moment thus to penetrate the vastness of the unknown must constitute a master link between human intelligence and the Infinite. With that definition of the spectroscope, we may leave it for the present.

DRAWING ASIDE THE VEIL

Scarcely had the full import of the master key just described impressed itself on the minds of men when the great Russian chemist, Mendeleeff, and the German, Lothar Meyer, each independently of the other, discovered that, back of the seeming chaos of the elements and their properties, law and order reigned supreme. Out of the chaos had emerged a system, and they had found its secret. A fundamental principle, a controlling rhythm, like the harmony of a musical composition, seemed to transform the accumulated aggregations of isolated facts into simple relationships. No longer need the chemist grope in the darkness of an inexact science. The facts of nearly a century of hit-and-miss discovery were about to be marshaled into a new order which should forevermore keep in step with the marching song of fundamental law. For it was found that, if starting with hydrogen, the lightest, the elements are arranged in the order of their increasing atomic weights, they form themselves into a table of natural periods and groups in which the elements in any group bear a close resemblance to one another in their respective properties and chemical behavior. In the beautiful language of Robert Kennedy Duncan, "Just as the pendulum returns again in its swing, just as the moon returns in its orbit, just as the advancing year ever brings the rose of spring, so do the properties of the elements periodically recur as the weights of the atoms rise."

As originally foreshadowed by John Newlands in 1863, every eighth element seemed to repeat the properties of the eighth element preceding it. The "law of octaves," he called it. Thus the elements might be arranged in horizontal periods and vertical columns, or groups. The arrangement did not prove to be quite so simple as that, but with certain modifications, dictated by

Periodic Table

Periods	Group 0 (A B)	Group I (A B)	Group II (A B)	Group III (A B)	Group IV (A B)	Group V (A B)	Group VI (A B)	Group VII (A B)	Group VIII
1	He=4	Li=6.94	Gl=9.1	B=11	C=12.005	N=14.01	O=16	F=19	
2	Ne=20.2	Na=23	Mg=24.32	Al=27.1	Si=28.3	P=31.04	S=32.06	Cl=35.46	
3	A=39.88	K=39.1	Ca=40.07	Sc=44.1	Ti=48.1	V=51	Cr=52	Mn=54.93	Fe=55.84 Co=58.97 Ni=58.68
4		Cu=63.57	Zn=65.37	Ga=69.9	Ge=72.5	As=74.96	Se=79.2	Br=79.92	
5	Kr=82.92	Rb=85.45	Sr=87.63	Y=89	Zr=90.6	Cb=93.5	Mo=96		Ru=101.7 Rh=102.9 Pd=106.7
6		Ag=107.88	Cd=112.4	In=114.8	Sn=118.7	Sb=120.2	Te=127.5	I=126.92	
7	X=130.2	Cs=132.81	Ba=137.37	La–Lu 139–175	Ce=140.25	Ta=181.5	W=184		Os=190.9 Ir=193.1 Pt=195.2
8		Au=197.2	Hg=200.6	Tl=204	Pb=207.2	Bi=208			
9	Nt=222.4		Ra=226		Th=232.4		U=238.2		

FIGURE 3

The periodic grouping of the elements with symbols and atomic weights. Some of the more recently discovered elements are not shown.

the necessities of stubborn facts, it proved to be the search-light which revealed an orderly, systematic grouping of the elements in accordance with their atomic weights and properties. It is interesting to know that this generalization, known as the Periodic Law and one of the most far-reaching and significant in the whole history of theoretical and applied chemistry, when first suggested by Newlands, was received with open ridicule by contemporary chemists. Not until Mendeleeff and Lothar Meyer, seven years later, had shown conclusively the existence of such a fundamental relationship did the idea rise above the skepticism of timid souls.

Now, the supreme test of any scientific generalization is the way in which it agrees with and explains observed facts. Scientists have never been able to proceed in accordance with the philosophy of the old gentleman who, when told that the facts did not support his contention that the earth is flat, retorted, "So much the worse for the facts." But the Periodic Law has met every requirement. In a marvelously beautiful and simple way it has explained known facts, correlated and systematized existing knowledge, corrected errors, harmonized with new knowledge as fast as it was discovered and actually predicted with startling accuracy fresh discoveries.

When Mendeleeff prepared his table in 1869, it contained many gaps. These represented the places of elements not then discovered. One by one, however, as these missing elements were found, their properties escorted them to the exact places which their respective atomic weights dictated that they should occupy. They could not have escaped if they would. One notable example is to be found in the discovery by Lord Rayleigh and Sir William Ramsay in the nineties of the last century of the rare gases of the atmosphere, five in number. Now, these elements were found to have no chemical affinities whatever. They were wholly unrelated to any of the other elements. With no ties of kinship, where should they be put? If the new law provided no place for them in the periodic grouping, it must certainly be in some way defective. To some extent, it could not express the truth. But, lo, their atomic weights placed them in a group by themselves, preceding all the other groups, as naturally as though they had been made to order and their places of abode erected in advance. A law which thus harmonizes with a new discovery must have something back of it other than fictions of the imagination. It must have some counterpart in reality. In the eternal scheme of things, it must express some measure of truth.

A still more striking confirmation of this great law had already been made. In 1870, Mendeleeff proclaimed his perfect faith in the law which he had formulated by boldly predicting the discovery of three elements. In accordance with their respective positions-to-be in the table, he called them eka-boron, eka-aluminum and eka-silicon. From their associations in each case, that is from the elements in the table on either side and above and below the positions which the new elements were to occupy, Mendeleeff predicted not only the atomic weights of the elements but their physical and chemical properties, the compounds they would form, and even the specific gravities and colors both of the elements and of many of their compounds. He little thought that he would live to see this prophecy fulfilled. Yet he did, gloriously fulfilled. In scandium from Scandinavia, gallium from France, and germanium from Germany, these elements found their exact counterparts. Almost to the letter did they meet the conditions laid down by the Russian chemist. As though a lightning flash had rent the heavens and drawn aside the veil which obscures the ethereal blue, this prophecy and its fulfilment betokened the dawn of a new era in the science of chemistry.

Yes, and this law corrected errors. The atomic weights of some elements as determined at that time indicated positions in the periodic table at variance with those dictated by the properties of the elements themselves. In any particular case this could mean just one of two things. Either there was some flaw in the law or the atomic weight was erroneous. A redetermination of the atomic weights in these doubtful cases, in almost every instance, proved the latter to be the truth. There are several exceptions, the explanation of which is not yet clear.

The Periodic Law suggested new lines of investigation. It stimulated effort. For nearly a quarter of a century, it dominated chemical thought. It contributed the inspiration which the breath of discovery always imparts and without which progress ceases. It raised the empirical methods of chemistry to the rank of a real science. It gave promise, too, of still greater discoveries yet to come. May there not be an evolution of the elements from the simplest to the most complex? Is there not some primal stuff out of which elements arise in regular sequence? Can we not push back this mystery of the atoms and peep within? These were some of the questions which presented themselves and to which for a generation chemists and physicists have addressed themselves with marvelous success.

More and more it became clear that within the atom are the issues of life, the mysteries of energy and matter

and the ultimate explanation of this universe of stars and
solar systems, plants and animals, human beings and
civilizations. In other pages we shall resume this fascinating inquiry.

A TREASURE-HOUSE OF CHEMICAL WEALTH

And now I want you to come with me to a little home
laboratory in the outskirts of London. It is the Easter
vacation of the year 1856. Before us we see a lad of
seventeen years, later to be known as Sir William Perkin.
It is just dusk of an apparently unsuccessful day's work.
He picks up a flask half filled with a sticky mess of chemicals. His first impulse is to throw the stuff away. Then,
as though restrained by the hand of destiny, he pauses.
Grasping a bottle of alcohol, he fills the flask, and,
behold, there flashes into view a beautiful purple dyestuff. It is mauve, the first of the aniline colors. Standing there in the twilight, could young Perkin have drawn
aside the veil and peered into the future, he would have
seen emerging from that black, foul-smelling coal-tar all
the colors of the rainbow, the most delicate perfumes
known to Nature, the explosive of the battle-field and the
healing balm of the hospital, powerful drugs for the
stilling of pain and the allaying of fever, preservatives
and antiseptics, a sweet five hundred times sweeter than
sugar, photographic chemicals, and much more. No
treasure-house of fabled lore ever yielded a greater
wealth of riches than has coal-tar under the magic touch
of the research chemist.

But you know the romance of coal-tar. You recall
how a group of German chemists under the superb

leadership of Adolph von Bayer, after seventeen years
of intelligent research and an expenditure of twenty-
eight million gold marks, wrested from Nature the secret
of synthetic indigo. You are familiar with the story of
alizarin and with many other triumphs in this fascinating chapter of chemical discovery. The significant
thing to note here is the turning of chemical interests
into new channels. Organic chemistry took on new life.
A new branch of chemical industry was born. Brains
and capital began to be poured into the preparation of a
host of useful compounds. A fresh impetus of incalculable value was given both to theoretical and applied
chemistry. A chemical renaissance, which has not yet
passed, took possession of the stage. Many of the foremost chemists of the second half of the last century
turned to this virgin field of endeavor.

Here was a challenge to chemical genius, both stimulating and fascinating. The chemist had ceased to be
a mere analyst. He had become a creator. Out of the
wastes of industry he had learned to fabricate the wealth
of the Indies. Under his magic touch, the black smoke,
which soiled architecture, fouled the air and injured
health, turned to gold. Compounds innumerable, he
fashioned in his flasks and retorts. He had fathomed the
secret of molecular architecture. The structure of
molecules, he could alter at will. He might design a new
dyestuff or drug and go into his laboratory and build it.
If the substance proved to have commercial value, a
plant for its production arose almost overnight. The
chemistry of the carbon compounds unrolled before him
in limitless reaches. No longer did organic substances
come into being only through the agency of life. The

chemist himself became their creator. No wonder that a
golden age of chemistry, outstripping by far the boldest
flights of alchemistic fancy, seemed at hand. Yes, the
happy worker in this new wonderland of creative effort
seemed to be entering upon a glorious heyday of chemical triumphs, which bade fair to eclipse the proudest
achievements of earlier times.

One of the most notable of the early workers in this
field was Kekulé. From 1865 to 1885, his influence upon
the development of the chemistry of carbon compounds
was greater than that of any other chemist. He had been
a pupil of Liebig, who was a pioneer in the realm of
organic chemistry, and among his own students he numbered Adolph von Bayer, Emil Fischer and Victor Meyer,
all of whom achieved distinction as organic chemists.
Kekulé is remembered now chiefly for his brilliant
solution of the problem of the "benzene ring." Benzene is the first in a long series of carbon compounds,
from which are derived many of the most important
substances of organic chemistry. The benzene molecule
contains six atoms of carbon and six atoms of hydrogen.
For long, the way in which these atoms are united in the
molecule was a baffling puzzle. Kekulé had thought long
and deeply on it. No intelligent work on the synthesis
of benzene derivatives could be done until this matter
had been settled. How Kekulé arrived at a solution, he
has told us in his own words.

"During my stay in London I lived for a time in
Clapham Road near the Commons. I frequently spent
the evening with my friend, Hugo Müller, in Islington,
on the other side of that enormous city. We talked about
many things, but chiefly about our beloved chemistry.

On one beautiful summer day, I traveled through the busy streets of that metropolis in the last omnibus, and as usual rode outside on the top of the omnibus. I began to dream. The atoms began to play antics before mine eyes. I had always seen each little particle in motion, but had never before succeeded in determining the nature of their motion. That day I saw how two smaller ones often united to form a pair, how the larger ones seized two of the smaller ones, and how the still larger held three and even four of the smaller, and how they all moved in vortices. I saw how the greater formed a row, and how the smaller were drawn along at the ends of the chain. . . . The call of the conductor, 'Clapham Road,' awaked me from my dreams but I spent the night in transferring to paper at least sketches of each of these dream pictures. Thus arose the structure theory.

"The benzene theory had a similar origin. During my stay in Ghent, Belgium, I lived in a fine room on the main street. My work room faced on a narrow side street, which, during the day, had no light. This was no disadvantage to a chemist who spends all of the days in the laboratory. I sat in this room and wrote on my text-book. It did not go well. My thought was on other things. I turned my chair to the fireplace and fell half asleep. The atoms again played antics before mine eyes. Small groups kept themselves modestly in the background. My mind's eye, trained by repeated sights of a similar kind, now distinguished larger forms of various shapes. Long rows united, becoming much thicker; all in movement snake-like twisting and turning. And see, what was that? One of the snakes seized his own tail, and thus confusedly appeared the picture before mine eyes. I awoke as by a flash of lightning. This time also I spent the remainder of the night working out the consequences of the hypothesis."

The picture of the snake-like form seizing his own tail was that of the benzene ring. In that moment, the genius of Kekulé perceived how the six atoms of carbon in the benzene molecule unite with one another to form a ring with an atom of hydrogen attached to each. The truth of this dream conception has been tested many times. And now the X-ray actually confirms the picture. This formula of benzene proved to be a dominating factor in chemical thought and work for at least two decades after it was announced. It played a rôle in the

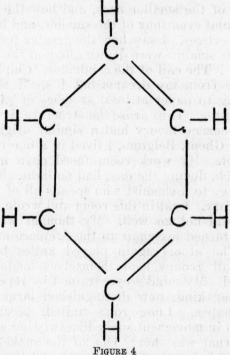

FIGURE 4
The benzene ring. Six atoms of carbon are linked with six of hydrogen.

chemistry of carbon similar to that of the periodic system of Mendeleeff in inorganic chemistry. This Kekulé formula accounted for many known facts and suggested numerous lines of investigation. In particular, it was of the utmost assistance in the synthesis of new compounds. The chemist could get a picture in two dimensions of the thing he was trying to build, and it proved, too, to be in accord with the chemical facts. All the world has been made the debtor of this dreamer whose visions revealed fundamental secrets of the atoms and the molecules. Fantastic though they seemed, these dreams marked a turning-point in the progress of chemical thought. Kekulé, however, sounded this note of warning: "If we learn to dream we may find out the truth; but let us avoid publishing our dreams before they have been tested by the wide-awake intelligence."

MORE ABOUT MOLECULAR ARCHITECTURE

Still, there was something lacking in the pictures of carbon compounds as conceived by Kekulé and his contemporaries. These pictures were in two dimensions only. Manifestly, molecules exist in three dimensions. Something more was needed. Louis Pasteur, pioneer investigator and brilliant worker in many fields, provided the clue. It came as the result of a microscopic examination of the crystal salts of tartaric and racemic acids. Pasteur found that the sodium and ammonium salts of these two acids were identical in every respect, except that the tartrate deviated the plane of a beam of light passed through it to the right, while the racemate had no effect upon the light. In this work he made use of an instrument called a polariscope and of an optical effect common to many crystal substances. The difference in this instance observed by the young investigator seemed trivial and by many would have been passed over without further thought. Not so, however, to the inquiring mind of a Pasteur. Under the microscope, this

French scientist discovered that not all of these crystals were symmetrical. The tartrate crystals had facets, or tiny faces, on one side. The racemate crystals did too. But—and here was the point—in the tartrate crystals the facets were all on the right-hand side, while in the racemate crystals they were on both sides. With infinite patience, Pasteur separated the crystals of the racemate salt into two piles. Those having the facets on the right-hand side proved to be identical with the tartrate and now rotated the beam of light to the right just as the tartrate did. Those having the facets on the left-hand side rotated the beam of light to the left. A mixture of the two in equal parts would not produce any rotation at all.

But what has this to do with the molecules of carbon compounds? A great deal. Just at this time a new investigator came upon the scene in the person of van't Hoff, a man who had a more profound influence upon the development of theoretical chemistry during the last quarter of the nineteenth century than any other chemist. These differences in the optical activity of certain carbon compounds meant much to this Dutch scientist. With the clear vision of the genius that he was, van't Hoff saw that this difference must be due to some peculiarity of the carbon atom itself. What it was became for a time the sole object of his thought.

One tell-tale bit of evidence afforded a clue. A right-hand crystal of a racemate salt was the mirror image of a left-hand crystal. One crystal was not symmetrical with respect to the other. It was impossible to superimpose one crystal upon the other so that the two would exactly coincide at all points. Pasteur had seen that

"An asymmetric [unsymmetrical] grouping of the atoms, corresponding to an object and its mirror image, must be present." In other words, the atoms within the molecules of one crystal must have a directly opposite arrangement to those of the atoms in the molecules of the other crystal. To understand this difference, stand in front of a mirror and hold up your right hand. It is the left hand of the image in the mirror which is being raised. The mirror gives a right and left inversion. Although a crystal of one sort can not be made to coincide, point for point, with a crystal of the other sort, its mirror image could be made to do so.

Now, the controlling atom in the molecule of one of

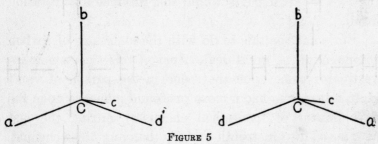

FIGURE 5

These diagrams illustrate the asymmetric groupings of the atoms within the respective molecules of tartrate and racemate crystals with which Pasteur was dealing. In no position can the two be made to coincide point for point. The lines radiating from the central carbon atom represent different directions in space.

these optically active salts is the carbon atom. The carbon atom, as well as the atoms of all other elements, possesses a property called *valence*. This may seem like a rather formidable term, but we must familiarize ourselves with it. It means the capacity which the atom of one element has to hold in combination the atoms of another element. The valence of hydrogen is taken as one. From this as a starting-point we may obtain the valences of a number of other elements. An atom of chlorine will hold in combination one atom of hydrogen. This makes the valence of chlorine also one. An atom of oxygen will hold two atoms of hydrogen. Its valence is two. An atom of nitrogen will combine with three atoms of hydrogen, making its valence three. We think of an atom as having a certain number of unitary chem-

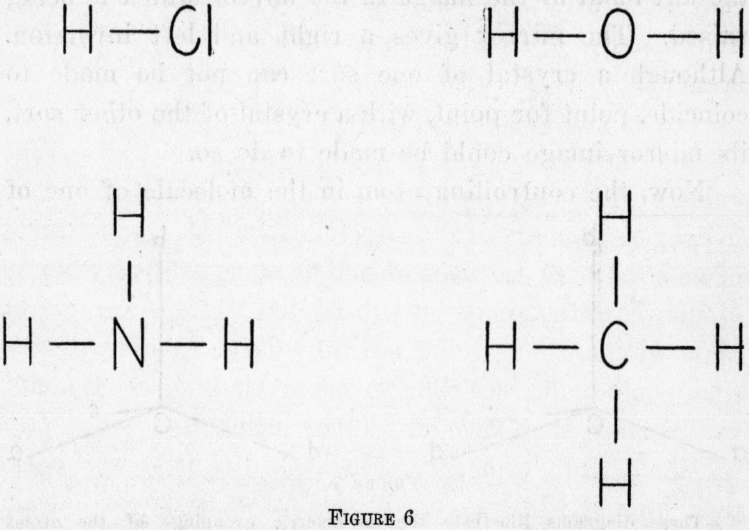

$$H-Cl \qquad H-O-H$$

$$
\begin{array}{ccc}
& H & \\
& | & \\
H-N-H
\end{array}
\qquad
\begin{array}{ccc}
& H & \\
& | & \\
H-C-H \\
& | & \\
& H &
\end{array}
$$

FIGURE 6

These four structural formulæ illustrate the meaning of valence. The atom of chlorine combines with one atom of hydrogen and has a valence of one. Oxygen combines with two atoms of hydrogen and has a valence of two, while nitrogen and carbon have valences of three and four respectively. Often an element may have more than one valence. Nitrogen in its various compounds has five.

ical affinities, which seek to satisfy themselves by uniting with the atoms of other elements to form compounds. In any compound, all of these bonds of union must be satisfied. Atoms always seek partners. If the atoms of no other element with which they may unite are present, the atoms of the same element unite with each other. Some of these chemical affinities, as in the case of the molecules of water, are very strong. It requires a great deal of energy to break the bonds asunder and to obtain the elements in the free state. In many instances, these bonds are weak. This is true of the chemical affinities between the atoms in a molecule of nitroglycerin. These affinities are easily broken, and, as the atoms fly apart, they do so with the liberation of vast quantities of energy and usually with irreparable damage to the adjacent scenery.

Let us get back to the carbon atom and the picture of the molecule in which it plays the leading rôle. Now, the valence of the carbon atom is four. It unites with four hydrogen atoms, forming methane, a chief constituent of natural gas. In place of one or more of the hydrogen atoms, however, may be substituted various groups of other atoms, thus giving rise to a large number of distinct compounds. Carbon forms myriads of compounds, vastly more than does any other element.

Van't Hoff, whom we side-tracked a little way back, took up the problem of the optical activity of carbon compounds. He sought the explanation in the structure of the molecule itself and found it. He saw, as others must have done and as Le Bel contemporaneously with him did see, that the molecule of a carbon compound exists in three dimensions in space. Van't Hoff asked the question, "What must be the geometric form of such a molecule that one molecule may differ from another as a mirror image differs from its object?" That is, what must be the configuration in space of the central carbon atom and its four combined groups to produce an unsymmetrical molecule. For it was perfectly clear to van't Hoff that the form and structure of the crystal of a salt of racemic acid, for instance, must depend upon the form and structure of the constituent molecules.

The first step in the solution was the very obvious conclusion that the only geometrical configuration in three dimensional space which will permit of a central

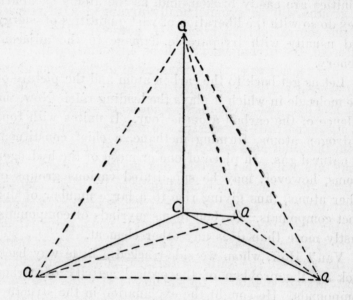

FIGURE 7

Grouping of the atoms in the tetrahedral molecule of a carbon compound. The carbon atom is at the center of the tetrahedron with the four combined atoms at the ends of the lines drawn from it to the respective vertices. If these atoms or groups joined to the central carbon atom are all different, the grouping is an asymmetric one.

carbon atom and four combined groups is that of the *tetrahedron*. If your knowledge of solid geometry has grown somewhat hazy, look in an encyclopedia or dictionary for a description and representation of this form. It is a solid bounded by four equilateral triangles. Therefore, as *tetra-* indicates, the solid has four corners.

Now, van't Hoff imagined the carbon atom to be at the center of this solid with the four imaginary valence arms extending to the four corners. At each corner was a combined atom or group of atoms as the case might be.

A little thought will show that, if the combined atoms or groups at the four corners are all alike, these atoms or groups will be symmetrically arranged with respect to the central carbon atom. If, however, they are all different, the arrangement will be unsymmetrical.

In the latter case, the arrangement of the atoms about the central carbon atom may be such as to give rise to two and only two groupings. That is, two different types of unsymmetrical tetrahedra are possible, each differing from the other as a mirror image differs from its object. They are not superposable, one upon the other. One rotates the plane of polarized light to the right and the other rotates it to the left. But when molecules representing these two types are present in equal proportions, there is no optical activity. That is what Pasteur found in the case of the salts of tartaric and racemic acids. The tartrate exhibited optical activity, while the racemate did not. This was because the tartrate contained molecules of but one type, while the racemate contained molecules of both types in equal quantities. The optical activity of one neutralized that of the other.

Van't Hoff had solved the problem. There could be no question about it. Analysis showed that in all cases of optical activity the molecule contains a carbon atom combined with four different groups. In other words, there is present what chemists call an "asymmetric" carbon atom. It was also clear that the tetrahedral form of the molecule holds in all other cases, whether the carbon atom is combined with four different groups or not.

Where this is not true, there is an absence of optical activity. That is all.

At last chemists were able to make pictures of these molecules of carbon compounds as they must appear. Although it is utterly impossible with the most powerful microscope to see a molecule, the configuration of its atoms in this instance is a mathematical certainty. There could be no other arrangement which would satisfy the known facts. This view is not an idle speculation. It rests upon a formidable array of the most reliable evidence ever adduced in support of any scientific theory.

Of what value was this conception? How could it benefit the progress of chemistry to know the arrangement of the atoms within the molecule? Why did chemists at once recognize that it marked a turning-point in the development of the science? Because it substituted for the hit-and-miss chemical synthesis of earlier years a rational plan of molecular architecture. Chemists could then, with much more certainty than theretofore, build in the imagination a new carbon compound, envision its structure in every detail, even in three dimensions of space, and then construct it with as much precision as an artist fashions a piece of statuary. Just as the architect must prepare the plans of a cathedral before its construction can begin, so must the chemist be able to picture the molecular structure of a compound before its materialization can proceed. Without this conception born in the imagination of van't Hoff, the host of dyestuffs, drugs, medicinals, lacquers, perfumes and what-not, which have literally been made to order, would not now be commonplaces of the workshop, home and hospital. There is not an individual in civilized life, from the humblest to the most exalted, who is not a debtor to this Dutch chemist. The discovery by Paul Ehrlich of salvarsan, or "606," was a deliberate and monumental adaptation of van't Hoff's purely theoretical research to a great purpose. What to van't Hoff was a labor inspired only by an unquenchable thirst for truth alone became in the hands of contemporary and later chemists the most practical working plan of the laboratory and chemical plant. It is the same old story. Material progress forever rests upon the discovery of fundamental truth. That is the keynote of every advance, whether physical or spiritual. It always has been so. It always will be so. This discovery by van't Hoff is the corner-stone in the edifice of organic chemistry. Did pure research have no other achievement to its credit, this alone would be proof supreme of the everlasting value of the pursuit of truth for truth's sake.

ELECTRICITY AND CHEMICAL ACTION

Great gaps in our knowledge of pure and applied chemistry would exist to-day, had not some one discovered the fundamental relationships existing between electricity and chemical activity. Whole industries would be non-existent. Great blocks of natural wealth would remain untapped. Metallurgy would be in a vastly more primitive state. Electrochemical industries such as those centering about a Niagara or a Muscle Shoals would not even be dreams. Had not some one tamed the lightning and learned its laws of action upon chemical compounds, the material progress of the last half-century would present a radically different picture. It is difficult to conceive of what modern chemistry would be without electricity. Electricity proved to be the magic key which unlocked a multitude of doors and made possible the solution of a host of problems. Giant that it is, it has leveled mountains of scientific difficulty and tapped immeasurable reservoirs of chemical wealth. Under its influence, the luxuries of yesterday have become the necessities of to-day. Once more the world must acknowledge its debt to the devotees of pure and applied research.

You recall how Sir Humphry Davy, in the laboratory of the Royal Institution, made the first successful application of the electric current to the solution of a chemical problem. His pupil and successor, Michael Faraday, a quarter of a century later in the same laboratory, discovered two of the fundamental laws of electrochemical action. The first was a simple demonstration of what one would naturally expect to find. He was studying the electrolysis of solutions, that is, the chemical changes which occur when an electric current is passed through solutions of chemical compounds. He found that the quantity of metal deposited upon the negative electrode of his electrolytic bath is proportional to the amount of current used. If he doubled the current, twice as much metal by actual weight was found to be deposited in a given time.

The second discovery was much more significant. Faraday found that for the same quantity of current the amount of metal deposited from a solution is proportional to the atomic weight of the metal divided by its valence. Thus the atomic weight of silver is 108 and its valence 1, while the atomic weight of copper is

63.6 and its valence 2. Now, the quantity of current which will deposit 108 grams of silver from solution in a certain time will deposit only 31.8 grams of copper. The same was found to be true in the case of all other metals. It at once became possible to determine what are known as the electrochemical equivalents of the metals; that is, the quantity of metal in each instance which will be deposited by one ampere of current in one second of time. This placed the whole art of the electrochemical deposition of metals upon a scientific basis. It was a distinct gain. In later years, when the electrolytic refining of metals on a large scale became possible, these laws enabled the engineer to design electrolytic apparatus and plant equipment in accordance with the exact requirements of the undertaking. In many other ways these fundamental discoveries have paid enormous dividends. Faraday, however, saw none of all this. Just as in his epoch-making discovery of the laws of electromagnetism, his only concern was to add to the sum total of human knowledge. He did not scorn practical results, but they were a secondary consideration.

This second of Faraday's laws, too, had a still deeper meaning. There seemed to be some exact relationship between the atomic weight of a metal and its ability, when in solution, to conduct the electric current. A new weapon of attack upon the mysteries of the atoms had been placed in the hands of the investigator. This relationship at once made it possible to check up the atomic weights of metallic elements as found by other methods and determine their accuracy. And so a very practical gain was accomplished, for the reliability of many chemical calculations, both of theoretical and industrial importance, depends upon the accuracy with which these numbers have been determined. But most important of all, these discoveries of Faraday aroused scientific curiosity. They stimulated investigation. They gave promise of still richer rewards in the years to come,—a promise which time has abundantly fulfilled.

Still, until long after the work of Faraday, the real nature of electrolytic action was a mystery. Just why an electric current should decompose a compound in solution, no one knew. Neither was it known why the current should decompose one compound and not another. Sodium chloride, ordinary salt, in solution is readily broken up, while sugar will not conduct the current at all. So also of many other compounds. Chemists came to recognize two groups,—the electrolytes and the non-electrolytes, those which undergo decomposition by the electric current and those which do not. But this classification did not at all help to answer the ages-old question "Why?"

Grotthuss more than a century ago and Clausius several decades later had attempted explanations. Still, the solution remained a baffling mystery until the coming of Arrhenius in the eighties of the last century. In 1884, Svante Arrhenius, a young Swedish chemist, came to work in the laboratory of van't Hoff. In the following year, he published a paper which proved to be little short of revolutionary in its influence upon the future of chemical thought and practise. In it he proposed the *theory of the electrolytic dissociation* of those compounds which in solution conduct the electric current.

In accordance with this theory, Arrhenius assumed that some or all of the molecules of an electrolyte in solution dissociate, or break up, into two parts, one of which is positively charged with electricity and the other negatively charged. Non-electrolytes, those compounds which do not conduct the current in solution, do not thus dissociate. These charged parts into which the molecules dissociate, he called *ions*. Ions are the real conductors of the current in a solution. They take the place of the copper conductor outside of the solution.

Let us illustrate. A molecule of sodium chloride consists of one atom of metallic sodium combined with one atom of gaseous chlorine. Just how a solid and a gas may unite to form a solid compound, we do not know. However, in accordance with the electrolytic dissociation theory, a molecule of this compound breaks up in solution into a positively charged sodium ion and a negatively charged chlorine ion. Every drop of the solution contains millions of these ions. When electrodes connected with the positive and negative poles of a battery are suspended in the solution a current flows, and bubbles of gas immediately appear about each electrode.

The ionization of sodium chloride is shown as follows:

$$\overset{+}{\text{Na}}\text{Cl} \quad \rightarrow \quad \overset{+}{\text{Na.}} \quad + \quad \overset{-}{\text{Cl}}$$

Na Cl	Na.	Cl
Sodium chloride	Sodium ion	Chlorine ion

Now, what happens is this: One of the electrodes inserted in the solution is positively charged and the other is negatively charged. Positive electricity attracts negative and negative attracts positive. Immediately the positive electrode draws negatively charged ions of chlorine to itself and the negative electrode draws positively charged ions of sodium. The chlorine ion in coming in contact with the electrode gives up its charge, thus becoming an ordinary atom of chlorine. It then unites with another discharged ion, becoming a molecule of ordinary chlorine gas, which bubbles off. The sodium ion likewise gives up its charge, becoming an atom of ordinary metallic sodium, which, having lost its protective electric charge, decomposes a molecule of water and liberates hydrogen gas. About the negative electrode, to

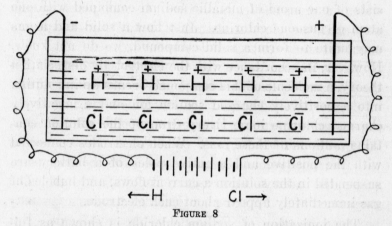

FIGURE 8

Electrolysis of a solution of hydrochloric acid. The positively charged hydrogen ions are drawn to the negative pole, or cathode, where they give up their charges and pass off as hydrogen gas. At the same time the negatively charged chlorine ions are attracted to the positive pole, or anode, where they likewise give up their charges and pass off as gas.

which the sodium ions pass, sodium hydroxide accumulates, which is the compound formed when metallic sodium is brought in contact with water. This is one bit of evidence in favor of the theory.

It will be seen that the electric current does not decompose the compound in solution. The compound is already dissociated. The current simply serves as a directive force to guide the ions to their respective electrodes. A very feeble current, not possessing nearly enough energy to decompose the molecules of a stable compound, will nevertheless to some extent effect this electrolytic separation. The theory at once threw a flood of light upon this long-standing puzzle. For it was known that a current so weak that, if passed through water for one hundred and fifty years, would liberate only a cubic centimeter of gas, would still decompose water in measurable quantities. It was plain enough now that the electric nature of many compounds account for their electrochemical behavior.

Arrhenius had been led to the development of his theory from a consideration of the comparative effects of electrolytes and non-electrolytes in lowering the freezing point and raising the boiling point of solutions. As every one knows, salt dissolved in water lowers the freezing point. It also raises the boiling point above the normal temperature for pure water. The amount of the lowering or raising, as the case may be, depends upon the quantity of dissolved salt. Not only salt, but all compounds which will dissolve in water will produce these effects. It had long been known that an electrolyte, such as sodium chloride, will produce a much greater effect upon the freezing point or boiling point of a solution than will a non-electrolyte, such as sugar. That is, a given molecular quantity of sodium chloride will lower the freezing point or raise the boiling point of water in which it is dissolved more degrees than will an equivalent molecular quantity of sugar. Let it be said in passing that chemists are able to weigh out quantities of any two compounds which will contain in each approximately the same number of molecules.

It seemed perfectly obvious that the change in the freezing point or boiling point must be due to the molecules of the dissolved compound. But why the foregoing difference in the behavior of electrolytes and non-electrolytes? This is the sort of problem which the inquiring mind of the scientist delights to tackle. He knows there is a reason. Nothing ever happens by chance. The explanation may be obscure, the puzzle baffling. Still, somewhere in Nature's treasure-house of secrets, he knows the answer is to be found. And so he searches, buoyed up by the calm assurance that his labor can not be lost.

In the light of Arrhenius' theory of electrolytic dissociation, the problem of the freezing and boiling points became sun clear. If a large proportion of the molecules of an electrolyte are dissociated into ions, each having the same effect upon the freezing point or the boiling point as an undissociated molecule has, while the molecules of a non-electrolyte do not thus dissociate, then the effects observed are precisely those which should be expected. Fact and theory were found to coincide beautifully.

In support of his theory, Arrhenius produced an abundance of evidence. Solutions of electrolytes did behave as though they contain positively and negatively charged ions. These ions actually did appear at the electrodes when a current was passed through a solution. It seemed clear enough, too, that the extent of dissociation should depend upon the dilution of the solution, that is, upon the quantity of water in proportion to the amount of dissolved salt or other compound. In a very dilute solution, all of the molecules might be dissociated into ions. It would also seem to follow that a dilute solution should have a *relatively* higher degree of electrical conductivity than a concentrated solution, although the latter is *absolutely* a better conductor. In other words, as between a concentrated and a dilute solution, the more salt, the more current—but less current in proportion to the amount of salt. And such was found to be the case. Again the theory accounted for the facts as they were.

And now, for the first time, it became possible to define the terms *acid* and *base* with scientific precision. Acids and bases are the two fundamental types of chemical compounds. It had long been known that, when an acid and a base combine, a salt and water result. But exactly why, no one knew. What is the essential element in an acid? For many years, it was thought to be oxygen. Indeed, the name itself means "acid-former." Analysis showed that most acids do contain this element. However, no chemist was able to find oxygen in hydrochloric, the strongest of the common acids. Only hydrogen and chlorine seemed to be present. Still, for long, it was thought that chlorine must be a compound of oxygen and a hypothetical element named *murium*. But the most zealous search failed to reveal it. And then a number of other acids were discovered in which chemists could find no oxygen whatever. It did gradually become apparent, however, that all acids have in common the element *hydrogen*. Furthermore, inorganic or mineral acids and some organic acids too are electrolytes. In solution they give hydrogen ions. In all cases this was found to be true. Not all compounds which contain hydrogen, however, are acids,—only those which yield hydrogen ions in solution. A molecule of cane sugar, for instance, contains twenty-two atoms of hydrogen, but it gives no ions in solution, and, therefore, has neither the properties nor the composition of an acid.

Chemists now know that an acid is a compound which in solution gives hydrogen ions. These ions are positively charged and appear at the negative electrode when an electric current is passed through the solution. The characteristic properties of an acid, such as the sour taste, the changing of the color of certain compounds known as indicators, and the action upon a metal to produce hydrogen gas, are due to these hydrogen ions. Manifestly, too, the strength of an acid depends upon its ability to dissociate into ions. That acid is strongest which for a given concentration of solution yields the largest percentage of hydrogen ions. This was in accordance with the theory, and the means of testing it was ready at hand. The strongest acid should have the highest degree of electrical conductivity. And such was found to be the case. A vast realm of chemical facts became amenable to the new principle of scientific correlation. In perfect unison, fact and theory marched abreast. Once more the vision of the researcher blazed the way for chemical progress.

The following equation illustrates the meaning of ionization and what happens when an acid is dissolved in water:

$$HCl \rightarrow \overset{+}{H} + \overset{-}{Cl}$$

| Hydrochloric acid | Hydrogen ion | Chlorine ion |

Likewise, it was shown that a base is a chemical compound which in solution gives what the chemist calls *hydroxyl ions*. These are negatively charged groups, each consisting of the combination of an oxygen atom and a hydrogen atom. As has already been stated, when an acid and a base are brought together in solution, water and a salt result. It is now clear why water should be one of the products. A positively charged hydrogen ion from the acid unites with a negatively charged hydroxyl ion from the base, giving a compound containing two atoms of hydrogen and one of oxygen. This is, of course, water. The process is called neutralization, and as a matter of fact this production of water is the only chemical action taking place in bringing it about. The salt ions remain in the undissociated state until the water has been driven off by evaporation. The neutralization of any acid by any base always consists in this union of a hydrogen ion and a hydroxyl ion to form water. Thus, all cases of neutralization are reduced to a single process. Out of the heterogeneous mass of imperfect knowledge previously obtaining, simplicity emerged supreme.

The following equations show respectively the ionization of a base and the union of the hydrogen and hydroxyl ions to form water and a salt in the neutralization of an acid and a base:

$$NaOH \rightarrow \overset{+}{Na} + \overset{-}{OH}$$

Sodium hydroxide   Sodium ion   Hydroxyl ion

$$\overset{+}{Na}\overset{-}{OH} + \overset{+}{H}\overset{-}{Cl} = H_2O + \overset{+}{Na}\overset{-}{Cl}$$

Base   Acid   Water   Salt

This fact of neutralization also explained why the heat obtained in bringing together equivalent quantities of any acid and any base should always be the same. It is due to the production of water, and under these circumstances the quantity of water in one case is always the same as in every other case. Another puzzling problem had come under the sway of a known principle of chemical action. Its mystery had vanished as naturally as the sun converts the blackness of the night into the brightness of the morning.

These and many other known facts assumed a new meaning. Much of chemical phenomena, theretofore imperfectly understood, became readily intelligible. In particular, chemical activity seemed to be electrical in nature. Subsequent discoveries have tended to confirm this hypothesis. In support of the new theory came such stalwart defenders as van't Hoff and Ostwald. Many more quickly fell into line. To-day, I know of but one chemist of distinction who holds out against the overwhelming mass of evidence arrayed in support of this revolutionary conception of chemical action. And this theory appeared at an opportune time. Just as inorganic chemistry needed a new base from which to attack the problems confronting it, this conception, second only to the periodic grouping of the elements, came upon the scene. Fruitful beyond the dreams of its projector, it to-day dominates much of the instruction in our schools and colleges. It is gratifying to know, too, that Arrhenius is still living, happy in the consciousness that a product of his own research has proved to be a foundation stone of the present edifice of chemical fact and theory. To few is it given to enjoy such a privilege to the full.

PRACTICAL CONSIDERATION

Ions play a large part in maintaining the health of the human organism. A deficiency in the ions of metallic calcium in the blood is characteristic in cases of rickets. Rickety children are frequently subject to a form of convulsions known as tetany. This condition may usually be relieved by the injection into the blood of a solution containing calcium ions. An excess of calcium ions, however, has a very toxic effect. Too high a concentration of potassium ions enormously reduces the action of the heart and may produce death. When one has a sour stomach, the cause is an overabundance of hydrogen ions. In other words, there is too much acid in the stomach. For this condition, we take sodium bicarbonate, ordinary baking soda, for this destroys the acid by neutralization and therefore eliminates the hydrogen ions.

The gastric juice of the stomach contains considerable hydrochloric acid at all times. In such diseases as beri-beri, heart disease, cancer and anemia, the supply is insufficient. Normal health depends upon a slight degree of alkalinity of the blood, which means that there must be present a small excess of hydroxyl ions. The capacity of the human organism for maintaining this condition at all times is remarkable.

What would we do without the storage battery for motor starting, ignition and lights? Here is one of the most important applications of the chemical effects of the electric current. When we charge a battery, it does not take up electricity as a sponge takes up water. Instead, the current produces in the plates a set of chemical changes, thereby storing in them chemical energy. After the battery is charged and the plates are connected in external circuit, a reverse set of chemical changes converts the chemical energy back into electrical energy. As we all know, in driving a car the generator continually charges the battery, the charge usually being sufficient to keep the plates in condition.

To distinguish a storage cell from the ordinary voltaic cell, it is called a secondary cell. Faraday and others experimented with such cells, but it was Planté of France who in 1860 invented the first successful storage battery. This was the beginning of the present lead plate cell. Edison has followed it with another type, which is so impervious to abuse as to be well worthy of the description, "Built like a watch: rugged as a battleship." In my laboratory, I have forty of these cells which have given splendid service for many years.

In the electrolytic refining of metals, in electroplating and electrotyping, chemistry and electricity meet in a vast field of the highest usefulness. And as we shall see, the very nature of matter itself is electrical.

We have now sketched in outline the more important events in the progress of chemistry from the time of the alchemist to the mighty flood-tide of recent achievements. Much more might have been written. Many aspects of chemistry have had to be omitted. This book is not an encyclopedia. However, in succeeding pages we shall frequently have occasion to dip back into these formative years, picking up here and there a thread of chemical discovery and showing how it was carried forward to be woven into the fabric of modern triumphs.

Thus far, the purpose has been to paint the historic background out of which present progress grew.

We can not leave this period, however, without a word regarding Wilhelm Ostwald, a pioneer leader of the first magnitude in the inauguration of the new era in chemistry. As an experimental investigator of the highest ability, he did research work in many fields. But it is as an organizer that he has made his most profound influence on chemical thought. He took the loose, empirical knowledge of a generation ago and welded it into an exact science, supplying by his own researches much of the material to effect his purpose. Just forty years ago, he founded the *Journal of Physical Chemistry,* the most important publication of its kind in Europe. He is also the author of text-books which have had a wide and lasting influence. Thirty years and more ago, he reached the conclusion that energy and matter are one. In this, he anticipated Einstein by a decade. As a director of chemical research, he has played an important rôle. Many of the leading chemists of recent times have been his students. And Ostwald is still living, an heroic figure in the great forward movement of the science of which he has been so large a part.

And we should mention the classic synthesis of the sugars and the proteins by Emil Fischer, possibly the greatest organic chemist of any time. Neither should we forget the so-called "phase rule" of Willard Gibbs, one of the really great contributions to pure chemistry made by an American scientist. Announced in the Transactions of the Connecticut Academy of Sciences in 1876, it was so clothed in mathematics that Gibbs' fellow chemists did not appreciate the epochal importance of his generalization until years after. It developed with all the precision of mathematical treatment the fundamental principles underlying chemical equilibrium. Its industrial applications have been many, particularly in the field of alloys, in an understanding of the structure of steel, and in the solution of problems related to the manufacture of Portland cement. The practical results flowing from these applications afford a capital example of the debt industry owes to fundamental research.

I hesitate to mention other names, for in so long a list some well meriting recognition would surely be passed by. It is not the purpose of this book to give an exhaustive treatment of the subject.

In the following chapter, we shall come back to the closing decades of the last century to describe those epoch-making discoveries which led to our new knowledge of the atom and of those marvelous miniature worlds of the unseen, rivaling in the majesty of their perfection the infinitely vast cosmic systems of the heavens above.

CHAPTER III

Atoms, Electrons and Protons

EARLY CONCEPTION OF ATOMS—CROOKES' DISCOVERY—
CATHODE RAYS AND THEIR NATURE—RÖNTGEN AND THE
X-RAY—INVESTIGATIONS OF SIR J. J. THOMPSON—ELEC-
TRONS—RADIOACTIVITY—BECQUEREL AND URANIUM—MADAME
CURIE DISCOVERS RADIUM—ALPHA, BETA AND GAMMA RAYS—
RADIUM EMANATION—LIFE HISTORY OF RADIUM—DISINTEGRA-
TION PRODUCTS OF URANIUM—A PEEP WITHIN THE
ATOM—ATOMIC NUMBERS—DISINTEGRATION CHART FOR
URANIUM—ISOTOPES—AGE OF THE EARTH—FIRST ALCHE-
MIST—THE PROTON—STRUCTURE OF THE ATOMIC NUCLEUS—
PROTON IDENTICAL WITH HYDROGEN NUCLEUS—PROUT'S
HYPOTHESIS—PARADOXICAL DIMENSIONS OF NUCLEUS—
TRANSFORMATIONS OF ELEMENTS—SUBATOMIC ENERGY—AN-
NIHILATION OF MASS AND PRODUCTION OF ENERGY—EINSTEIN'S
EQUATION—REPORT OF TRANSMUTATION OF HYDROGEN INTO
HELIUM—POSSIBLE SOURCE OF SUN'S ENERGY—COSMIC
RAYS—MILLIKAN'S EXPERIMENTS—THEIR SIGNIFICANCE—
UTILIZATION OF ENERGY OF ATOM—X-RAY SPECTRA—MOSELEY
AND THE ATOMIC NUMBERS—X-RAY PATTERNS OF ATOMS AND
MOLECULES—MEASURING THE CHARGE ON AN ELECTRON—
ELECTRONS AND CHEMICAL ACTION—LANGMUIR'S THEORY—
THE BOHR ATOM.

WE ARE already on speaking terms with atoms, but
we have not peeped within. We have not gained a
glimpse of that marvelous miniature planetary system of
perfect law and order, infinitely small, and yet, in the

majesty of its movements and the complexity of its structure, challenging comparison with the solar systems of the celestial spaces. And of electrons and protons, the constituent members of an atomic family, we have yet to learn.

The story of these modern explorations of discovery goes back to the eighties of the last century and the rising of that vast flood-tide of new knowledge of radio-activity and the electrical nature of matter which has marked an epoch in the progress of science. Let us not delay the beginning of its narration.

Until this violent upheaval in century-old ideas of the constitution of matter, scientists were perfectly certain that the ultimate units of which the elements are composed were infinitesimally small, indivisible particles, probably spherical in form and simple in structure. Indeed, despite variations, this early idea of atoms held the center of the stage. No divine edict had announced such a view. It had simply grown up as the most logical way of thinking about the smallest particles into which matter might be divided by physical and chemical means. But a scientist is never a fundamentalist. He never allows inherited ideas from an age of imperfect knowledge to gain a steel-trap grip on his intellectual processes. Always keeping step with the marching song of new discoveries, when the facts point the way, he discards an outgrown idea as readily as he does a threadbare garment or an outworn pair of shoes.

The man who blundered into this virgin continent of unexplored possibilities was Sir William Crookes. Most every one in these days has seen an X-ray tube. The progenitor of that veritable herald of a new era was an electric vacuum tube devised by Crookes. Something like a generation ago, this British investigator conceived the idea of pumping the air from a glass tube, into either end of which he had sealed a metallic electrode, and then connecting these electrodes with a high voltage source of electricity. Wonderful color effects resulted from this electric discharge in high vacuum. Pure research was this,—merely gratifying the whims of a scientist's insatiable curiosity to know what will happen under a new set of conditions. Little did Crookes realize that he stood at the dawn of a new day. But he began to experiment, and soon he had the whole scientific world studying this new fact of Nature and trying to unravel its meaning.

Let us state that one of the electrodes in a Crookes tube is known as the anode and the other as the cathode. One is the positive terminal and the other the negative. The mysterious rays came from the cathode, or negative terminal. In a darkened room, these rays manifested themselves in three ways: they produced a brilliant glow, or fluorescence, as scientists call it, in the walls of the glass tube; a metal object placed in their path became very hot; and this object also cast a sharp shadow on the opposite wall of the tube. Such were the observed facts, and as unlikely a set of phenomena as ever rewarded the researches of a pure scientist. Although it was rash to dream of anything of practical value flowing from such fantastic effects, they were soon poking holes all through the venerable structure of chemical and physical knowledge.

Of what did these rays consist? That was the first big question presenting itself. Were they simply a new form of ether waves, or did they consist of infinitesimally small particles shot off from the cathode at tremendous velocities? The only way to answer such questions is to try experiments, and the scientists took off their coats and went to work. One point was quickly settled. In another tube, Crookes placed a small track consisting of two slender rails and carrying a light metal paddle-wheel with its axles resting freely upon the rails. When the tube was excited, this little wheel began to revolve and to move along the track toward the anode. It seemed clear enough that the cathode must shoot off missiles of some sort. Waves in the immaterial ether could not produce motion. But what was the nature of these infinitesimal particles? More experiments were necessary.

Since these particles came from the cathode, it seemed a likely guess that they might be negatively charged. Whether this might be so was not difficult to discover. The positive pole of an ordinary magnet was brought near to an excited tube. Immediately, the stream of particles moved in a curved line directly toward the pole of the magnet. To make this effect visible, a vertical strip of cardboard which had been coated with a thin layer of a zinc sulfide, a substance which under the influence of cathode rays, fluoresces brilliantly, was placed lengthwise of the tube. Just in front of the cathode terminal was inserted a screen having a narrow slit. Now when the tube was excited, a bright line of light appeared along the whole length of the cardboard. When, however, the positive pole of the magnet was brought near to the side of the tube, this line curved downward toward the magnet. The positive pole of a magnet will attract only the opposite kind of electricity. Therefore, it became certain that these tiny bullets were

negatively charged. Other experiments showed that they
actually impart negative charges to bodies upon which
they fall and that they sometimes move with velocities
as high as one hundred thousand miles a second. Simply
stupendous revelations were these and of surpassing
interest, despite the fact that nothing which might be
labeled "practical" had so far resulted.

Still, these swarms of atomic meteors were wholly
confined within the walls of a small glass tube. Was it

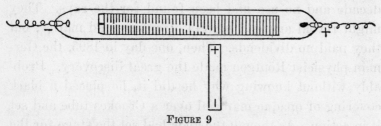

FIGURE 9
Apparatus by which the cathode particles were shown to carry negative charges of electricity. As they pass through the narrow slit at the
left and along the zinc sulfide screen, a trail of light is left, which curves
downward toward the positive pole of the magnet held at the side.

possible to induce them to come on the outside and display their charms in the open? The physicist Lenard,
now professor at the University of Heidelberg, first
succeeded in doing this. He provided a tube with a small
aluminum window one-eighth of an inch in diameter,
through which very feeble rays passed. But he used
only thirty thousand volts. Coolidge with his new
cathode-ray tube using three hundred and fifty thousand
volts, through a window of nickel foil two inches in
diameter, now shoots billions of these charged particles
into the air.

It was early discovered that it makes no difference of
what metal the cathode terminal is made. The results

were always the same. Negatively charged particles, identically similar in every case, appeared. Surely, a profound secret of Nature was in the offing. Could it be possible that here at last men had stumbled upon the primordial substance of which scientists from Aristotle down had dreamed? Indeed, it might be so. More experimenting should tell the tale.

Yet, scientists had been experimenting with this new "fourth state" of matter, as Crookes called it, for a decade and no use had been found for the rays. They might reveal ages-old secrets of energy and matter, but they paid no dividends. Then, one day in 1895, the German physicist Röntgen made the great discovery. Probably without knowing why he did it, he placed a black covering of opaque material over a Crookes tube and set it in action. As though the gods had set the stage for the coming of this event, there happened to be a prepared chemical screen lying near the tube. To the amazement of Röntgen, it immediately began to glow. Something very extraordinary was occurring. A new kind of radiation was emanating from the tube. In utter defiance of all the accepted ideas of orthodox scientific fundamentalists, these rays passed right through matter which had always been regarded as opaque to any kind of light waves. Further experiments showed that this mysterious radiation penetrated living flesh and all sorts of substances. In short the X-rays were born. Shadowy, ghost-like silhouettes of coins in a purse, nails in a shoe, the bones of the hand or what-not were soon commonplace evidences of the new manifestation. The secret was soon out. Wherever these swarms of negatively charged particles strike an object within a Crookes tube, an ex-

ceedingly penetrating radiation is set up. At first a
baffling mystery, it has long been known that these rays
consist of ether waves so exceedingly short that it requires two hundred and fifty million of them to measure
an inch and the rate of vibration producing them is three
quintillion per second. It did not take long to pile up
such a record of achievement to the credit of the X-ray
that no one longer questioned the value of the preceding

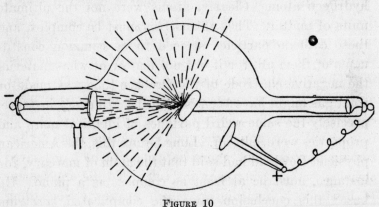

FIGURE 10

An X-ray tube. The cathode particles are brought to focus upon the
metal screen near the center of the bulb, where by impact the inconceivably
short waves in the ether known as X-rays are generated.

years of research. Once more the veil of mystery had
been lifted. A deep insight into ultimate realities had
been gained. Men stood upon the threshold of a new
world.

And now Sir J. J. Thomson took up the investigation
from a different angle. He sought to know how heavy
one of these cathode particles is, or, as the scientist says,
its mass. To the uninitiated, this, of course, seems a
wholly impossible feat. But by methods of extraordinary precision it was not long until Thomson had

determined to his own satisfaction and to that of the whole scientific world ever since that one of these negatively charged particles has a mass about one eighteen-hundredth as great as that of an atom of hydrogen. The most recent determination gives the fraction as one eighteen-hundred and forty-fifth. Now hydrogen is the lightest known element, and yet here were particles of matter lighter by nearly two thousand times than the hydrogen atom. Clearly, atoms were not the ultimate units of matter. They themselves must be complex, and these cathode particles seemed to be common constituents of them all, for it did not matter of what material the negative electrode of the Crookes tube was made or what gas might have been in the tube. In every instance, precisely the same weird particles of identical mass and properties were split off. Long before this, the American physicist Rowland had said that the atom of mercury, for instance, must be at least as complex as a piano. He based this conclusion upon the complicated spectrum produced by mercury vapor in incandescent state. When viewed with the spectroscope, it is seen to possess a large number of spectral lines. Rowland could not reconcile such complexity with a simple structure of the atom. To him the thought was irresistible that so many vibrations in the ether could not proceed from a simple source. Within the atom must be a world of marvelous complexity. And so it has proved.

Already you have guessed that these cathode particles are the familiar *electrons* with which your radio vacuum tube swarms. They boil off from the hot tungsten filament of the tube, and their control, through the plate and grid, by the wireless waves in the ether enables you to "listen in on the universe." A stream of electrons surges along a copper wire, and we have an electric current. The lightning flashes, and countless trillions of these subatomic fireflies zigzag from cloud to cloud or mayhap to the earth. All space seems to be filled with them. They are the working capital of the universe. Apparently ultimate units of matter, quite recent observations indicate that they may be compound.

Sir J. J. Thomson did not stop with his determination of the mass of the electron. He wished to know whether there might be anything more to this cathode particle than a simple negative charge of electricity. Was there a tiny hard core of what we call matter bearing an electric charge, or was the electric charge the whole thing? Already Thomson and Lorentz had shown that a moving charge of electricity can possess both mass and inertia, the two fundamental properties of all matter. It was not difficult to measure both the negative charge of the electron and the velocity with which it moved. Then Thomson proceeded to demonstrate, both theoretically and practically, that an electric charge of that magnitude moving with the observed velocity would account for precisely the quantity of mass which the electron was known to possess. In other words, the electron is nothing but negative electricity, a mere point of energy. A revolutionizing idea was this. Hard, solid matter had resolved itself into great aggregations of centers of force. In a sense, it had become intangible, elusive, unreal. The atmosphere, the ocean deeps, the rock-ribbed hills, and the substance of living organisms had become but moving points of electrical energy. The vast complexity of the universe, so far as ultimate units were concerned, seemed to resolve itself into a wonderful simplicity. In speaking of this new knowledge, Sir William Crookes said: "We have actually touched the borderland where matter and energy seem to merge into one another—the shadowy realm between the known and the unknown. I venture to think the greatest scientific problems of the future will find their solution in this borderland, and even beyond. Here, it seems to me, lie ultimate realities, subtle, far-reaching, wonderful."

RADIOACTIVITY

Still, men had not yet glimpsed the interior of an atom. One thing seemed perfectly sure: an atom is marvelously complex. Its supposed simplicity had vanished. But just how far the pendulum had swung in the opposite direction did not appear. It is axiomatic that negative charges can not exist without the corresponding positive charges. Here were negative electrons. Where were their brothers of positive electrification? The most rigid search did not reveal them. The best that could be done was to accept the provisional hypothesis of Sir J. J. Thomson, namely, that an atom is an aggregation of negative electrons moving about a center of positive electrification. But no one deluded himself with the thought that this was more than a half explanation. All the batteries of science were now turned upon the atom.

Just at this moment, occurred one of the most propitious discoveries in the whole history of science. Radioactivity came upon the scene to throw a flood of light upon the mysteries of energy and matter and upon the structure of the atom in particular. We have not yet

ceased to marvel at the revelations in this new field of
inquiry nor to fail to find new vistas of unexplored truth.

The man to approach this new fact of Nature, waiting
patiently throughout the ages to take its place in the
constantly growing edifice of human knowledge, was
Henri Becquerel, of the University of Paris. The phenomena of X-rays had aroused his curiosity, and scientific curiosity is the most prolific source of discovery that
the world has ever known. Becquerel began to investi-
gate the light-giving properties of phosphorescent
substances. May it not be possible, he asked, that the
radiations of some of these substances will also have the
property of penetrating opaque matter? For his purpose, he selected the metal *uranium*. I do not know what
hand of destiny may have led him to make this choice.
Certainly, it was a most happy one. He exposed the
metal to sunlight, carried it into his dark room and
placed it upon a photographic plate wrapped in heavy
black paper. I can imagine the keen interest with which
this savant developed the plate. He had put a momen-
tous question to Nature, and he knew that the answer
would be forthcoming. But what would it be? The
developed plate told the tale. It had been darkened.
Here was a radiation which, like X-rays, would penetrate
opaque matter and produce chemical changes in the compounds on a prepared plate. Becquerel now substituted
thin sheets of metal for the black paper. The result was
the same. Without knowing it, he was blazing pioneer
trails in the shadowy borderland of a new world. One
day the sun forgot to shine. Wrapping a photographic
plate in black paper, Becquerel placed the uranium upon
it and thrust the two into a drawer. There, almost for-

·gotten, they remained for several weeks. Then, the curiosity of the scientist asserted itself once more. Could it be possible that uranium metal not having first been exposed to sunlight would affect a photographic plate? Becquerel developed the plate. Again, the shadow-image gave the answer. Uranium, independently of any external stimulation, did emit the new rays. But suppose it did? Of what value could that be? Let us see.

There happened to be working with Becquerel at that time in his Paris laboratory a Polish girl, whom all the world has come to know as Madame Curie. As you know, she asked and received permission to make a systematic search to discover whether any of the other elements might also possess radioactive powers. She found only one, *thorium,* which did. But one day she made a scientifically startling discovery. She found that pitchblende, the parent mineral from which uranium is obtained, exhibits a degree of radioactivity four times as great as that given off by all the pure uranium which could be extracted from the sample itself. What did it mean? The answer was perfectly clear: pitchblende must contain some other element more radioactive than uranium itself.

The possibility of discovering a new element was alluring. Assisted by her youthful husband, Pierre Curie, this Polish girl in a strange capital began the search. Starting with a ton of pitchblende presented to them by the Austrian Government from its rich mines at Joachimsthal, Bohemia, the Curies essayed the herculean task. In this search, they availed themselves of Becquerel's discovery that these rays are able to ionize a gas, or make it a conductor of electricity, thus discharging a gold-leaf electroscope whenever a radioactive substance is brought near to it. So delicate is the test that a quantity as small as one fifty-billionth of a gram may be detected with perfect ease, and Professor Soddy says that probably one-tenth that amount would not escape discovery.

The first product of this expedition of discovery was the finding of a strongly radioactive element, which Madame Curie named *polonium* in honor of her native country. But another residue showed the presence of a still more active element, and the search continued. Finally, the element was cornered. In 1898, the Curies separated a few milligrams of a substance two and a half million times as radioactive as uranium. I do not need to tell you that this new element was *radium*. Viewed with the spectroscope, it disclosed a perfectly definite bright-line spectrum, and its atomic weight was soon determined to be two hundred and twenty-six, fitting it into a niche in the periodic table which had been waiting for it for nearly a generation. It was found to darken photographic plates, ionize the air, excite phosphorescence, liberate large quantities of heat, produce chemical changes and destroy minute organisms.

The whole scientific world was immediately aflame with the discovery. It was quickly discovered that the new element is a wonderful source of energy. Every three-quarters of an hour a gram of it gives off enough heat to raise the temperature of the same quantity of water from the freezing point to the boiling point. Its energy-content is more than a million times greater than that of coal. It did not take long to learn, too, that men can neither hasten nor stay this liberation of energy.

They may stand on the side-lines and watch it, but that is all. Neither intense heat nor exceeding cold will influence the process in the slightest degree. Still, men were as yet groping only in the twilight zone of partial discovery. The great vistas of subatomic worlds had not been glimpsed.

RADIUM RAYS

Three investigators of the first rank, Sir Ernest Rutherford, Sir William Ramsay and Professor Frederick Soddy, immediately took up the investigation of the properties of radium. The first and last of these pioneers are still at work. To Rutherford we owe the first systematic analysis of the complex radiations emanating from radioactive substances. The result was the discovery of three distinct sets of rays, which he named *alpha rays, beta rays* and *gamma rays*. But what of their nature and what did they reveal regarding the structure of the atom? We shall see.

The alpha rays turned out to be positively charged particles shot out of radium atoms with velocities approaching twenty thousand miles a second. Their penetrating power is small, but they are exceedingly efficient in ionizing gases and rendering them conductors of electricity. And, to the bewilderment of the scientific world, when these particles were collected and examined with the spectroscope, they proved to be identical with helium gas. An epoch-making discovery in its effect upon the orthodox notions of chemical elements was this. The old idea that an element is a substance which can not be changed into anything different from itself by any known means broke down. Here was an element, radium, spontaneously decomposing and thereby giving rise to another element, helium. Surely, here was natural alchemy. True, man can neither initiate nor influence the transformation, but, as we shall see, it gave him the clue which has enabled him to batter the atoms of other elements to pieces and become a real alchemist. We shall hear much of alpha particles in succeeding pages.

The beta rays were soon proved to be *streams of electrons* projected from radioactive atoms with velocities ranging from sixty thousand to one hundred eighty thousand miles a second. In other words, they are identical with the cathode particles of a Crookes tube. They are attracted by the positive pole of a magnet, while the alpha particles are deflected in the opposite direction. Their penetrating power proved to be great. A sheet of aluminum foil .005 of a centimeter thick will completely stop alpha particles, but it has no effect upon the beta rays. The advance-guard of atomic exploration was taking great strides in extending the frontiers of human knowledge. Certain it now was that the atoms of all elements contain electrons and that the atoms of radioactive elements in addition hurl forth enormously heavier positively charged particles, thus giving rise to another element. Fascinating was the search. Still, the main army of attack had only reached the coastal region of the unknown continent.

The gamma rays, having a penetrating power much greater even than that of the beta particles, proved to be identical with X-rays, except that they are of shorter wave length and more intense. They are simply exceedingly short waves in the ether set up by the impact of beta particles on surrounding matter. The bombardment of electrons in a Crookes tube produces ordinary X-rays. The electrons from a radioactive element give the gamma rays.

Following close upon the heels of these revelations came a remarkable disclosure. Rutherford dissolved a sample of radium salt in water and evaporated the solution to dryness. The result was the production of an intensely radioactive gas, which he collected and named *radium emanation.* It proved to be a new element, *niton,* of atomic weight two hundred and twenty-two, just four less than that of radium, and taking its place in the periodic table along with the rare gases of the atmosphere. At the same time helium gas, already known to be a disintegration product of radium, formed. Now the atomic weight of helium is four. Therefore, it became apparent that the two initial products of radium decay are these two elements, accompanied by the liberation of a ceaseless supply of energy. Evidently, something of extraordinary interest was happening within the atom. Soon it was to surrender it secrets.

The next link in the chain was the discovery that the activity of the new element niton rapidly decays from day to day until at the end of thirty days it has become practically zero. At the same time, it successively passes through a series of disintegration stages, giving rise at each stage to a new product. The end product proved to be lead, but lead of a different atomic weight from that obtained from ordinary ore. Another thought-provoking fact was this, the real significance of which will appear a little later.

The rate at which radium decays was soon established and from this it at once became possible to calculate its

average period of life. This period may be stated as
follows: In seventeen hundred and thirty years, half of
any given quantity of radium will have decomposed. In
another equal period half of the remainder will decompose, and so on. In order that there should be any left
in the earth now, it seemed that in past geologic time
there must have been prodigious quantities present in
the rocks. Still the geology of the rocks and their fossil
records disproved any such conclusion. Only one alternative was left. Scientists were compelled to believe
that radium is being produced from some other element
as fast as it disappears. With that other element, which
turned out to be uranium, and its revelations of atomic
structure we are now concerned.

DISINTEGRATION PRODUCTS OF URANIUM

I wish to proceed with this discussion unhurriedly,
with plenty of time to grasp the details of the pictures
which will present themselves. A multitude of facts of
the most fascinating nature awaits us. We can not
assimilate them in a moment. With patience the whole
will be made plain. First, before we can interpret the
disintegration of uranium, certain preliminary ideas, to
be elaborated more in detail later, must be introduced.

Let us start off with the scientist's present conception
of the structure of the atom. To get a better view, we
will magnify the sizes of all atoms and molecules ten
billion times. On this scale, a bird shot would be as large
as the earth, and we shall find an average atom to be
about three feet in diameter. And what do we see?
Surely, not the hard, smooth, shining sphere which the
ancients and even scientists until quite recently imagined.

Instead, we behold a vast solar system with central sun and planets which revolve about it at almost inconceivable velocities. We look again, and to our bewildered gaze find that the atom appears to be almost infinitely porous. How could we ever have thought it solid? Between the planetary electrons and the central nucleus, and between the electrons themselves, are great dreary wastes of space, relatively vaster in comparison than the spaces between the members of our own solar system. Far away at the center of the sphere, we descry the nucleus, no larger than a pin point even on the immense scale we are here considering. As we shall see, this is probably the most paradoxical unit of all creation. Although inconceivably small, vastly smaller than an electron, practically all of the mass of the atom is stowed away within this solar treasure-house. This is not a fiction of a disordered brain. As much solid evidence exists in support of this conclusion as of any hypothesis of science. Indeed, this is much more than an hypothesis now.

Quickly, we examine the atoms of other elements and find that they are all built after the same pattern. In every one there is the central nucleus and revolving electrons. The only difference we note is in the respective numbers of planetary electrons in the atoms of the different elements. Hydrogen has a single electron, winging its solitary way about an orbit of truly "celestial" proportions. The atom of helium, the next in order of weight, is seen to have two electrons, each in a different orbit. The atom of lithium shows three, and so on until we come to uranium, the heaviest, which exhibits a marvelously complex system of central nucleus and ninety-two revolving electrons. We no longer wonder at the

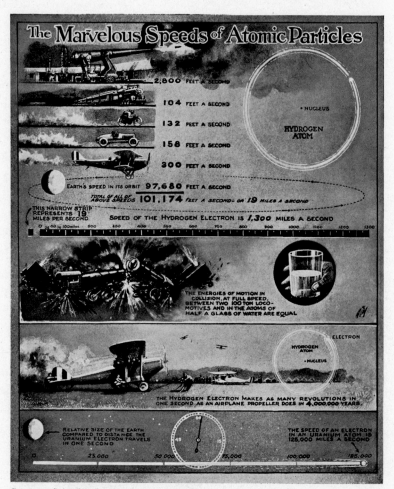

Interesting facts regarding the electron

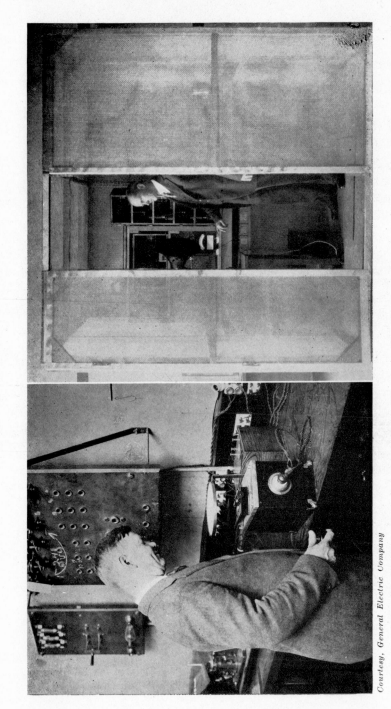

Courtesy, General Electric Company

Apparatus for obtaining X-ray spectra of the elements

The X-ray is assisting in the solution of a multitude of scientific and industrial problems

Listening to the patter of electrons from the hot filament of a vacuum tube amplifier

With similar apparatus electrons from the disintegration of uranium have been heard

large number of spectral lines which one of these heavy elements gives when its atoms are in the highly excited state of incandescence and its orbital electrons are stimulated to unwonted activity. The velocity with which these electrons move is estimated by Rutherford sometimes to reach ninety-three thousand miles per second, half that of light. What dreamer of a generation ago would have been bold enough to paint a picture of molecules inconceivably small, made up of atoms infinitely smaller, which in turn are electronic systems as majestic in their reign of perfect law as the stupendous systems of the starry spaces? And yet, such is the undoubted truth.

Let us pause to note one immensely important fact. We have seen that in the atom of hydrogen we have a single planetary electron, in helium two, in lithium three and so on until we reach ninety-two in uranium. There seems to be a perfect sequence, each heavier atom adding another electron. That is, we can number the elements in order from hydrogen to uranium. This has been done, and the numbers one to ninety-two are known as the *atomic numbers*. They are even more significant than are the atomic weights of the elements. This number gives the position of the element in the periodic table. As is apparent, too, it means the number of negative electrons revolving about the central nucleus. But it has another meaning. Let us see what it is. As you have doubtless already guessed, the nucleus must be positively charged. Otherwise, it could not hold in their orbits the negative electrons. Still the atom as a whole is electrically neutral. Therefore, the number of positive charges on the nucleus must equal the number of planetary electrons. In other words, the atomic number stands for the number of positive charges on the nuclear "sun" as well as for the number of revolving "planets." Indeed, these charges have actually been measured and found to agree in each case with the atomic number. The electrical attraction of the nucleus for the electrons corresponds to the force of gravitation in our own solar system, and we know that the electrons must be in motion about the nucleus; otherwise they would be drawn into it, with the consequent annihilation of the whole mass of the atom and the liberation of a vast quantity of energy. But we are getting ahead of the story. Let us defer no longer the account of the actual disintegration of uranium. It will throw a flood of light upon this whole field of atomic structure.

Now I want you to examine very closely with me the accompanying diagram. In following the trail of uranium from the upper right-hand corner until its disintegration products toboggan to the bottom of the cascade and half of its mass has been transformed, we pass over a period estimated as ranging from five to eight billions of years. Fortunately, we shall not require that time to make the explanation. Along the horizontal axis of this diagram, we have the symbols of certain elements and the atomic numbers from 81 to 92. In two instances, 85 and 87, symbols are missing because these elements have not yet been discovered. Along the vertical axis, we have the atomic weights. If for example we wish to know the atomic number of an element appearing in the diagram, we drop a vertical line to the horizontal axis, and to find its atomic weight we carry a horizontal line across to the vertical axis.

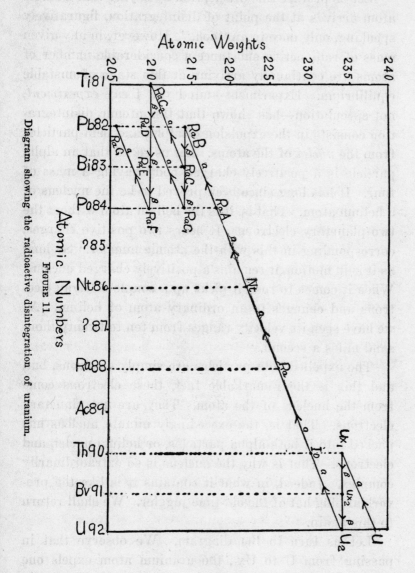

Diagram showing the radioactive disintegration of uranium.

FIGURE 11

Let us preface this description by saying that a single atom arrives at the point of disintegration, figuratively speaking, only once in an "eon." However, in any given mass of radioactive substance a considerable number of atoms are continually arriving at this stage of unstable equilibrium. Experiment—mind you I say *experiment,* not speculation—has shown that this atomic disintegration consists in the expulsion of alpha and beta particles from the *nuclei* of the atoms. Let us recall that an alpha particle is a positively charged body having a mass of four. It has long since been proved to be the nucleus of a helium atom. That is, it is the helium atom without the two planetary electrons. It bears two positive charges, corresponding in this with the atomic number. So long as it is in motion, it remains a positively charged nucleus. When it comes to rest, it picks up a couple of stray electrons and changes to an ordinary atom of helium. As we have seen its velocity ranges from ten to twenty thousand miles a second.

The expelled beta particles are simply electrons, but, and this is the remarkable fact, these electrons come from the nucleus of the atom. They are not planetary electrons. That is, the exceedingly minute nucleus has packed into it both alpha particles, or helium nuclei, and electrons. That is why the nucleus is so extraordinarily complex. Indeed, in what it contains it is like the proverbial plug hat of the old-time juggler. We shall return to this again.

Let us turn to the diagram. We observe that in passing from U to Ux$_1$, the uranium atom expels one alpha particle. Let us see what this does to the partly disintegrated atom. Since the alpha particle is a helium nucleus of mass four and carrying two positive charges, the transformation results in reducing the atomic weight of the atom by four and the charge on its nucleus by two. In other words, we have a new element Ux_1. Since the atomic weight of uranium is 238, the atomic weight of the new element is 234, and its atomic number is 90. That is, where U has 92 positive charges on the nucleus, Ux_1 has only 90. This is not an imaginary element. Its atomic weight and properties have been determined, and it is just as much a reality as hydrogen or oxygen.

In the next stage, we pass from Ux_1 to Ux_2. This consists in the expulsion of a beta particle, or an electron, and we represent the change on a horizontal line. Let us see why. The mass, or weight, of an electron is practically zero. You will remember that a hydrogen atom is 1,845 times as heavy as an electron, and that the entire mass of an atom is concentrated in the nucleus. Therefore, in going from Ux_1 to Ux_2, the atomic weight remains the same. In other words, we have the paradoxical coincidence of a new element of precisely the same atomic weight as the preceding one. Such an occurrence would have been unthinkable in the older chemistry. To-day, it is an experimental fact. But, why is it a new element? How does it differ from the one which gave it birth? First, let us remember that this electron comes from the nucleus and thus subtracts from the nucleus one negative charge, for all electrons are negative. This is equivalent to increasing by one the positive charges on the nucleus. And when we change the positive charges on the nucleus, we change the atomic number of the element and the number of planetary electrons. In this case the atomic number becomes 91, and the nucleus simply picks up another *orbital* electron, for electrons are everywhere and a nucleus will always acquire as many as it needs to neutralize its positive charges, just as our sun sometimes captures a comet and makes it a part of its own system.

Following the diagram, we see that Ux_2 expels another beta particle, or nuclear electron, and passes to U_2. Again the atomic weight remains the same, but the positive charges on the nucleus increase by one, thus bringing the atomic number back to 92, the same as that of uranium with which we started. And here we arrive at a most significant chemical fact. The elements U and U_2 each have the same atomic number, the same number of planetary electrons, and identical chemical properties. They can be separated only by physical means. Practically the only difference is that of atomic weight. In this, the second is four less than that of the first. As we shall see, there are many examples of this phenomenon. To designate it, Professor Frederick Soddy, one of the pioneer leaders in the investigations of radioactivity, coined the name *isotope,* which means "the same place." That is, these two elements, differing only slightly in physical properties and in atomic weights, are isotopes of each other.

This new fact of Nature at once offered an explanation of one very puzzling circumstance. It was supposed by early investigators that the atomic weights of the elements should be whole numbers. But the stubborn facts of chemical analysis soon dissipated this idea. Many atomic weights certainly were not whole numbers. The mystery now vanishes, however, for it is known that where a decimal atomic weight occurs the ordinary form of the element is made up of a number of isotopes in varying proportions. The atomic weight of each is a whole number but the combined result is not. Let us take lead, the atomic weight of which is given as 207.2. This element is known to have isotopes having atomic weights of 204, 206, 207 and 208 respectively, and it is thought that there are two others of atomic weights 205 and 210. It was lead from radioactive sources which gave the first hint of isotopes, and Professor Theodore W. Richards, of Harvard, made the atomic weight determination which gave the proof. Let us say in passing that Professor Richards is the world's leading authority in the field of atomic weight investigations.

Let us return to the diagram. From U_2 we have a straight toboggan slide for a long stretch, along the pathway of which five new elements are born. This isotope of uranium first expels an alpha particle, or helium nucleus, thus reducing the atomic weight by four and changing the atomic number from 92 to 90. We now note on the vertical dotted line three elements, Ux_1, ionium, and thorium. These are isotopes. Each has the same atomic number, the same equality of positive and negative charges between nucleus and planetary electrons, and the same chemical properties. Their atomic weights differ and also their physical properties somewhat. All three are radioactive.

Ionium now expels from its nucleus an alpha particle, giving birth to radium, and the process is repeated three times more in succession. In each instance the atomic number is reduced by two and the atomic weight by four. The average life periods of these elements range from one hundred thousand years for ionium to only thirty-eight and a half minutes for radium B.

Let us remember that these transformations are perfectly spontaneous and absolutely unalterable. Nothing which man can do affects them in the slightest. The most powerful chemical reagents or the most intense heat or cold are wholly without influence. And in these volcanic-like nuclear eruptions prodigious quantities of energy are liberated. Let it be clear, too, that the source of this energy is the nucleus and not the planetary electrons. These heavy elements, which may have evolved slowly throughout the ages from lighter ones, at length acquire the characteristics of atomic instability and from causes utterly beyond the scrutiny and control of human beings gradually disintegrate.

Radium B now expels two beta particles, or electrons, in succession, giving rise to Ra C and Ra C₁ respectively. Here again, we have the birth of new elements without a change in atomic weights. In each case the charge on the nucleus changes, thus giving a new atomic number, and the chemical and physical properties change, but the mass of the atom remains the same. Such combinations of elements are known as *isobares*.

From Ra C, you will note that there is a choice of two paths leading to Ra D. The nucleus of Ra C may expel a beta particle, giving Ra C₁, and then an alpha particle. Or it may erupt the alpha particle first, giving Ra C₂, and follow this with the expulsion of a beta particle. As a matter of fact both routes are taken, for both Ra C₁ and Ra C₂, are known. Radium D expels two beta particles, giving rise to two isobares, the latter of which, Ra F, thrusts out an alpha particle and shoots down to Ra G, where this long joy-ride ends.

Radium G is an isotope of lead, as are also Ra D and

Ra B Bismuth, of atomic number 83, is seen to have two isotopes, and polonium, atomic number 84, has three.

All along this pathway of subatomic transformations helium gas has been formed. From uranium to radium G, if we assume that we start with a single atom of uranium, nine atoms of helium have been produced. As soon as the alpha particles, or helium nuclei, come to rest or greatly reduce the speeds with which they were expelled, they pick up two more planetary electrons in each case and become ordinary atoms of helium. Also along this royal highway of radioactive disintegrations, fifteen new atomic species have been formed. Nine of these are identified by ordinary spectroscopic and chemical means.

The elements *thorium* and *actinium* also give disintegration series, each ending with lead. As we shall see, it is the dream of the modern alchemist to carry this disintegration by artificial means downward to gold. In addition to the foregoing elements, potassium and rubidium also emit beta rays, probably becoming calcium and strontium respectively. It is by no means uncertain that some of the other elements are slightly radioactive.

A wonderfully interesting little instrument, known as the spinthariscope, was devised by Sir William Crookes for viewing directly the impact of alpha particles from a radioactive substance. A screen covered with zinc sulfide is placed at the bottom of a small tube and just above it is suspended a tiny bit of some radium salt. Fitted into the top of the tube is a magnifying lens. Upon looking through the lens, hundreds of minute flashes of light are seen. The screen appears to be bombarded by an incessant rain of projectiles. Here is direct proof of the disintegration of radium.

A pupil of Sir J. J. Thomson, C. T. R. Wilson, has devised a beautiful method of photographing the path of an alpha particle. It is well known that dust in moist-laden air affords centers about which visible clouds of water vapor will condense. In dust-free air it is difficult

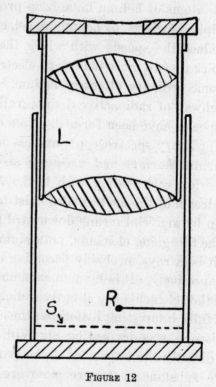

FIGURE 12

The spinthariscope. The bombardment of alpha particles from the radium compound placed at R produces splashes of light on the zinc sulfide screen S.

to form such clouds. If, however, the molecules in the air can be ionized, that is, changed into positively and negatively charged particles by knocking electrons free from their atoms, these ions will serve as centers of condensation. As we have seen, swiftly moving alpha particles thus ionize the air. Taking advantage of this fact, Wilson shot alpha particles into a chamber of moist-laiden, dust-free air and at the same time photographed the trail of condensed water vapor left along the pathway of the moving projectiles. Evidence of atomic disintegration of a most beautiful and convincing character was thus obtained.

THE AGE OF THE EARTH

And now if your brain is not in too much of a whirl, let us see how the known rate of decay of a radioactive substance enables us to calculate the approximate age of the earth's crust. We must base our estimate upon the activity of uranium, for this is the oldest radioactive element and the parent of all the others. The average life period of uranium is usually given as five billion years. This means, as you will recall, that in five billion years half of any given quantity of uranium will decay and in another equal period of time half of the remainder and so on. That is, half of the atoms in the original mass of the element will have passed through all the disintegration stages and been converted into lead.

From the foregoing, it must be clear that the amount of lead present in a uranium mineral gives us a clue as to the age of the mineral itself. Now, in the oldest geologic formations uranium minerals have been found containing one-tenth lead. That is, since the uranium atoms in this mineral began to disintegrate, only one-tenth of them have undergone the process. This means that the average period is only one-fifth complete, for, if the average period had now expired, half of the mineral instead of a tenth should be lead. In other words, the rock formations in which these uranium minerals were found are a billion years old. Some determinations have made this period a billion and a quarter years. There can be little doubt as to the general accuracy of these estimates. The earth is vastly older than men formerly supposed. The biologists who have been scraping along on the bare hundred millions of years doled out to them by the geologist may now have almost infinite periods of time for their life processes.

In 1925, at a meeting of the American Chemical Society in Los Angeles, Dr. Willis R. Whitney demonstrated the audibility of the disintegration of the atoms of uranium. Using an ordinary radio amplifier and loud-speaker, he broadcasted the impacts of the alpha and beta particles, so that they could be distinctly heard throughout the large auditorium. The audience might have listened to the impacts of those subatomic entities for five billion years and still only half of the specimen of uranium would have been exhausted. Just previously to this demonstration, Wilson with his expansion chamber had made visible the tracks and collisions of electrons and the ionization of atoms due to X-rays. Millikan had enabled the audience to see the continuous motion of an isolated electron in an electric field. And the patter of the shower of electrons on the positive plate of a radio amplifier was made audible.

Analysis of surface rocks of the earth's crust indicates that there is enough radioactive material to a depth of twelve miles to supply all the heat which our planet radiates into space. If, as seems certain, radioactive substances exist below this depth and no compensating heat-absorbing process is in progress, there must be an accumulation of heat in the interior of the earth which will eventually appear at the surface and manifest itself in a very rapid radiation. When that time arrives, this geologic epoch will end and a new one begin. However, we have no need to worry, for this event is doubtless many millions of years in the future.

THE FIRST ALCHEMIST

Radioactivity had been an established fact for two decades before any one deliberately sought to disrupt the atom and in so doing produce atoms of lighter elements by the artificial disintegration of heavier ones. Then, in 1918, Rutherford attempted to shoot high-velocity alpha particles from a radium preparation into the atoms of such light elements as aluminum, boron, nitrogen, sodium, phosphorus, and silicon. These alpha particles, moving with velocities of about twelve thousand miles a second, are the most energetic projectiles at the command of the scientist. But let us remember that they are helium nuclei and therefore, like all atomic nuclei, exceedingly minute. As a result, an alpha particle used in this way as a missile passes straight through the great wastes of space in the planetary systems of most atoms. Only occasionally does it collide with a nucleus.

However, Rutherford produced a most remarkable result. In a number of instances, he actually succeeded in disrupting the nuclei of lighter elements and driving out of them positively charged particles having a mass identical with that of the hydrogen atom. Here was a great discovery, the full significance of which will soon be apparent. First, let us note that from aluminum he obtained hydrogen and magnesium, from phosphorus hydrogen and silicon, from sodium hydrogen and neon, from nitrogen hydrogen and carbon, and from boron hydrogen and beryllium. These and similar transformations have been duplicated by other workers. At last, alchemy was an accomplished fact, and a common constituent of the nuclei of all atoms seemed to be hydrogen, a circumstance to which we shall return shortly.

In his experiment with aluminum, Rutherford used a metal tube, across one end of which he placed a glass plate coated with zinc sulfide, a substance which we have seen has the property of glowing under the influence of radium rays. Into the other end of the tube, he thrust a little of radium A. When this substance is at a distance of more than seven centimeters from the screen, the zinc sulfide will not glow, because the alpha particles are stopped by collisions with the molecules of air before reaching it. Between the bit of radium A and the screen, Rutherford placed a very thin sheet of aluminum. But, and this is the remarkable thing, he placed it at a distance much greater than seven centimeters from the screen. One would expect that the zinc sulfide would entirely fail to glow. And yet, it did not. A very faint fluorescence appeared upon the screen. Something remarkable was happening. This glow could not be due to the impact of alpha particles from the radium A. It was too far removed. Surely, the cause must be particles erupted from the aluminum atoms. Rutherford proceeded to measure, by means of their deflection in a magnetic field, the mass and velocity of an individual particle. The mass turned out to be precisely the same as that of the hydrogen atom, and the velocity obtained showed an energy content forty per cent. greater than that of the individual alpha particles from radium A. Either here was the creation of energy, or the dislodged hydrogen atoms had been in motion before bombardment by the alpha particles. The latter alternative is the inevitable one.

What did this discovery mean? In the first place, it is perfectly clear that these hydrogen particles came from the nuclei of the aluminum atoms. The alpha particles from radium A are completely stopped by the aluminum target. Outside the nuclei of the aluminum atoms being bombarded are only the planetary electrons, and an electron is negatively charged and has a mass only one eighteen-hundred-forty-fifth that of a hydrogen atom. Let us remember that a hydrogen atom consists of a positive nucleus and one solitary planetary electron. Like all other atoms, its mass is concentrated in the nucleus. When intact with its electron, the atom of hydrogen is neutral. These hydrogen particles emitted by aluminum nuclei, however, are positively charged. Therefore, it seems certain that they are the nuclei of hydrogen atoms, just as the alpha particles are the positively charged nuclei of helium atoms.

Let us consider further that up to this time nuclear eruptions of radioactive atoms had yielded only electrons and alpha particles. But here were the nuclei of lighter atoms being made to disrupt positively charged particles of only one-fourth the mass of an alpha particle and turning out to be identical with the hydrogen nucleus. Could it be possible that the nuclei of all atoms consist of beta particles, or electrons, and hydrogen nuclei? Indeed, such is the present view and one which seems to be almost, if not quite, established. And now we must have a name for this new primordial unit of atomic structure, the hydrogen nucleus. It has been called the *proton*. Until further conquests are made, electrons and protons will remain the two ultimate entities of all atoms. Both have been proved to exist within the atom, and, so far as we know, nothing else does exist. Sir J. J. Thomson, however, has recently hinted that certain observations indicate that the electron, too, may be complex. Still, this remains to be demonstrated. We may say that the electron is a minute quantity of negative electricity and that the proton is a similar quantity of positive electricity, but the nature of each is a complete mystery. These are blanket notions for our ignorance. We do not know wherein lies the source of the attraction of the one for the other, or why that in different aggregations they give rise to ninety-two distinct fundamental elements of chemical composition. We need not, however, abandon the quest. Some day, the veil may be drawn farther aside and fuller, deeper glimpses of ultimate reality gained.

STRUCTURE OF ATOMIC NUCLEUS

Let us not imagine that we are at the end of the journey. This new knowledge of the proton has given very precise information regarding the necessary structure of the atomic nucleus. We have now seen that this nucleus is composed of electrons and protons. Infinitely small as nuclei are, into each of these magic caskets must be packed a definite number of these entities of ultimate reality. But how many in each instance? Practically, the entire mass of the atom is concentrated in the nucleus, and it is made up of the combined mass of the protons present. Since the mass of a proton is one and it is more than eighteen hundred times as heavy as an electron, the mass of the electron may be ignored.

Now, suppose we take the atom of uranium, the heaviest of all. Its atomic weight is 238. If this entire mass is due to the protons in the nucleus and each proton has a mass of one, there must be 238 protons packed into this nuclear center. No other conclusion is possible. Now a proton carries one positive charge. This would seem to give to the nucleus of the uranium atom 238 positive charges. But the atomic number of uranium is 92, and we have seen that this is the same as the number of positive charges on the nucleus. Furthermore, this charge has actually been measured and found to be 92. How are we to convert 238 charges into 92? There is only one way: the nucleus must also contain negative electrons and just enough to neutralize all but 92 of the positively charged protons. In other words, there must be present in the nucleus the difference between 238 and 92, or 146 electrons. That electrons are actually present in the nuclei of atoms, the eruption of beta particles from radioactive elements proves.

The same is true of the atoms of all other elements, except that of hydrogen. The nucleus of the hydrogen atom consists of a single proton. There is no nuclear electron. About it, however, revolves a single planetary electron, just as in the case of uranium there are ninety-two planetary electrons. Helium has a mass of four. The nucleus of its atom, therefore, contains four protons. But since the nucleus bears but two positive charges, corresponding with the atomic number, there must be two nuclear electrons. To neutralize the two free charges on the nucleus, two planetary electrons revolve in orbits about it. Oxygen of atomic weight 16 and atomic number 8 has in its nucleus sixteen protons and eight electrons, with eight planetary electrons in the exterior orbits. And so we might continue with each of the other elements. These conclusions are perfectly logical. We can not escape them. They are compelled by the stubborn facts of experimental research.

This discovery of the proton and its identity with the hydrogen nucleus have born fruit in an interesting and unexpected way. In 1815, Prout put forth the hypothesis that the atoms of all the other elements were simply aggregations in various combinations of the hydrogen atom. Since the atomic weight of hydrogen is practically one, that would have made the atomic weights of all the other elements whole numbers. But it soon became quite manifest that many of these atomic weights were not whole numbers. Our knowledge of isotopes, however, has shown us that they really are, and now we know that the nuclei of all atoms are built up from hydrogen nuclei. Thus this idealistic guess of an early worker has found its counterpart in reality.

It was only the atoms of the lighter elements that Rutherford, the first one hundred per cent. alchemist, was able to shatter. The net positive charge on the nucleus of the heavier atoms, such as mercury, silver, gold and platinum, was too great for the alpha particle to buck. Being itself of like charge, the alpha particle was turned back, or deflected, as it approached the heavy nucleus. According to the path of this deflection, Rutherford was able to calculate in each instance the number of positive charges on the nucleus of the heavy atom, finding it always equal to the atomic number of the element.

Still, it was found impossible to shatter the atoms of such light elements as carbon and oxygen, whose atomic weights are 12 and 16 respectively. These atomic weights are simple multiples of four, the atomic weight of helium. Now the helium nucleus, as we shall see, is an exceedingly stable unit, never having been successfully attacked. It doubtless consists of four hydrogen nuclei and two nuclear electrons, held together by tremendous forces, the real nature of which is yet a complete mystery. The fact that the atoms of carbon and oxygen can not be broken down makes it exceedingly probable that their nuclei consist respectively of three and four helium nuclei, or alpha particles, thus leaving no free protons to be knocked out by the alpha projectiles from radium A. Aluminum, however, has an atomic weight of approximately 27. This allows for six alpha particles and three extra protons in its nucleus. Apparently, these extra protons are somewhat loosely held and easily dislodged.

One paradoxical fact regarding the nucleus of an atom we must not fail to mention. If we were to magnify the hydrogen atom until the orbit of its single electron were equal in diameter to the orbit of the earth, or 186,000,000 miles across, the nucleus, consisting of a single proton, would be only 3.5 miles in diameter, while the planetary electron would have a diameter of 6,500 miles. In other words, although the proton is more than eighteen hundred times as heavy as the electron, its size is less in almost the same proportion. Despite the fact that into the nucleus of a uranium atom are packed 238 protons and 146 nuclear electrons, the size of this nucleus is less than that of a single electron. The same is true of the nuclei of all other atoms. Therein lies the paradox. This conclusion is not a mere guess. Instead, it is based upon experimental evidence. In bombarding a light element with alpha particles, only one alpha particle in ten thousand strikes a nucleus. Most of them pass straight through the atom, neither colliding with a nucleus nor a planetary electron. So porous is the atomic structure and so exceedingly minute the nucleus that only rarely does an alpha particle obtain the chance opportunity of making a head-on collision.

THEORETICAL TRANSFORMATIONS

In 1925, the scientific world was startled by announcements coming out of Berlin and Tokio that in each capital mercury had been successfully changed into gold. The real dream of the alchemist had at last been accomplished. To be sure only the minutest quantity had been produced. Still, it was asserted that the thing had been done. Dr. Adolph Miethe of Germany and Dr. H. Nagaoka of Japan were the respective claimants to this unique distinction. The principle upon which each operated is perfectly sound. Each was perfectly honest. It is regrettable that other workers have not been able to substantiate their claims. However, despite the exceeding care with which the mercury was purified in advance, the traces of gold obtained must be ascribed to the presence of impurity. Still, let us have a look at the method employed and the principle involved, for they are of great theoretical interest and may become of practical importance.

The method in each instance consisted in passing an electric discharge through mercury vapor. This means that these would-be alchemists shot into the mercury vapor high-speed electrons. Their hope was to cause an occasional electron to penetrate the nucleus of a mercury atom and stay there. Let us see what this would do. The atomic number of mercury is 80 and that of gold 79. That is, the nucleus of a mercury atom possesses 80 positive charges and that of an atom of gold 79 charges. Suppose one negative electron should be lodged safely within the nuclear fold of the mercury atom and find there a haven of rest. This electron would, of course, neutralize one positive charge and thereby reduce the atomic number from 80 to 79, that of gold. In fact, a mercury atom would have been transformed into an atom of gold. As we shall see, this neutralization of one positive charge would doubtless mean the annihilation of a nuclear proton with the liberation of a certain amount of energy. However, that was to be expected and only incidental to the process.

This theory is perfectly logical, and it seems entirely probable that it may yet work. Dr. Paul D. Foote, of the Bureau of Standards, states that "when the scientist is able to utilize an electric field of ten million volts, there is small doubt but that every element may be produced by transmutation. To do this on a large scale of production, to make it a commercial enterprise, is an entirely different proposition. I doubt if many of us will live to see its realization. But when that time comes, this world will be a true haven of rest for all its inhabitants. There will be no poverty, no suffering and no labor; atomic energy will do the work for all mankind. Humanity will be emancipated by the scientist."

It may be that the new cathode-ray tube of Dr. W. D. Coolidge may make possible this very transformation. He now shoots electrons in prodigious quantities at one hundred and fifty thousand miles a second. With the super-tube which he plans to build, he hopes to be able to shoot these projectiles with velocities approaching that of light. Were Coolidge to turn this new weapon of science upon mercury vapor, the long sought transformation might become a reality. Should that dream come true, the modern alchemist could start with lead, which is cheap and abundant, and by a series of successive transformations arrive at gold. Since the tube already constructed produces as many electrons as does a ton of radium, a battery of such tubes, or, better, of the projected super-tubes, should be able to produce gold in quantity. The immediate effect of this event, however, would be to precipitate deep and wide-spread disaster to the monetary and currency systems of the world, for all are based on the intrinsic value and scarcity of the yellow metal. Debts would become as dust in the balance. All could be easily and speedily paid. Government securities, based as they are upon gold, would become worthless. Gold as a relatively cheap and abundant metal would come into its own in the field of art. And yet, its preciousness having vanished, there would no longer be any distinction or uniqueness in its possession. One other factor, however, must be reckoned with, namely, the power cost of transformation. Still, it seems certain that the annihilation of protons in the transformations would liberate vastly more subatomic energy than would be required in the process. That is, we should at last be utilizing to some extent that vast quantity of latent energy locked up within the atoms in infinite supply. This is the energy to which Doctor Foote referred in the quotation just made.

This picture may seem fanciful. Possibly it is. Still, it would be a rash individual who would assert that it may never come to pass.

Let us view this transformation of the metals from a different angle. Mercury has three isotopes, the atomic weights of which are respectively 198, 200 and 202. Suppose we could cause the atomic nucleus of the first isotope to emit a proton, just as protons were knocked from the atoms of aluminum, boron, nitrogen and other light elements. The result would be to make the atomic weight 197. But this is also the atomic weight of gold. In so doing, we should have found another highway from mercury to gold. Then, if we could cause an atom of gold to emit an alpha particle, we should reduce the atomic weight by four and obtain iridium, still more valuable than gold. Again, if we could eliminate one alpha particle from each of the three isotopes of mercury, we should have the three isotopes of platinum. Or we might start with lead and by the same processes arrive at gold, platinum and iridium. Were these to become practicable, we might have at small cost non-corrosive metals for cooking utensils and many other purposes. Just fancy an automobile body built of sheet gold or a skyscraper constructed of structural platinum!

And so the alchemist dreams on, as did his picturesque progenitor of an earlier period. Let no one say that his dream shall not some day become a glorious reality.

SUBATOMIC ENERGY

The *controlled* liberation of the vast reservoirs of subatomic energy locked up within the electronic systems of the atoms in infinite quantity,—yes, that is the dream of dreams which has captured the fancy of many a modern scientist. To-morrow, these swiftly moving entities of ultimate reality may become the tireless servants of men. Why not?

Sir Oliver Lodge has estimated that the energy latent within the atoms of an ounce of water would lift all the German ships sunk at Scapa Flow and place them high and dry on the mainland. Professor Le Bon, of Paris, asserts that the energy imprisoned within the smallest French coin is equal to eighty million horse-power. As small a quantity as one-seventieth of a grain of radium hurls into the air thirty million electrons per second, to say nothing of the alpha particles emitted. The complete disintegration of a single gram of radium evolves two billion nine hundred million calories of heat, or more than a million times more than that obtained from the combustion of an equal quantity of coal. No wonder the research scientist dreams of liberating for the use of his fellowmen these illimitable supplies of original energy. But can it be done? Is there any evidence that such liberation is taking place anywhere in the universe? Let us see.

I wish to approach this subject of energy from electrons and protons in another way. Let us not think, just now, of setting free this intrinsic energy through some

strategic attack upon the atom. We have already hinted
at the annihilation of protons and electrons. We shall
now follow along this path and see where it leads.

As we have seen, it seems highly probable that the
nuclei of all atoms consist of protons, or hydrogen nuclei,
together with electrons condensed into an exceedingly
minute space. And, since the mass of an electron is
practically zero, the entire mass of an atom is due to the
protons compressed into its nucleus. For instance, the
helium nucleus, or alpha particle, seems to have been
evolved by the condensation of four protons, or hydrogen nuclei, into a most compact unit.

Now, we have said that the mass of a hydrogen atom,
which is the same as that of a proton, is *practically* one.
It is, but it is not quite that. Taking the atomic weight
of oxygen, which is 16, as a standard, the number for
hydrogen turns out to be 1.0077. This has been determined many times with the utmost accuracy, and there
is no possibility of error. It is also true that the atomic
weight of helium is precisely 4. As a simple matter of
arithmetic, we see that the mass of four protons will be
4.031, and not 4. If a helium nucleus is formed by the
condensation of four protons, what becomes of the extra
0.031 of mass? It seems to have been annihilated. But
this is a revolutionary idea. It seems to be in direct
violation of the law of the conservation of matter, which
says that matter can neither be created nor destroyed,
but may be changed from one form to another. Still, it
is not in violation of this law, for Einstein has shown
that matter may be transformed into energy. Furthermore, he has worked out for us the exact law governing
this transformation. Let us state this law in the beau-

tifully precise, but to some barbarous, language of mathematics: $E = C^2 m$, where E is the energy, C the velocity of light, and m is the mass which is being transformed into energy.

Since the energy obtained depends upon the square of the velocity of light, a very large number, we see that the energy from the transformation of even a trifling quantity of matter becomes enormous. Dr. Paul Foote asserts, that ''if the hydrogen in two teaspoonfuls of water be converted into helium, 200,000 kilowatt hours of energy is set free, representing $20,000 worth of electrical current, or ten thousand dollars to the teaspoonful.''

We can readily understand that, in this transformation, for each 4 grams of helium formed 0.031 gram of hydrogen has been changed into energy. This has doubtless been accomplished by the neutralization of protons through union with electrons. Since a proton is nothing but a minute quantity of positive electricity and an electron is an equal quantity of negative electricity, it is perfectly apparent that, if the two can be made to coalesce, they will disappear. But their disappearance is accompanied by the liberation of energy. If, too, this neutralization can be effected in any other way, energy will be the product. As we shall see, possibly such transformations are somewhere taking place. Somewhere planetary electrons may be falling into the atomic nuclei, with the consequent destruction of the atoms and the liberation of vast quantities of energy.

Should one gram of hydrogen be thus annihilated, in accordance with the Einstein equation, it would yield electric power equal to $2,600,000. The complete destruction of the atoms in a pound of gold would produce ten billion kilowatt hours of energy, worth at ten cents a kilowatt hour a billion dollars. The transmutation of a fraction of a pint of water would liberate sufficient energy to drive a battle-ship across the ocean and back at full speed. Here is ancient alchemy entirely eclipsed. No pursuer of the Philosopher's Stone ever dreamed of attaining to such prodigious quantities of wealth and power.

In the autumn of 1926, the report came from Germany that Professor Paneth and Doctor Peters, of the University of Berlin, had succeeded in transmuting hydrogen into helium. To bring about this supposed transformation, these German chemists made use of palladium, a heavy rare metal, which in the spongy state has the property of absorbing a thousand times its own volume of hydrogen gas. Not only does it absorb the gas but it also changes it from the molecular state to the atomic, a condition in which hydrogen is much more active. For instance, if a little of this spongy paladium is dropped into a flask of hydrogen and oxygen, so active does the hydrogen become that the two gases unite with explosive violence. For twelve hours, a stream of hydrogen was passed over palladium in finely divided state. Then, with the spectroscope they were able to detect in the hydrogen the principal lines of the helium spectrum. The quantity of helium thought to have been formed was exceedingly small, estimated to be only a few thousand millionths of a cubic centimeter (a small thimbleful). Consequently, it was impossible to know whether the theoretical destruction of mass with the resulting production of energy had been accomplished or not. It was thought that this energy might have passed off in the form of the exceedingly penetrating cosmic rays of which we shall presently learn.*

It will be recalled that, in 1867, Sir Norman Lockyer discovered with the spectroscope enormous quantities of helium gas in the atmosphere of the sun. With the discovery of radioactivity a generation later, this came to be a highly significant fact. It at first seemed plausible to assume that the sun contains large quantities of radioactive material, which through disintegration and the consequent expulsion of alpha particles from the atomic nuclei produces helium and at the same time supplies the heat necessary to maintain the celestial fires. However, this assumption of such large quantities of radioactive elements in the sun as would be required to supply the solar heat has seemed untenable. It is now supposed that this energy arises from the actual destruction of the sun's mass in accordance with the Einstein equation. The evolution of hydrogen nuclei into helium nuclei with the partial annihilation of mass would account for the helium in the sun's atmosphere and for part at least of the sun's energy. There may be other destructions of mass within the sun as well. Professor A. S. Eddington says, "We are to suppose that a proton and electron run together, their electric charges cancel and nothing is left but a splash in the ether which spreads out as an electromagnetic wave carrying off the energy." Professor Eddington also asserts that, if the entire mass of the sun is available for conversion into energy, the present radia-

---

*Report has since come that later experiments have unfortunately failed to confirm this transformation. We must still hope that fact and theory may yet be made to coincide.

tion may be maintained for fifteen trillion years to come. He puts the mass of the sun which thus disappears each year at one hundred and twenty trillion tons. It is surely comforting to know that we shall not need to worry about the immediate cooling off of our central orb with the early necessity of closing out business on this planet.

Let me emphasize that this discovery of the equivalence of energy and mass and the theoretical possibility of converting the latter into the former is an outstanding development of recent progress in the chemical and physical sciences of the utmost importance. Whether or not we are ever able to initiate the process and profit thereby, it has thrown a penetrating search-light upon the probable source of celestial energy.

A highly significant circumstance is the presence of helium nuclei in the atoms of all the radioactive elements. Is it not probable that they are also present in the nuclei of the atoms of all other elements? Only when an atom becomes top-heavy and unstable does it spontaneously thrust them out. Does it not seem reasonable to suppose that an evolution of the elements from hydrogen nuclei, or protons, to radioactive atoms is in constant progress? May it not be true that in the cosmic crucibles of the stars, as Professor Eddington has indicated, this process with its consequent destruction of mass, accounts for the ceaseless radiation which diffuses throughout all space? Let us see if there is any evidence upon this point.

COSMIC RAYS

Early in the present century, Dr. Werner Kolhoerster, a German scientist, first observed a highly penetrating form of rays, which seemed to come from every direction of the depths of space, with the same intensity at midnight as at noonday. These rays were recently studied by Dr. Robert A. Millikan, of the Norman Bridge Laboratory, at Pasadena, California. The disclosures made by Millikan, and their interpretation, tell a wonderful story.

Millikan performed his experiments at Lake Muir, near the summit of Mount Whitney, at an elevation of 11,800 feet, and at Arrowhead Lake 7,000 feet lower. To detect the rays he had devised a very delicate self-recording electroscope. When he sunk this in the water of the lake, the instrument continued to record the presence of the rays to a depth of forty-three feet. Not until this depth had been exceeded did the electroscope cease to register. Now, it must be remembered that these rays before striking the water had passed through the earth's atmosphere, which is equivalent in its opposing power, to twenty-five feet of water. Thus, we see that these cosmic rays have a penetrating power enabling them to pass through sixty-eight feet of water, equivalent to six feet of lead. The most penetrating of ordinary X-rays, such as are used in hospitals, will pass through only a half-inch of lead. Therefore, these cosmic rays, being generated somewhere out in space, are nearly one hundred and fifty times more powerful than the X-rays with which we are familiar.

But we have a form of X-rays more penetrating than those of the laboratory. As we have seen, these are the gamma rays emitted by all radioactive elements and produced by the impact of the expelled beta particles upon surrounding matter. Let us remember that X-rays

Dr. Robert A. Millikan (left) and his research assistant, Dr. I. S. Bowen

In the Norman Bridge Laboratory of Physics, California Institute of Technology

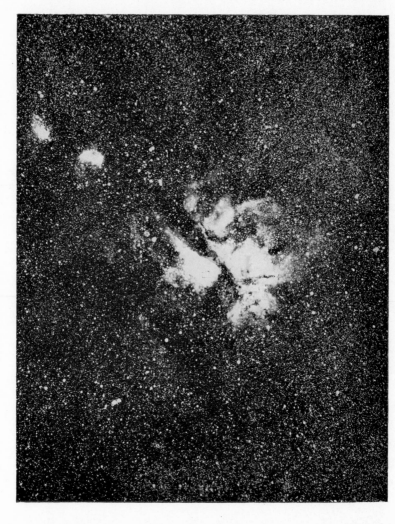

The nebula in Carina

Nebulæ are thought to be a source of the exceedingly penetrating *cosmic rays*. In them, atomic evolution and disintegration are quite likely giving rise to transformations enormously more energetic than **any** produced in our laboratories

are exceedingly short waves in the ether, produced by the impact of electrons upon the target of an X-ray tube. These impacts set up a very rapid vibration which manifests itself in the ether waves of X-rays. The more penetrating gamma rays are due to a still more rapid vibration, resulting in still shorter wave lengths in the ether. Therefore, the conclusion is irresistible that these cosmic rays, of vastly greater penetrating power than that either of X-rays or gamma rays, are due to nuclear transformations within atoms somewhere out in space, but transformations enormously more energetic than any with which we are familiar in our laboratories. This conclusion is based upon the fact that the rate of vibration of an emitted ray and, therefore, its penetrating power are proportional to the energy released in the subatomic change which produces it. As Millikan says, it seems certain that all through space atomic nuclear changes are taking place at least fifty times more intense than those observed in radioactive disintegrations.

And now comes the most significant deduction of all. The energy factor of these nuclear changes, as indicated by the frequencies of the cosmic rays, corresponds very closely with that which would be set free in the theoretical destruction of mass involved in the production of helium from hydrogen. The frequency, or rate of vibration, of these rays is also in close agreement with the calculated frequency emitted in the neutralization of nuclear protons by planetary electrons. That is, these cosmic rays give every indication of arising from the birth of helium nuclei and the destruction of atomic mass.

What is the explanation? How is it that these rays

can come from every direction of space, being not at all more plentiful from the region of the sun than from any other quarter? Is not the answer to be found in the hypothesis that the stars and spiral nebulæ in all directions are giving rise to these energy changes? Atoms in the utmost profusion are constantly being born and perishing. In this vast sweep of cosmic change, may there not be atomic evolution followed by atomic disintegration and annihilation? Is not the cycle, measured in units of time beyond our power to grasp, from proton and electron to star and, through processes with which we are not yet familiar, back again to primal proton and electron? The evidence produced by Kolhoerster and Millikan answers "yes."

It should be stated that new experiments show that the intensity of these cosmic rays varies with the aspect of the heavens. It is at a maximum when the Milky Way is most nearly overhead. When the constellations of Andromeda and Hercules are most favorably placed, too, the radiation is more intense than at other times. These results, however, do not alter the conclusion that these rays originate in every quarter of the heavens.

Let us have one more aspect of this field of inquiry. Can we resist the thought, already hinted at, that the radiant energy from the stars, energy released through the destruction of atomic mass, is somewhere, possibly everywhere, in interstellar space giving birth to electrons and protons? If not, what becomes of it? We are told that energy can not be destroyed. Does this radiant energy travel on in the form of ether waves forever and ever, here and there chancing to do a little useful work upon some planet, but otherwise accomplishing nothing?

Rational judgment forbids such a conclusion. To-morrow, the work of the scientist may make clear the answer.

UTILIZATION OF THE ENERGY OF THE ATOM

It has long been the dream of the practical scientist to discover means of setting free the energy of the atom and harnessing it to do the world's work. Dr. T. F. Wall, of Sheffield, England, has been working upon a method by which he hopes to disrupt the atom through the cumulative effect of oscillating electric fields so timed as to bring them precisely in tune with the magnetic fields produced by the movements of the planetary electrons in their orbits. That the atoms of some elements actually exhibit magnetic fields is a recent discovery of experimental physics. However, Doctor Wall has as yet announced no result. That a sympathetic vibration of proper frequency may disrupt atoms, just as similar vibrations of lower frequency detonate the molecules of T. N. T. or nitroglycerin, is entirely plausible. However, a chief difficulty of great practical importance is the possibility that, should this feat be accomplished, all the atoms of the earth would be detonated at once and our planet thus be resolved into primeval chaos and abruptly brought to an end.

It is the secret of the *controlled* liberation of this sub-atomic energy which the scientist seeks. Should he attain to it, as he may at any time do, he will stand at a turning-point in the evolution of the race comparable to that of the cave man when he had gained the mastery of fire. Stretching before him will extend vistas of achievement of such dizzy vastness as to dwarf into insignificance all the proudest triumphs of preceding centuries. Energy and power problems will vanish. Human toil will all but disappear. The world's work will be performed by the illimitable supplies of energy forever flowing from subatomic reservoirs. Indeed, the millennium will be at hand.

Is it desirable to attain the goal? Should it be realized, will this superabundance of material power result in intellectual stagnation? Or will new problems present themselves, worthier goals for human striving, widening horizons and higher levels of attainment? May we not believe that, so long as the race is here, objects summoning forth the best that lies within the heart and brain of man will be provided for his effort?

The highly practical individual may ask, "In what way does this knowledge of the atom benefit mankind? Where are the tangible results?" Indirectly, we do use the energy within the atom. The commercial success of such enterprises as long distance telephone communication, radio telephony, the X-ray, artificial illumination, industrial processes involving photochemical changes, electrochemistry, photography and much more depends upon what goes on within the atom. It is the same old story. Fundamental research must forever precede practical achievement. And who would exchange the widening of mental horizons and the growth in intellectual stature resulting from the new knowledge of the atom and all that it implies for any conceivable quantity of material wealth? From this continual discovery of fundamental truth issues the perennial springs of spiritual enlightenment as well as the resources of material progress.

THE X-RAY AND WHAT IT REVEALS

One of the first discoveries regarding X-rays was the apparent impossibility of dispersing them into various colors as the raindrops or a triangular glass prism disperse ordinary sunlight. When the ether waves of sunlight pass through a three-cornered piece of glass, the direction of their motion is changed. We say that the ray of light is bent. And the rays at the violet end of the spectrum are bent more than are those at the red end. The result is the separation of the light into its component colors, so that we obtain a spectrum on a screen. X-rays will not undergo this change for the reason that the wave lengths in the ether are too short, being ten thousand times shorter than those of visible light.

One of the best means of producing a spectrum of ordinary light is by means of what is known as a diffraction grating. This is a piece of glass upon which are ruled exceedingly fine lines, very close together. Sometimes there are as many as fifteen or twenty thousand lines to the inch. In order to scatter the light and produce a spectrum by the passage of light through such a grating, the spaces between the lines must be less than the wave lengths of the light being examined. However, the most closely ruled grating which can be made is too coarse for X-rays. The wave lengths in the ether are shorter than the spaces between the lines. For more than a decade, this physical barrier baffled every attempt to produce X-ray spectra.

Then, in 1912, it occurred to Laue, a Swiss physicist, that the very minute, regularly-spaced atoms in crystalline substances might afford a natural, ready-made diffraction grating for the dispersion of X-rays. Here are atoms already arranged by Nature in perfect, regular sequence, tier on tier, rank, file and column, in exceedingly close spacing. Laue's prediction was put to the test and brilliantly verified. The spaces between the tiers of atoms were found to be smaller than the wave lengths of X-rays. By this method, it at once became possible to analyze the light of X-rays or to employ it in the study of the atomic and molecular patterns of crystal specimens. Here was a new field of extraordinary interest. Much work has been done in it by the Braggs in England and in this country by Doctor Hull, of the General Electric Laboratories.

The most fascinating application of this new means of attack, however, proved to be its use in the determination of the atomic numbers of the elements. Seizing upon the discovery, Moseley, a young English physicist, who lost his life by a Turkish bullet at the Dardanelles, proceeded to map the X-ray spectra of the various elements. Now the character of the spectrum depends upon the element used as the target in the X-ray tube. In each case, the wave length will be somewhat different, thus producing a different set of lines. To obtain the spectra of liquid and gaseous elements, solid compounds of those elements were used. For instance, the spectrum of chlorine gas may be obtained by using solid sodium chloride as the target in the X-ray tube. The spectral lines of metallic sodium having been previously determined, the additional lines must be those due to chlorine.

Let us examine still further the method of attack and the revelations which were made. Using a certain metal, say silver, to receive the rain of electrons from the cathode of the X-ray tube, the tube was put into action. The X-rays produced were reflected from the face of a crystal, used in place of a diffraction grating, and the resulting spectrum, consisting of a series of well-marked lines, was photographed. By a simple comparison of the relative positions of these lines with the positions of the known lines of the ordinary spectrum, it was possible to determine the wave lengths and frequencies of the X-ray ether waves. For each element a characteristic spectrum was obtained. But as Moseley proceeded with this spectrum analysis from element to element, there began to emerge a most remarkable result. It is stated thus: "The square roots of the wave frequencies varied in progressive, stepwise fashion from element to element, giving a series of equal whole number steps that would, if complete, run approximately from 1 for hydrogen to 92 for uranium." If an element were lacking, a conspicuous gap unmistakably denoting its absence appeared in the series. Only three such gaps now remain to be filled. Their atomic numbers are 43, 85 and 87 respectively. Elements 43 and 75 were reported discovered by Professor Walter Noddack, of Berlin, in 1925, but experiments at the Platinum Institute of the Russian Academy of Sciences failed to substantiate the claim, thus making their discovery doubtful. News is just at hand, however, stating that Doctors Walter and Ida Noddack have succeeded in obtaining in pure form a small quantity of rhenium, element 75. It turns out to be a black powder, which unites readily with a number of other elements.

The question arises, "How do we know that there

may not be more than 92 elements?'' We do not. However, the existence of any beyond that number is quite doubtful. Such elements would be exceedingly unstable and strongly radioactive. There is no evidence of other elements of this character. Until it is forthcoming, we may safely assume that 92 is Nature's full complement.

There is something inspiring in the thought that along one line of scientific inquiry we are reaching the limit of possible advance. Of course, this does not mean that there is not much more to be known about the properties of the elements and their chemical behavior. But the fact that the number of types of elements is actually known holds the promise of ultimate conquests of truth in other domains. The word *types* has just been used, for, if we were to count the isotopes, the actual number of elements would be considerably larger than 92.

Of what value are these atomic numbers? In one important respect, they have cleared up difficulties regarding the placing of certain elements in the Periodic Table, which have perplexed chemists ever since Mendeleeff announced his law in 1869. According to their respective atomic weights, argon, potassium, iron, cobalt, nickel, tellurium and iodine did not fit into the niches which their chemical properties prescribed for them. The atomic numbers leave no doubt of their proper grouping. Furthermore, these numbers narrow the field of investigation. Chemists will no longer waste time in fruitless efforts to discover elements where no gaps exist. Neither will they believe that the spectra of any of the stars or nebulæ afford reliable evidence of celestial elements, unless they correspond with those dictated by the atomic numbers of Moseley. This universe seems

to be homogeneous. Only the primordial building blocks
found in our earth seem to exist anywhere. Pygmies of
the universe we may be, adrift upon this bit of rock and
sea and sky, and yet the possibility of all knowledge may
lie within our ken.

X-ray spectrum analysis has been fruitful in other
directions. It enables us to measure to an accuracy better than a hundredth of one per cent. the distance apart
of the layers of atoms in a crystal. Under the search-
light of its uncanny revelations, we are actually able to
determine the arrangement of the atoms within a crystal,
as for instance in the diamond. This appears to be a
lattice crystal in which each carbon atom is surrounded
by four others at equal distances from it. Each atom is
at the center of gravity of a tetrahedron, with the
others placed at the four corners of the solid. With what
satisfaction would not van't Hoff contemplate this picture, confirming as it does with wonderful accuracy the
molecular architecture which his genius constructed on
the basis of intellectual processes alone. And X-ray
microscopy has given us a perfect picture of the six-sided
benzene ring of Kekulé. These X-ray spectra reveal the
patterns and linkings of atoms within the molecules and,
therefore, enable the chemist to build models of these
units which can not be far from the truth. This new
method of investigation also makes possible the calculation of the density of a crystal substance with greater
accuracy than by its determination from older methods.
Or, knowing the density of the crystal, we may determine
the atomic weight of any atom in its composition, thereby
affording a check upon determinations made in other
ways.

Fascinating are these revelations of ultimate reality, and utterly beyond the wildest flights of fancy of the boldest dreamer of a generation ago. Who shall say

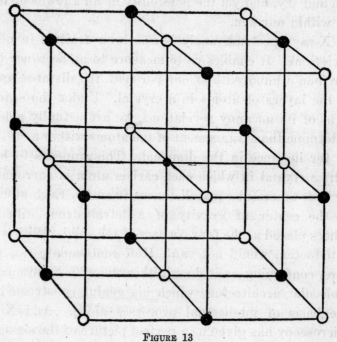

FIGURE 13

Structure of a crystal of sodium chloride as revealed by X-ray analysis. The black circles indicate the positions of sodium atoms, while the white circles give the positions of chlorine atoms.

that they do not pay dividends? To-morrow, they may be the working capital of new industries.

MEASURING THE CHARGE ON AN ELECTRON

In 1923, Dr. Robert A. Millikan received the Nobel Prize in physics for measuring the electric charge on an isolated electron. He accomplished this by measuring

the speed a single electron imparts to a drop of oil in a
magnetic field of known strength. It was found that the
speed and, therefore, the strength of the charge imparted
to the drop always increased by definite jumps, being
exactly two, three, four, etc., times what it was for the
simplest effect, that is, when but a single electron was
on the drop. By discharging the drop completely, he
was able to deal with it in the electrically neutral state.
From a multitude of observations, he determined with
the utmost precision the exact charge which an electron
bears.

In speaking of this research, Doctor Millikan says,
"He who has seen that experiment, and hundreds of investigators have observed it, has literally seen the electron. . . . The electron itself, which man has measured
in the manner just described, is neither an uncertainty
nor an hypothesis. It is a new experimental fact that
this generation in which we live has for the first time
seen, and which any one who wills may henceforth see."
Elsewhere, he has said, "Electrons of both the positive
(protons) and negative variety, are then merely observed
centers of electrical forces. . . . Further, since Rowland proved years ago that electrical currents are
simply electrical charges in motion, the proof that electrical charges are built up out of discrete electrical particles, electrons, carries with it the proof that electrical
currents such as pass through incandescent lamps consist
merely in the drifting of numerous swarms of these electrons through conductors."

Although the ultimate units of energy and matter,
this raw material out of which atoms are constructed,
thus seem to be greatly simplified, let us not delude

ourselves with the thought that we have in any way explained the real nature of these positive and negative charges and the force which holds them in its grip. Of these, we have not the slightest inkling. The mystery is as profound as ever. The pathway of discovery still stretches onward into the great unknown. Whither it will lead no man can say.

ELECTRONS AND CHEMICAL ACTION

It is the planetary electrons which are chiefly concerned in ordinary chemical changes. The nuclei always remain intact. Only in radioactive transformations or in such bombardments of the atom as those carried out by Rutherford are the nuclei disrupted. The number and distribution of the outer, or extranuclear, electrons determine the chemical activity of an element. In chemical combinations, each atom involved either gains or loses one or more planetary electrons. When the union is dissolved, however, the atoms either lose or recover a sufficient number of electrons to make their respective planetary complements and, therefore, resume their original states and properties.

Dr. Irving Langmuir, of the General Electric Laboratories, has worked out an ingenious theory to account for the great stability of certain elements and for the chemical activity of others. The rare gases of the atmosphere—helium, neon, argon, krypton and xenon—are absolutely inert. They have no chemical properties whatever. This chemical inactivity challenged the attention of Langmuir. Why should it be so? Of certain things chemists were sure: atoms are made up of positively charged nuclei and outer negatively charged electrons. In ordinary chemical reactions the nuclei are unscathed. Chemical action must, therefore, be due to relative degrees of instability among the planetary electrons. But what are the stable configurations? It became clear to Langmuir that the inert gases of the atmosphere held the key to the solution of the problem.

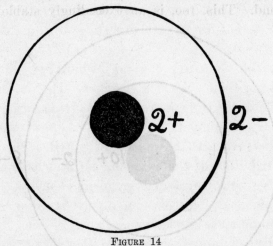

FIGURE 14

A simple illustration of the Langmuir conception of the atom of helium. A nucleus having two positive charges is surrounded by an outer "shell" containing two planetary electrons. This is one of the stable configurations.

The atomic numbers of these rare gases are 2, 10, 18, 36 and 54 respectively. As we have seen this number in each instance stands for the number of positive charges on the nucleus and for the number of planetary electrons moving in orbits about the nucleus. We may for convenience think of the atom as a nucleus with a certain number of concentric shells. In each shell, will be a definite number of planetary electrons. Thus, we may represent helium as shown in figure 14. It has but one shell, containing two electrons. Now, Langmuir assumed that the first shell of the atom of every element, except that of hydrogen, has two electrons. So far as helium itself is concerned, this is a very stable combination. Neon, the second of the inert gases, of atomic number 10, has ten electrons, two of which according to the Langmuir hypothesis are in the first shell, leaving eight for the second. This, too, is an exceedingly stable combi-

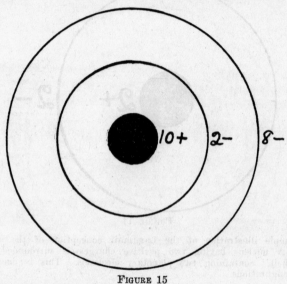

FIGURE 15

Illustration of the Langmuir conception of the atom of neon. Here, the nucleus, having ten positive charges, is surrounded by two outer "shells," the first, like helium, having two planetary electrons, and the other eight electrons. This also is a stable configuration.

nation. The eighteen planetary electrons of argon, he assumed to be distributed in three shells of two, eight and eight electrons respectively. Again, the combination is equally as stable as that of each of the two preceding. Krypton with thirty-six planetary electrons divided into shells containing two, eight, eight and eighteen electrons, while xenon gave two, eight, eight, eighteen and eighteen in the various shells. Langmuir assumed that these are the stable configurations and that the atoms of elements not possessing these electronic groupings in the outermost shells are all the while seeking to attain to them. The result is chemical action.

To illustrate how this works, let us take for example the union of sodium and chlorine to form ordinary table

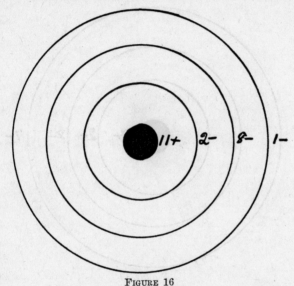

FIGURE 16

Illustration of the Langmuir conception of the atom of sodium. The outermost ''shell'' contains but one planetary electron. This is an unstable configuration. To gain stability, the atom needs to capture seven more electrons or lose one. Consequently, sodium is a chemically active element.

salt. The atomic number of sodium is eleven. As shown in the figure, this permits of shells of two and eight electrons respectively, but leaves a third shell with but a single electron. Thus, according to Langmuir, an atom of sodium can not be chemically inactive. It is all the

while trying to pick up seven more electrons to complete
the stable configuration for its outermost shell or to lose
that lone electron. Now, chlorine, as shown in the figure, has seven electrons in its outermost shell. It needs
to lose seven electrons or to gain one. As a matter of
fact, these elements are among the most chemically active
known. It is easy to see why they combine so readily to
form sodium chloride. According to this hypothesis, the

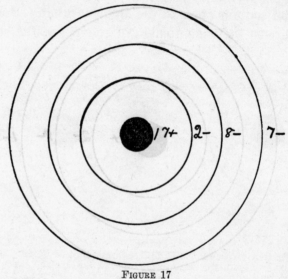

FIGURE 17

Illustration of the atom of chlorine. In this case, the outermost
"shell" contains seven planetary electrons. To gain stability, the atom
needs to capture one additional electron or lose seven. This, too, is a
chemically active element.

solitary electron in the outermost shell of the sodium
atom joins with the seven outermost electrons of the
chlorine atom. This change makes a stable system
among the electronic shells of each atom. Each shell
contains either two or eight electrons.

The foregoing picture explains, too, why sodium

chloride, though made up of exceedingly active and poisonous elements, is non-injurious and indeed palatable. Having lost an electron, the sodium atom is now positive. It has become an *ion*. Its properties have changed. Likewise, the chlorine atom, having gained an electron, is now a negative ion and vastly different in its activity. Thus, we see that the chemical union of these two elements consists in transferring an electron from the sodium atom to the chlorine atom. Here and elsewhere in the wide domain of chemistry, the electron

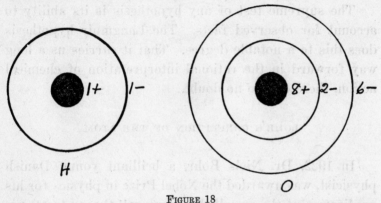

FIGURE 18

Illustrations of the atoms of hydrogen and oxygen in accordance with the Langmuir hypothesis. Both configurations are unstable, and both elements are chemically active. Since the atom of oxygen needs to gain two planetary electrons, it unites with two atoms of hydrogen, thus forming the molecule of water, a very stable compound.

appears to lie at the very heart of chemical action.

Let us take the familiar example of the union of hydrogen and oxygen to form water. The accompanying figures show the distribution of planetary electrons. The outer shell of the oxygen atom needs to gain two electrons to obtain the stable number eight. Therefore, it unites with two hydrogen atoms, each of which is unstable because it lacks an electron in its outer shell.

Thus, we have the molecule of water with its two atoms of hydrogen to one of oxygen.

Examples might be multiplied, but these serve to illustrate the undoubted dependence of chemical action upon electronic distribution. Although for chemistry the atom is still the fundamental chemical unit, its activity, as we have seen, would be impossible without the mobility of its constituent electrons. Where this mobility is lacking, as in the rare gases of the atmosphere, there is no chemical activity.

The supreme test of any hypothesis is its ability to account for observed facts. The Langmuir hypothesis does this to a notable degree. That it carries us a long way forward in the rational interpretation of chemical action, there can be no doubt.

BOHR'S CONCEPTION OF THE ATOM

In 1922, Dr. Niels Bohr, a brilliant young Danish physicist, was awarded the Nobel Prize in physics for his application of the so-called "quantum" theory to atomic structure. Our picture of the atom would not be complete without giving this latest conception of the relation between the movements of the planetary electrons and their radiation of energy. All the multitudinous properties of the elements depend upon the structure of atoms. It is within the atom that we must look for the secrets of energy and matter. Anything which throws light upon the solution of atomic problems is a distinct contribution both to chemistry and physics.

Bohr, as every scientist must, accepts the now established view of the structure of the atom with its positive

nucleus and planetary electrons. Using this as a starting-point, he builds upon it. He thinks of the planetary
electrons as revolving in fixed orbits of various diameters, but with a certain definite and invariable speed in
each orbit. These speeds may be 2, 4, 6, 8, etc., but

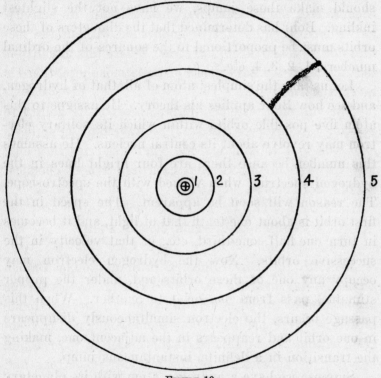

FIGURE 19

The atom of hydrogen in accordance with the Bohr quantum theory,
showing the five orbits and the single planetary electron making the jump
from orbit 5 to orbit 4, thus producing one of the bright lines in the
hydrogen spectrum.

within a given orbit the speed can never be more nor
less. In this respect, the planetary system of the atom
is regarded as differing from its infinitely larger counterpart of the heavens. It is entirely possible for an orbit

of a solar system to be changed to any conceivable degree by the appropriate external force. Not so, however, with an electronic orbit, but an electron moving within it, unlike a planet of a solar system, may move in definite jumps from one orbit to another. As to why an electron should make these jumps, we have not the slightest inkling. Bohr has determined that the diameters of these orbits must be proportional to the squares of the ordinal numbers, 1, 2, 3, 4, etc.

Let us take the simplest atom of all, that of hydrogen, and see how Bohr applies his theory. He assigns to this atom five possible orbits within which its solitary electron may revolve about its central nucleus. He assumes this number because there are four bright lines in the hydrogen spectrum when viewed with the spectroscope. The reason will soon be apparent. The speed in the first orbit is about one-tenth that of light, and it becomes in turn one-half, one-third, etc., of that velocity in the successive orbits. Now the hydrogen electron may occupy any one of these orbits and, under the proper stimulus, pass from one orbit to another. When this passage occurs, the electron simultaneously disappears in one orbit and reappears in the adjacent one, making the transition in a definite, instantaneous jump.

Suppose we have a hydrogen atom with its planetary electron moving in the fifth orbit. The electron jumps from the fifth to the fourth orbit. This jump gives a kick to the ether, sending out a pulse of light having a definite wave length and producing a certain bright line in the spectrum. When the electron jumps to the third orbit, a second pulse of light, but of different wave length, is emitted. This produces a second bright line in the spectrum. These jumps are repeated until the electron appears in the first orbit. It has in succession produced four lines in the hydrogen spectrum. Energy is imparted to the ether and, therefore, lines are produced in the spectrum only when the electron is moving inward. When we view the spectrum of hydrogen, we see all four lines at once. This is because some electrons are making each jump at the same time. But in any particular atom of hydrogen there is only one electron. An electron which has reached the innermost orbit may be made to pass backward to the outermost orbit through the absorption of energy. For instance, when light of the same wave lengths as that necessary to produce the four hydrogen lines in the spectrum is thrown upon hydrogen gas, the electrons will move outward, thereby storing up potential energy to be released when they again move inward.

Now hydrogen as we ordinarily obtain it, as for instance in a glass cylinder in a laboratory, emits no light and gives no spectrum. The electrons are revolving at definite speeds within fixed orbits. In order to make them jump from orbit to orbit, they must become excited through the application of some external source of energy. Let us suppose the hydrogen to be heated or subjected to an intense electric discharge. What is assumed to happen is this: electrons are dislodged from their orbits. In many instances, the electron of an atom is kicked entirely outside the five orbital paths, leaving the nucleus temporarily isolated, or ionized. Immediately, however, these dislodged electrons, attracted by the positive nucleus and under the violent agitation due to the external disturbance, begin to regain their positions in the outermost orbits. But they do not stop there. They begin to move inward jump by jump. The external stimulus causes some electrons to make this return journey without having been dislodged from the orbital paths. Manifestly, when this excitation begins, there will be billions of electrons in each of the successive orbital stages from the innermost one out. Consequently, multitudes of electrons will be making each jump at the same time. Therefore, the four hydrogen lines will appear simultaneously in the spectrum.

A beautiful theory is this. Is there any evidence to support it? Millikan asserts that the theory has been completely demonstrated. He says, ". . . the spectroscope has furnished the physicists with means for the quantitative testing of the recently developed laws of atomic mechanics, and it is to-day furnishing as exacting proof of the orbital theory of electronic motions as the telescope furnished a century earlier for the orbital theory of the motions of heavenly bodies."

Some experiments carried out by Millikan himself are wonderfully illuminating. In them, he made use of what he calls "high-vacuum, hot-spark spectrometry." Between electrodes very close together in a high-vacuum container, he passed a high-potential electric discharge, obtaining thereby an exceptionally hot spark. In this hot spark, he could examine with the spectroscope various elements. For his first experiment, he selected boron. Its atomic number is 5. Therefore, it has five planetary electrons in its various orbits. Of these, two have been proved to be close to the nucleus, as required by the Langmuir hypothesis of electronic configurations. The remaining three are several times more remote and are termed *valence* electrons. That is, they are the electrons which determine the number of atoms of another element which will enter into chemical combination with an atom of the element in question. As we have seen, they determine the chemical activity of the element.

Now, the hot spark employed by Millikan has an extraordinarily high degree of ionizing power, which means the ability to shake loose the outer orbital, or valence, electrons from the atom. From the character of the spectra produced, he was able to prove that the hot sparks stripped a great many atoms entirely free of these electrons. Then, he proceeded to calculate and predict just what frequency of vibration in the ether and what wave length, in each case, these electrons will produce when they jump back orbit by orbit toward the nucleus. This means that he was able to foretell precisely the kind of a bright line and its position in the spectrum which would be produced by each jump. He made this calculation on the basis of the known spectral lines produced by hydrogen. His prediction foretold the line which should appear in the spectrum when an electron from the stripped boron atom should jump from orbit 5 to orbit 4. Millikan then made a photograph of the hot-spark spectrum, and, when the plate was developed, there was the line just as he had predicted that it would be. This line, too, had never before been observed in the case of boron. This discovery was made entirely on the basis of the quantum theory as applied by Bohr to the structure of the atom, and a very striking confirmation did it give. In the astronomy of the atom, it is indeed comparable to the discovery of Neptune in the astronomy of the heavens.

Millikan next calculated the line which would be produced when the electron from the stripped boron atom on its return trip should fall from the third to the second orbit. Again the spectroscope verified the prediction. Continuing his experiments, he was able to predict and verify all the spectral lines of the stripped boron atom. He then made similar studies with equal success of the stripped atoms of bismuth, carbon, nitrogen, sodium, magnesium, aluminum, silicon, phosphorous and sulfur.

Additional proof from other sources has also been forthcoming. We must not forget to explain that the word *quantum* refers to the quantity of energy liberated when an orbital electron jumps from one orbit to another. That this theory has come to stay, there is no doubt. It no longer stands upon the firing line of scientific inquiry. It already occupies a secure and strategic position. It still further robs the atom of its mystery.

When we consider the large number of valence electrons in the atom of a heavy element and the various orbits which must be provided for them, we can readily account for the complex spectrum which these electrons make in their multitudinous jumps from orbit to orbit.

In concluding this chapter upon the atom, let us append the following statement from Rutherford, the world's greatest authority upon atomic structure:

"The movements of the outer electrons are responsible for the X-ray and optical spectra of the elements and their configuration for the ordinary physical and chemical properties of the elements. On the other hand, the phenomena of radioactivity and all properties that depend on the mass of the atom are to be definitely assigned to the nucleus. From a study of the radio-active transformations, we know that the nucleus of a heavy atom not only contains positively charged bodies but also negative electrons, so that the nuclear charge is the excess of positive charge over negative. In recent years, the general idea has arisen that there are but two definite fundamental units that have to do with the building up of complex nuclei, viz., the light negative electron and the relatively massive hydrogen nucleus which is believed to correspond to the positive electron.''

And now we have had the ''peep within.'' With the scientists of yesterday and to-day, we have literally explored the interior of the atom. Still, let no one fancy that the half has yet been told. On the frontiers of atomic investigations, much remains to be cleared up. Our knowledge of the atom and its constituent electrons and protons will grow with the years. That they will be fruitful years, there can be no shadow of doubt.

CHAPTER IV

CHEMISTRY AND POWER

PROBLEM OF POWER—WHAT OF THE FUTURE?—A SURVEY—
WATER-POWER—COAL RESERVES—PETROLEUM RESOURCES—
CHEMICAL SOLUTIONS—THE "CRACKING" PROCESS—ANTI-
KNOCK GAS—OIL SHALES—OIL SHALE PROCESS NOT NEW—A
TRANSITION PERIOD—INTERNATIONAL CONFERENCE ON BITU-
MINOUS COAL—BERGIUS' PROCESS FOR LIQUEFACTION OF
COAL—LIQUEFACTION A BOON TO BITUMINOUS INDUSTRY—
OTHER ROUTES FROM COAL TO AUTOMOTIVE POWER—WORK OF
FISCHER AND PATART—SABATIER AND CATALYSIS—METHA-
NOL—LOW-TEMPERATURE CARBONIZATION OF COAL—POSSI-
BILITIES AND ECONOMIES OF THE PROCESS—ARTIFICIAL
ANTHRACITE—POWER FROM COAL DUST—NO ROOM FOR
PESSIMISM.

POWER,—yes, that is the big problem which looms
large on the horizon of this little planet and seems to
grow more acute with each passing year. Power and
yet more power is the never-ending cry of every workshop in the world. It is the soul of our transportation
systems. Power is the basis of all industry. It trans-
lates itself into electricity. In a thousand ways, it is
fundamental to world progress. In early centuries,
bought with the sweat and grime of the bondsman, power
to-day seeks to emancipate mankind from the drudgery
of human toil. Back of all the smoke screens which mask

152

the grim specter of war is the greed for power. Power in abundance spells economic independence. It gives to a nation that most coveted of all objectives, its place in the sun, the source of all power. Power to subdue the earth, to develop to the full its resources, to surround man at little cost with every necessity and many luxuries, power to provide him with that economic surplus and leisure without which education, invention, science, art, literature, democratic government, enlightened statesmanship and organized religion would disappear and civilization be swallowed up in the abyss of barbarism,—that is the goal toward which science strives. Power in unmeasured quantity, with little or no effort, would bring the millennium.

What answer does chemistry offer to this supreme problem which has confronted every race of men from the cave man to the twentieth century? Listen to Dr. James F. Norris, of the Massachusetts Institute of Technology, in his presidential address at the seventy-second meeting of the American Chemical Society, in Philadelphia, in September, 1926: "I hold that it is not foolhardy to refuse to worry about the consumption of natural resources or to look to the future with confidence that science will always keep ahead of the needs of the world."

But here we are, adrift upon this tiny planet in an infinite ocean of space. Will the earth ever become bankrupt in its sources of energy? Will it cease to yield sufficient power for the maintenance of the race? Will this terrestrial clock run down, the wheels of industry fail to turn, and life disappear because our supplies of energy have vanished? Forever and a day is a long while. We are making prodigious inroads upon our original capital. Is there no limit to the supply?

Even now, the imaginary approach of a gasoline famine disturbs our slumbers and visions of motorless highways cast their shadows across our dreams and haunt our waking hours. Will that new car become a piece of junk and the horse be restored to supremacy on the city street and country road? Will the hands of time be turned backward because a basic source of energy has been exhausted? If so, how soon will the calamity befall us? Will it come in our day or will it only be a legacy which we shall bequeath to succeeding generations? Does no light gleam through the darkness? Is no progress being made in the solution of this problem, fundamental to the happiness and well-being of the nearly two billions of souls upon our earth? These are some of the questions which anxious thousands are asking. They deserve answers formulated in the light of all the knowledge which science makes available.

When thoughts of this kind weigh heavily upon me, I like to think of the old lady who worried a great deal about what the world would do for light when the whales were all killed and we should have no more oil for our lamps. Another avenue of escape is to step off a few billions of miles into space and see this "sorrowful star" and all its troubles vanish, swallowed up in the infinity of other worlds and solar systems. And then again, it comforts me to think of the young man in the patent office who in 1833 resigned his position on the ground that the inventions and scientific discoveries had all been made and he could not conscientiously draw a salary for a useless job.

A SURVEY

Let us take stock of the nation's energy reserves and then consider what the researches of chemistry are doing to insure an adequate supply of power for many centuries to come. If we can provide the "sinews of war" for a campaign of a thousand years, we may safely assume that posterity will take care of the next thousand years and so on until this planet shall mayhap have become a cold, dead world, winging its silent way through the infinite reaches of the celestial spaces.

Our tangible power assets may be stated as follows: falling water, coal, petroleum and natural gas. In addition, we have the energy of the tides, the direct energy of the sun, and the inconceivably vast reservoirs of subatomic energy locked up within the atoms of the elements. This last source we have discussed in another chapter. The energy of the tides, we shall some day learn to harness. Of course, the sun, the arbiter of planetary destinies, the molder of geologic climate and the mighty warrior of primitive peoples is the ultimate source of all our energy. Enough sunlight falls on the Desert of Sahara in twenty-four hours to be equivalent to the burning of six billion tons of coal, one-quarter of all that has been mined in this country from the beginning of the industry. If we could convert into power without loss all the energy in the sunlight falling upon the United States, it would in one minute equal the power we now use in a year. So long as the sun continues to shine we shall not be without an adequate source of power, and Professor A. S. Eddington, of Cambridge University, assures us that we may expect the present rate of radiation for fifteen trillion years. What the cost will be of converting this practically inexhaustible supply of power to human needs is the big question confronting scientists and engineers. But we need not despair. This planet is still in the heyday of vigorous youth.

Water-power—white coal,—that, to many, has seemed an adequate answer to power problems. Water, carried inland by the rays of the sun and condensing to form our lakes and streams, flows down the rivers and merrily tumbles over the cataracts in a never-ceasing supply of free and limitless power. It is a gift of the gods and costs us nothing. Why not let it turn the wheels of industry, light and heat our homes, drive our locomotives and smelt our ores? Why rack our brains with chemical problems related to the development of power when the energy of a thousand cataracts clamors to do our work? Let us see.

The United States Geological Survey recently estimated this natural resource to be 34,818,000 horse-power available ninety per cent. of the time or 55,030,000 horse-power available fifty per cent. of the time. Of this total, 11,176,596 horse-power had been developed up to January 1, 1926. By no means all of that which remains is adapted to practical development. Some sites are too small for present-day requirements. Others are too remote from industrial centers. Seventy per cent. of the potential water-power of the country is in the Rocky Mountain region and the states beyond. A competent engineering authority asserts that of our undeveloped water-power not to exceed ten million horse-power can be harnessed at a cost which will enable it to compete successfully with electric power generated by steam.

The best engineering judgment holds that never will "white coal" supply as much as fifty per cent. of the country's power requirements. Steinmetz, as a result of careful calculations, stated that, if all our water-power were developed, the output would be but slightly greater than that now produced by coal. In the states of the Atlantic seaboard, only eleven per cent. of the electric power is developed by water and in the country as a whole only twenty per cent.

The simple facts are that, except where we have a Niagara, a Muscle Shoals or a St. Lawrence power site, water-power can not successfully compete with steam-generated power. In recent years, thousands of small water-power plants, such as sawmills, gristmills and factories, have been abandoned. The required power could be had more cheaply by burning coal. The reasons are not difficult to find. The cost of developing water-power is much greater than that of a steam installation of the same capacity. Interest charges on the large initial investment, overhead, repairs and replacement expense prevent cheaper operating costs. The cost of power production by burning coal is constantly becoming less. In 1913, the most efficient development gave a horse-power hour for one and one-fourth pounds of coal. To-day, the same result is obtained from three-fourths of a pound, and recent indications are that this will soon be reduced to one-half pound. Water-power developments have not progressed as rapidly. Some of the large steam-electric plants of the country now utilize as much as twenty-five per cent. of the energy in the raw coal. Such plants as a whole average fifteen per cent., whereas a quarter of a century ago the efficiency was but seven and a half per cent. Rapid strides have been made in recent years in the development of power through the fundamental chemical process of fuel combustion. Water-power has not been able to keep the pace.

Water-power is a great natural resource. Where water-power is available in large blocks, as at Niagara or Muscle Shoals, it can and must be developed. Such power can compete with steam. Where coal is scarce or wholly absent, as in some of the Western States and in portions of Canada, water-power at once becomes the basis of industrial development. The immense industrial center grown up about Arvida, on the Saguenay River, in the Province of Quebec, would to-day be but an impossible dream had it not been for the "white coal" of that favored spot. Some day the energy of falling water may be able to compete more successfully with that from burning coal.

So much for water-power. Let us turn to coal. When the white man first set foot upon these shores, the United States Geological Survey tells us that there were 3,541,000,000,000 tons of coal of all kinds locked up in the coal measures of this country. Of this huge estate, we have to date used only 25,000,000,000 tons, and we are mining it at the rate of approximately 600,000,000 tons a year. At first thought, these reserves seem inexhaustible. We have scarcely scratched the surface of our fuel resources. Apparently, there is almost as much left as when the first lumps of this crystallized sunshine of a former geologic era were removed from their ages-old resting-place. With such immense credits in the bank of Nature, why should men worry about the exhaustion of our sources of power? As a matter of fact, there is no need for worry in our day and generation. With fifty-two per cent. of the total coal reserves of the world within the borders of the United States, our supply will meet every domestic and industrial need for several hundred years to come. Still, our anthracite will be gone in another century and we have already mined much of our best bituminous coal. Despite these disquieting facts, however, coal constitutes our basic power supply. More and more, scientists are turning to this crystallized debris of the primeval swamps and forests of an earlier age for the material motive power of civilization. In the present organization of society and industry, that nation which controls in largest measure this basic resource and its twin brother, iron, will dominate the commercial and political activities of the world.

It is when we take stock of our petroleum estate that the situation seems alarming. Here at once we are walking in a fool's paradise and struggling with a hideous nightmare. The almost undiminished output of this liquid motive power of transportation lulls us into a false sense of security. At the same time the grim specter of early exhaustion casts its ever-lengthening shadow across our pathway. To many minds, the peace of mankind hinges upon a plentiful supply of petroleum, equitably distributed throughout the world. It has become a national necessity, both in peace and war. For its possession, statesmen seem willing to wage war and spill the blood of innocent victims, caught in the maelstrom of struggling nations intoxicated with the lust for power. Petroleum the world must have. When it is exhausted, substitutes must be provided. To do so is the problem of chemistry.

Already the handwriting appears on the wall. The Federal Oil Conservation Board, in its recent report, estimated the total petroleum reserves to be about 4,500,000,000 barrels, which without importation will provide a supply for only six years. This does not mean that our petroleum will be exhausted in six years, for it will be impossible to obtain all of it within that period. These estimates, too, are only tentative. The extent of existing reserves can not be known with certainty, and new fields may be discovered. Already increased output has come from the Texas Panhandle and in particular from the Seminole field in Oklahoma. Whereas, in 1926, 27,000,000 barrels of crude petroleum were withdrawn from storage, the present prospects are that in 1927, 100,000,000 barrels will be put into storage. But this excess of production will doubtless only be temporary. Petroleum engineers have brightened the picture by assuring us that after present methods of pumping have yielded all they can, 26,000,000,000 barrels additional, now left as waste in the oil sands, can be obtained by known, but more expensive, methods of recovery. Often but a sixth and sometimes only a tenth of the oil in the pool has been secured. Much of it can never be brought to the surface. However, the application of artificial pressure, flooding with water, and the employment of mining methods may be relied upon to salvage part of this earlier waste.

Of the 9,000,000,000 barrels of petroleum produced in this country from the beginning of the industry up to June 30, 1926, one-third must be credited to the previous five years. That is the disquieting feature of the situation. That is what causes the automobile manufacturer to lie awake nights and turns his hair gray. We now have approximately twenty million motor-cars and trucks in operation in this country. It is estimated in the *Report of the Committee of Eleven* to the American Petroleum Institute that this number will reach thirty-one million by 1930 and that by 1950 it will be forty-five million. The saturation ratio for passenger cars, which is assumed to be one car for four persons, will be reached in 1938. Any increase after that will be due to population.

To meet the constantly growing demand for gasoline, production must be enormously increased. At the present rate of increase, the annual consumption of motor fuel will be four hundred and twenty million barrels in 1930. By 1950 it will have reached six hundred million and in 1975 seven hundred and thirty million, nearly as much as the total petroleum production for 1926.

When we consider that at present only thirty-five per cent. of the crude oil actually subjected to the refining process is converted into gasoline, we can understand how great the petroleum production must be to meet the need.

Besides gasoline for automotive vehicles, we have also to consider adequate supplies of fuel for Diesel engines, for the navy and ocean liners, and for domestic use. From where will this huge supply come? How will science solve the problem of providing it? Presently, we shall see what steps have been taken.

As to natural gas, it has never constituted any considerable factor in the nation's power supply, and its exhaustion will not be long deferred. In the exploitation of our oil fields, this gaseous fuel has been shamelessly wasted. A chief use of this gas is to bring the petroleum to the surface. With the exhaustion of the gas, more expensive methods of recovery must be employed. And then, too, this gas contains considerable quantities of gasoline which may be condensed and recovered. It sometimes comprises as much as ten per cent. of the total production. When this gas is blown into the air or is allowed to burn at the casing-head, as has happened in times past, a double loss is sustained.

Such in brief are the known and proved energy resources of this country to-day. What has chemical research been doing in recent years to insure their more economical utilization? In particular, what provision has been made for the conversion of other fuel materials into a form suitable for use in internal combustion motors? What assurance can the chemist give that the gasoline age is not to be but a flash in the pan, merely a fascinating joy-ride in the evolution of transportation systems? How can he justify the implicit faith of his fellows in the marvelous efficiency of the magic wand of science? Let us see.

SOLUTIONS OF THE PROBLEM

This planet has never yet been cornered. Mankind has never found itself in a place so tight that it could not be extricated. So long as the race is here we may be perfectly sure that the wherewithal to maintain it will be forthcoming. What would the cave man think, could he step into our world to-day? But we do not need to go back that far. I sometimes wander into Faneuil Hall, and, as I study the portraits of the founders of the nation, I try to picture how this age would seem to them could they once more tread the busy streets of Boston and behold the transformation which has been wrought in the brief space of a century and a half. Most of the achievements at the close of this first quarter of the twentieth century were not even dreams to the forefathers of that period. Dr. Willis R. Whitney, Director of the Research Laboratory of the General Electric Company, asserts that we have yet but barely scratched the surface of scientific discovery and invention. Although the skies may at times be overcast, the sun has never yet failed to reappear.

Let us now get down to the concrete illustrations of the tangible accomplishments of chemistry in the solution of this problem of providing a never-failing supply of cheap and abundant motor fuel. For it is motor fuel for which the world cries. In some way the chemist must ward off the threatened exhaustion of this precious store of energy.

For about a decade, the process known as "cracking" has been doing much toward making the most of existing supplies. Let us explain. We are already well acquainted with atoms and molecules. Petroleum is a mixture of hydrocarbons, that is, compounds whose molecules consist of atoms of hydrogen chemically combined with atoms of carbon. Some of these molecules contain but a few atoms. They are the light, volatile, that is, easily vaporized, constituents, and go to form the gasoline portion of petroleum. But unfortunately only a relatively small proportion of the crude petroleum consists of these light molecules. Was there any way to increase the gasoline yield? The chemist began to experiment. He knew that the bulk of petroleum consists of hydrocarbons containing a large number of atoms to the molecule. If in some way he might break these heavy molecules up, he saw that he could obtain lighter hydrocarbons similar to those in gasoline. In other words he sought to "crack" these heavy molecules, much as we crack nuts with a hammer and anvil.

We, of course, understand that petroleum is refined by a process of distillation in which the light, low-boiling constituents come off first, followed by the heavier ones in regular succession. It was against the heavier constituents, after the first run of natural gasoline had been obtained, that the chemist directed his heavy artillery. He put the residue into cracking stills in which he subjected the hydrocarbons to heat and pressure. A considerable proportion of the heavy molecules could not stand this treatment. They broke down into smaller and lighter ones. The result was more gasoline. The problem had been solved. This process has added hundreds of millions of gallons of gasoline to the country's supply every year. Without it, we should have been in the throes of a motor fuel shortage several years ago. Charles E. Hughes asserts that "the cracking process has done more for conservation than any legislative scheme could do under our constitution."

This process of cracking may be applied, not only to any type of crude oil, but also to the heavy tars obtained from the distillation of coal and wood. What an important potential supply of motor fuel this latter source offers, will be discussed a little later. As we shall see, too, the gasoline obtained by the cracking process possesses valuable properties as an automotive fuel not found in that derived from the original method of straight-run distillation. Dr. Gustav Egloff, an authority in this field, asserts that ultimately as much as seventy-five per cent. of all crude oil will be converted by the cracking process into gasoline. However, this process does not in any way increase the quantity of petroleum. It simply increases the proportion of gasoline at the expense of kerosene, fuel and lubricating oils. This has been a tremendous boon to the automobile industry. Without it, the gasoline age would have presented a vastly different picture. Still, it can offer no hope of prolonging this age.

A second development, and one which we have only just begun to utilize, is of even more significance than that of the cracking process. It is the chemical discovery of "anti-knock" gas. No one likes a knocker, and a gasoline motor no better than a human being. Translated into simple language, anti-knock gas means increasing the efficiency of the automobile motor by possibly one hundred per cent. It means doubling the power and mileage obtained from every gallon of gas fed through the carbureter. It means extending the period within which petroleum threatens to be exhausted by possibly a quarter of a century. It means the dawn of a new day in the automobile world.

First, let us see how gas which does not possess anti-knock properties behaves. It is well known to automobile engineers that the higher the degree of compression of the gaseous mixture in the cylinder of a motor before firing occurs, the greater will be the proportion of energy paid out in useful work on the crank-shaft. But unfortunately at a particular "critical" pressure, which is perfectly definite for any given kind of gas, this burning changes from a gradual and even combustion to an instantaneous explosion, producing a knock. The chemist says the mixture detonates. As a result, a large proportion of the energy of the charge is liberated as radiant heat to be absorbed by the piston and walls of the cylinder. It is wasted, and right there the efficiency of the motor stops. Owing to this detonating property of the gas, the higher efficiency to be derived from higher compression is impossible of attainment. It is supposed that the firing of a part of the gaseous mixture by the spark from the spark plug so compresses the unburned portion that this unburned portion becomes hot enough to ignite spontaneously, thereby detonating with a resultant knock.

This was the problem which confronted Thomas Midgley, Jr., a young Cornell chemist, and Thomas A. Boyd, of the research laboratories of the General Motors Company. In some way they must impart to gasoline anti-knock properties. If it could be done, the potential power of our gasoline reserves would be doubled at a single stroke. This was a plain problem of research, but it was research with a specific end in view. It is a capital example of what we call applied research as distinguished from pure research, or the pursuit of truth for truth's sake only.

These chemists made the happy discovery that minute quantities of certain chemical compounds, chief of which is tetraethyl lead, increase very largely the pressure possible before the knock will occur. It is believed that, when the ignition occurs in the motor cylinder, the tetraethyl lead in the gas suddenly decomposes into infinitesimal particles of metallic lead. Each of these particles forms a burning center, acting like a tiny spark plug and causing the flame front to travel quickly and evenly throughout the mixture without detonation. However this may be, the discovery has made possible the high-compression motor with its greatly increased efficiency. Anti-knock gas, it is asserted, will increase the gasoline mileage by fifty to one hundred per cent. Egloff believes the ultimate efficiency will be still higher. This contribution of the chemist to the solution of the gasoline problem will prolong by many years our waning supplies of motor fuel.

One may ask why this discovery is not more generally utilized. Already certain makes of cars are being equipped with motors having higher compression ratios. However, anti-knock gas is not yet universally obtainable. Practise always follows tardily along the pathway blazed by scientific discovery. So long, too, as the motorist may buy gas at the curb at the low prices now prevailing, there is little incentive for the automobile manufacturer to build motors designed to increase the economy of fuel consumption. Let the price of gasoline jump to a figure which jeopardizes the sale of automobiles and the manufacturer will be quick to seize upon this discovery of science and utilize it to the utmost. That time may arrive more quickly than we have imagined. Another factor which has operated against the introduction of tetraethyl gas was the early belief that the exhaust gases from motors in which this anti-knock compound had been used were exceptionally poisonous and a menace to the public health. A committee under the chairmanship of Dr. William H. Howell, professor of physiology at the Johns Hopkins School of Hygiene and Public Health, undertook an exhaustive investigation. As a result, such menace was not found to exist and the ban, imposed for a time, was speedily lifted. In fact, tetraethyl lead, by producing more complete combustion of the gas in the motor cylinder, very largely diminishes the danger of poisoning from that insidious foe of the unsuspecting motorist, carbon monoxide. Other substances than tetraethyl lead have been employed for knock suppression, and research in this field has only just begun. The time is coming when the high-compression motor and the light-weight car so widely used in Europe will also become the fashion in America.

Chemists have also determined that certain types of hydrocarbons possess natural anti-knock properties. Like certain individuals we know who smooth out difficulties, eliminate friction and prevent social riots, these compounds burn evenly under compression and without detonation. In particular, the hydrocarbons obtained by the cracking process are knock eliminators. This is especially true of the gasoline derived from the cracking of coal-tar, a product which is destined to form a big factor in the motor fuel supply of the future. The secret is to be found in the structure of the molecule. The smaller the percentage of hydrogen atoms to those of carbon, the larger is the measure of anti-knock properties. Such compounds burn quietly and evenly without detonation. When blended with hydrocarbons of the opposite type, they improve the qualities of the gasoline to a marked degree. Just as a goodly sprinkling of level-headed citizens may hold in check the explosive tendencies of a near-mob, so these unsaturated hydrocarbons, as they are called, control the situation in the cylinder of a gasoline motor. For such discoveries as these, every user of an automobile, and in this country that is almost every person, is indebted to the chemist.

In particular, anti-knock gas not only gives greater power and mileage, but it also makes possible a motor of marvelous smoothness, free from noise and vibration. In a practical way it adds to the pleasure of driving and saves money for the motorist. The scientist who can confer these favors is surely a benefactor of his fellows.

Still, while anti-knock gas will prolong the supply of our petroleum reserves, it can not increase the quantity. Something more is needed, some fresh resource which shall resuscitate an industry which in its manifold ramifications has come to be fundamental to the happiness of millions and to the economic well-being of our national life. When the time arrives that we can not obtain abundant supplies of liquid petroleum merely by sinking a hole in the ground, what shall the nation do? Without waiting for that emergency to precipitate itself upon us, let us forecast the solution of the problem.

A VAST RESOURCE

Lurking in the oil shales of which this country has prodigious quantities, is a potential source of motor fuel so vast as to provide a veritable silver lining to the threatening clouds of petroleum shortage. Professor Ralph H. McKee, of Columbia University, our greatest authority in this field, asserts that, without utilizing oil-bearing rock producing less than thirty gallons to the ton, we possess enough of such deposits to yield twenty times as much petroleum as our wells have delivered to date from the beginning of the industry. The Committee of Eleven places our oil shale deposits at 394 billion tons and estimates a yield of 135 billion barrels on the basis of an average production of 14.4 gallons per ton. So rich are some of these shales in oil that they will produce upward of fifty gallons to the ton.

Regarding these deposits of fuel oil, the Report of the Federal Oil Conservation Board had this to say: "The oil shale and oil sand deposits of the country are of more promise in the future outlook. Very large areas of such shales exist, many of them containing as much as a barrel of oil per ton of shale. Their utilization is solely a question of price. There can be no doubt that these shales will some day be brought into production. They form an almost unlimited reserve and may, therefore, be taken as the final protection of our people in the matter of essential supply."

Mr. Harry H. Hill, chief petroleum engineer, United States Bureau of Mines, in speaking of this resource, says: "In Europe much is being done to distill oil from coal. But extracting it from shales is more appealing. Scotland has worked its shales for seventy-five years. We have vastly greater and richer deposits here. There is no doubt of the possibility of extraction; just a question of cost. Scotch shales are producing twenty-five gallons per ton; we can get much more. Scotch seams are 3½ to 10 feet thick; ours are many times that. Shale resources are so vast as to insure against deficiency in oil, once the price is high enough."

Dr. V. C. Alderson, former president of the School of Mines, Golden, Colorado, has declared that "so vast is the oil-shale field in Colorado that if there were 100 oil-shale plants in operation, each treating 2,000 tons a day, the easily accessible supply would last for 700 years." Assuming a barrel of oil per ton of shale, this would mean an annual production of 73,000,000 barrels, a very considerable item in the nation's fuel supply. And Colorado represents but a fraction of the total reserves.

Similar statements might be multiplied. Let us see, however, what the development of this resource involves. By oil shale we mean a rock impregnated with oil, but oil so tenaciously held in the pores of the rock that it will not flow and, therefore, can not be obtained by the ordinary methods of drilling and pumping. This rock must actually be mined, brought to the surface, crushed and distilled in retorts. The scientific and technical difficulties encountered in the development of practical processes of distillation and recovery have been great. Much research has been done in this field, and the progress to date gives certain promise that when the summons comes these vast reservoirs will meet the nation's need. The solution of the problem has been entirely in the hands of the chemist and the engineer. Where they have blazed the way, the capitalist and promoter are sure to follow as soon as the development of the industry promises to show a profit. In one important respect, the utilization of our oil shales will be free from the uncertainty and financial loss attending the development of oil-well territory. There will be no wild-catting. The enormous loss involved in drilling, only to find dry holes will be eliminated. The extent of our oil shales is very definitely known. Their development will mean no more risk than has that of our coal deposits.

The distillation of oil shale is not a new process. According to Dr. G. C. Riddell, a consulting engineer of New York, it began in France in 1838 and in Scotland before 1850. Shale pits in the latter country three thousand feet deep testify to the former extent of the industry, and, indeed, it has not yet been abandoned there. In our own country, oil was being distilled from shales of Utah and Pennsylvania in 1850. Only the discovery of liquid petroleum in immense quantities prevented the building of an oil-shale industry of large proportions. The Patent Office shows that one hundred and eighty-six patents have been issued in this country for the production of oil by the distillation of shale rock. Doctor Riddell asserts that in California during the last three years oil has been distilled from shale rock at a cost of less than one dollar a barrel, which is much less than the average cost of producing oil from American wells. It is by no means certain that the combined ingenuity of the chemist, the engineer and the industrial organizer will not solve the problem of producing oil from shale rock at a cost which will eventually exceed little, if any, that of oil obtained by present methods of drilling and refining. Of this we may be perfectly sure—when the need arises, chemistry will effect improvements and economies in the pioneer methods now available of such a character as may be necessary to utilize this vast resource.

One problem looms large in the minds of many who attempt to envision a motor age dependent for its liquid fuel upon the oil from shale rock. What can be done with the immense quantities of spent shale after the oil has been distilled? Those who have seen the culm banks of the anthracite regions can have but a faint picture of the huge proportions which it is believed these mountains of refuse must assume. And yet, already uses are being found for this material. It can be used in the construction of roads, for the making of concrete building blocks, in the manufacture of cement and as a filtering medium for the sugar industry. Still other uses may be discovered. Certain it is, however, that this difficulty will form no insuperable obstacle to the development of the resource.

In one important respect, oil from shale rock is of superior quality. It is rich in those unsaturated hydrocarbons possessing anti-knock properties. Especially is this true of the gasoline to be obtained by the cracking of this oil.

Just when shale oil will come on the market can not be told. As has already been indicated, it is a matter dependent upon cost and competition. As the present industry wanes, shale-oil production will grow. Doubtless the two will run side by side for many years, the one supplementing the other. It is more than likely that during this period of adjustment, a period marked by the passing of the old order and the coming of the new, the prices of petroleum products will be abnormally high. It will require high prices to stimulate shale-oil production. When, however, the new industry has been placed upon an established basis, we may confidently look to the chemist and the engineer to effect economies in operation which will give the maximum of value at the smallest practicable expense to the public.

Cheer up. Do not scrap that car or refuse to buy a new one. The gasoline will not give out.

Before proceeding with further developments, let us make it clear that, while we stand at the dawn of a new era in gasoline production, present supplies are drawn almost entirely from the petroleum issuing from drilled wells, of which more than seventy per cent. of the world's total is produced in the United States. Formerly, the supply of gasoline was derived entirely from the first "runs" in the ordinary refining of crude oil, and the price of gasoline was governed by the price of crude. Now, the cracking of the fuel oil which remains affords the larger volume of the gasoline supply, and the price is determined by that of fuel oil instead of crude. In other words, the control of the situation has passed from the hands of the producer to that of the refiner. In 1923, when the cracking process was just beginning to be adopted on a large scale, the "spread" between fuel oil and gasoline was twelve cents a gallon. To-day, it is seven or eight, and it is bound to be still less. That is, not only has this triumph of modern chemistry more than doubled the quantity of available gasoline, but by fixing a new basis for the determination of prices it has greatly reduced the cost to the consumer.

We must bear in mind, too, that the production of gasoline is by no means the sole consideration in the refining of petroleum. It is a matter of vast importance, particularly for our navy, that the supplies of fuel oil shall not be impaired. Fuel oil is also used in Diesel engines and for domestic heating. The demand for fuel oil made by the world's navies and ocean liners is becoming prodigious. The *Olympic* on one round trip

Power from water, at Arvida, Canada

The newest center of electrochemical industries in America

Plant in the Oklahoma fields for "cracking" petroleum. (Dubbs Process)

Courtesy, Dr. Friedrich Bergius, of Heidelberg, Germany

Bergius' apparatus for the liquefaction of coal

Courtesy, Consolidation Coal Products Company

Carbonized briquets of bituminous coal

A substitute for anthracite made by the recently developed low-temperature process consumes seven thousand five hundred tons of oil, and the *Majestic* burns eight hundred tons a day. The rapid introduction of oil furnaces for household heating still further augments the demand. Lubricating oils, too, are a product of petroleum refining.

It can be readily seen that the cracking process, which has as yet by no means been carried to the limit of practicability, produces gasoline at the expense of these other products. The operation of the inexorable laws of supply and demand and of economic necessity may be trusted to take care of the situation. Eventually, a balance will be struck. In the meantime, the chemist will bend his energies to the solution of new problems and to the task of making it certain that the supplies of these products so vital to national and private well-being are provided in abundance and at costs which shall not become excessively burdensome, much less prohibitive.

Valuable by-products obtained in the cracking process are gas and coke. Not only is this gas important as a fuel, but it may also be used as a raw material for the synthesis of alcohols and other chemical derivatives. The chemist allows nothing to escape unutilized, and at every turn in the pathway of research he finds fresh possibilities for new developments.

NEW VISTAS

Those of you who followed the trend of developments at the International Conference on Bituminous Coal, held at Pittsburgh in the autumn of 1926, know what a vast storehouse of unmeasured natural wealth our huge fuel estate affords us. Possibilities which a decade ago were little more than dreams are now entering upon the commercial stage. Recent progress has been swift and certain. In the light of the disclosures made before the sixteen hundred scientists and fuel technicians assembled from all over the world at the Carnegie Institute of Technology, present methods of utilizing our bituminous coal may soon appear to be as obsolete and primitive as does the stage-coach in the field of transportation. Indeed, the irreparable waste attending them may be regarded by future generations as little short of criminal. Hitherto almost unsuspected sources of power to supplement our waning reserves of petroleum, gas in greater abundance for fuel and power, a clean smokeless semi-anthracite for domestic heating, a new source of dyes and drugs,—these are some of the additional benefits which this crystallized sunshine of a former geologic age may be made to yield in response to the summons of the research chemist.

Just now we are interested in the problem of power. How can bituminous coal be made to yield us more? In particular, how may it be so processed as to enable it to supplement and possibly entirely replace, if need arises, our sources of petroleum? How can it lay the ghost of a gasoline shortage so that this specter of gloom may never return to haunt us? If we can once be sure that the gasoline will not give out, there will be little left to take the joy out of life. Let us see what this conference had to offer.

Probably the most promising of the processes outlined at Pittsburgh for the production of motor fuel from bituminous coal was that of Dr. Friedrich Bergius, of Heidelberg, Germany. Back in 1912, Doctor Bergius began what will doubtless come to be regarded as one of the classic researches in the history of industrial chemistry. For thirteen years he worked, expending millions of dollars, employing a small army of men, and solving a multitude of baffling chemical and engineering problems of the first magnitude. His goal was the development of a direct method for the conversion of bituminous coal into a petroleum-like fuel oil. Even before the Great War he saw the danger to his own and other countries lurking in the dependence of one nation upon another for its supply of gasoline for automobiles, motor-trucks, launches and farm tractors. Beneath the thin disguise of a score and more of artificial smoke screens, he saw that European international relations were soaked in oil. In particular, he wished to free his own country from bondage to American petroleum. Chemist that he was, he believed in his ability to solve the problem. His presence at the Pittsburgh Conference and the testimony he gave proves him right.

The first two years of Doctor Bergius' research were spent in the study of coal. In minute detail, he studied its chemistry and physical structure. From every part of the world, he obtained samples of coal,—thousands of them. In his knowledge of coal, he became probably the world's foremost expert. Then, equipped with this vast store of first-hand information, Bergius proceeded to make coal in his laboratory. He sought to duplicate processes of Nature which had required millions of years for their completion. And he succeeded. Starting with sawdust, he converted it into coal. He produced almost every gradation of coal from lignite to a substance resembling anthracite. When this preliminary research had made him master of the raw material with which he was to work, he attacked the supreme problem of converting coal into oil. This direct liquefaction of coal seemed to him to be the only artificial process which could hope to provide an adequate supply of motor fuel.

We already know that petroleum consists of hydrocarbons, that is, compounds whose molecules are composed of atoms of hydrogen and carbon chemically combined. Analysis showed Doctor Bergius that bituminous coal contains carbon and hydrogen in the ratio of sixteen to one, while the average ratio of these elements in petroleum is eight to one. If in some way he could succeed in doubling the hydrogen content of the coal, hydrocarbons resembling those in petroleum might be expected to form. Thus the problem took shape.

Of course, the preliminary work of experiment and research had to be done in the laboratory. At once, seemingly insurmountable difficulties thrust themselves into the foreground. Bergius sought to drive hydrogen at enormous pressure into coal heated in steel drums. But when the drums were opened, he found nothing but coke. The heat had been too great. The action had been precisely that which occurs in an ordinary city gas plant. He soon learned that hydrogen combines to form hydrocarbons at a much lower temperature than that required for the coking process. There seemed to be going on in his steel drums a sort of competition between the chemical reactions which produce coke and the desired one which results in petroleum. But the battle was now on, the enemy was in the open, victory seemed in sight.

Bergius' next step was to grind the coal almost to a powder and mix it with a heavy oil. Then he devised special pumps by which this mixture together with hydrogen could be forced into the steel drums under pressures of three thousand pounds to the square inch. A very carefully designed system of temperature control enabled him to keep the reaction chambers at the proper heat, for the process was very sensitive to temperature changes. The hydrogenation process, or the chemical union of

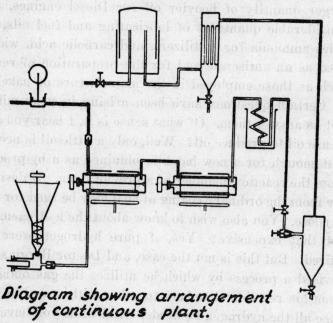

Diagram showing arrangement of continuous plant.

FIGURE 20

This diagram of the plant equipment used in the Bergius process for the liquefaction of coal is reproduced through the courtesy of Doctor Bergius.

hydrogen with carbon, seemed to begin at a temperature of about three hundred degrees Centigrade and to be complete at four hundred and fifty degrees. Two changes appeared to occur side by side in the steel drums. Hydrogen united to form hydrocarbons, and large molecules of hydrocarbons decomposed, or cracked, to form smaller ones. When the process was complete, the product was found to be a complex mixture of gaseous, liquid and solid hydrocarbons similar to those coming from natural petroleum. Upon refining the artificial petroleum obtained from a ton of common bituminous coal, it is found to yield about forty-five gallons of gasoline, a larger quantity of heavier oil for Diesel engines, and considerable quantities of lubricating and fuel oils, besides ammonia for fertilizers, and carbolic acid, widely used as an antiseptic and for the preparation of resins such as those employed in the manufacture of bakelite.

Certain questions have been arising in your minds. Let us answer them. Of what sense is it, I hear you say, to use oil to produce oil? Well, only a little oil is needed and enough for a new batch is obtained as a by-product from the reaction chamber of a previous run. If desired, tar from the ordinary coking of coal may be used for this purpose. You also wish to know about the hydrogen. Is not that expensive? Yes, if pure hydrogen were required. But this is not the case, and Doctor Bergius has devised a process by which he utilizes the gas obtained from his reaction chambers together with steam to produce all the hydrogen he needs. And while you have not asked about the coal, let it be said that very low grades may be employed. Brown coal, lignite and coal screenings are perfectly adaptable to the process. Thus, coal which is utterly unsuited for ordinary industrial purposes may be converted into petroleum. There is just one other point about which you wish to know, and that is the price of gasoline produced by this process. That factor has not yet been determined. Regarding it, Doctor

Bergius says, "From a financial and economical point of view, the plant for the liquefaction of coal must be compared with all the equipment and machinery necessary for the production of crude oil from the well through the various refining steps. It is not necessary to include the cost of mining coal, since there are already available great quantities of fine coal and screenings as well as easily acquired lignite, brown and the like. Another favorable factor is the stability of the production, since a coal deposit can be depended upon to produce over a much longer period than any oil field."

There is no doubt that under the stimulus of a petroleum shortage this process could be carried to a commercial success. It has already passed the experimental stage. Even now two plants for the "berginizing" of coal are in operation in Germany with a combined production of one million barrels of petroleum products a year. The International Bergin Company with strong financial backing has been organized at The Hague. Every country in Europe is interested in the process, and America may be sooner than she is now aware.

Dr. A. C. Fieldner and Dr. R. L. Brown, of the Pittsburgh Experiment Station, United States Bureau of Mines, in a paper presented at the seventy-second meeting of the American Chemical Society, said of the Bergius process, "Assuming that two tons of coal yield one ton, or six barrels of crude oil, then two hundred and fifty-two million tons of coal would be required to produce the 1925 production of 755,852,000 barrels of petroleum. In other words, our present bituminous coal mined per annum would need to be increased about 50 per cent."

Provided the cost of production could be brought to a practicable figure, such an undertaking would by no means lie outside the realm of possibilities. In the light of present progress in this particular field and with the record of achievement already to the credit of chemistry in the petroleum industry, there can be no reasonable doubt that in bituminous coal we are assured of an abundant supply of moderately-priced motor fuel, whenever the need shall arise to make it available. In the no distant future, we shall in all probability be drawing upon three sources of supply, namely, petroleum from our waning well territory, from our oil shales, and from the liquefaction of bituminous coal. It is a waste of time and utterly useless to lose any sleep over what we shall do in the event of an imaginary gasoline famine.

In a totally different direction, the utilization of bituminous coal for the production of petroleum would prove a boon to industry. To increase by one-half or more the demand for coal would smooth out the difficulties of the coal-mining industry and redeem it from economic chaos as nothing else could. Of course, the more rapidly we mine this natural resource, the sooner will its end arrive. However, it is estimated that we have in this country 1,600,000,000,000 tons of bituminous coal. We now mine about a half-billion tons a year. Suppose we were to increase the annual output to a billion tons, we should not reach the bottom of our national coal bin until the expiration of one thousand six hundred years. We must remember, too, that for the liquefaction process of Doctor Bergius we shall not need to use high-grade bituminous coal. Lignite and screenings are perfectly adaptable.

In the face of such heartening possibilities, the man who persists in worrying over the imminence of a gasoline shortage is a pessimist of the Dark Ages and deserves nothing better than to be cast upon an island of the sea, where he may indulge for the rest of his natural lifetime his propensity for self-created gloom.

OTHER HIGHWAYS

We have as yet by no means exhausted the avenues to motor freedom and abundant supplies of liquid fuel. Simultaneously with the work of Bergius, Professor Franz Fischer, of Germany, and General Georges Patart, of France, have been developing other routes from coal to automotive power.

In a paper read at the Pittsburgh Conference, Professor Fischer gave the results of his many years of research and outlined his method for the complete conversion of coke into synthetic motor fuel. His first step is to pass steam through highly heated beds of coke. Coke, being nearly pure carbon, unites with the oxygen in the steam to form the gas carbon monoxide and liberate hydrogen. Thus a mixture of these two gases, carbon monoxide and hydrogen, is obtained. This mixture is ordinary water gas, so widely manufactured in city gas plants for domestic heating and lighting. This part of the process was extremely simple. The real problem lay beyond.

If in some way these two gases might be made to combine, Professor Fischer saw that combustible compounds could be obtained suitable for use in automobile cylinders. Here was the vision. Somewhere must lie the path to success. Fischer determined to find it.

Right here I must introduce you to a new form of chemical action. When I say "new," I mean new to you. It is not new to the chemist. He calls it by the somewhat unique name of *catalysis* and has employed this phenomenon in his business for many years. As we shall learn later, some of the most important processes in chemical industry depend upon it. Dr. Paul Sabatier, a distinguished French chemist, has done some of the most notable work in this field. A number of years ago, he undertook to condense ordinary acetylene gas, consisting of two atoms each of carbon and hydrogen to the molecule, into heavier hydrocarbons, whose molecules should contain more atoms of these elements and which should be similar to those found in petroleum. He passed a mixture of hydrogen and acetylene through a heated tube, but nothing happened. Then Sabatier made a discovery. By some inspiration of genius, he was led to introduce finely powdered nickel into his tube. When he now passed the mixture of acetylene and hydrogen over the nickel, a brilliant incandescence resulted and liquid drops of petroleum-like hydrocarbons condensed at the end of the tube.

Now the finely divided nickel is a catalyst, and the action just described is a catalytic process. The nickel by its mere presence is able to effect a chemical action which would not otherwise take place, or at best would proceed very slowly. When the reaction is over, it is found that the nickel has not been affected at all. This catalytic agent is like the manager who arranges a prize-fight between two pugilists, but does not himself take part in the combat.

It was to this sort of chemical action that Fischer

turned in his attempt to combine hydrogen and carbon monoxide into synthetic motor fuel. He heated these gases, together with various metallic catalyzers, in copper-lined reaction chambers at temperatures of from 300 to 425 degrees Centigrade and at pressures ranging from 150 to 250 atmospheres. At the same time the Badische Anilin Und Soda-Fabrik was working along similar lines. So, too, was a group of French chemists under the direction of General Georges Patart. The first result was synthetic methanol, the scientific name for wood alcohol, about which we have heard so much in recent years. The reported cost both from German and French sources varies from eighteen to twenty-seven cents a gallon, giving a cheaper product than that obtained from the American practise of distilling wood.

This was a step in the right direction and a decided victory. Road tests showed that while methanol can be used in automobile cylinders, it gives only about half the mileage per gallon as is obtained with gasoline. Furthermore, it will not mix readily with gasoline. It requires five per cent. of water to prevent back-firing, but it can be used in high compression motors and undergoes combustion without knocking.

However, Professor Fischer had only begun. Associated with him was Doctor Tropsch, and with a different catalyzer they continued the investigation. This time instead of pure methanol they obtained a mixture of higher alcohols and compounds known to the chemist as aldehydes and ketones together with acids and hydrocarbons having as many as eight or nine carbon atoms to the molecule. This product Fischer called synthol and found it to be a much more satisfactory motor fuel than methanol alone. A decided disadvantage, however, is the low yield of only twenty-seven per cent. as compared with a yield of 85 to 90 per cent. for methanol.

Another disadvantage was the high pressure required. But continued research with the employment of still other catalyzers has finally made it possible to carry out the process at ordinary atmospheric pressure. Furthermore higher hydrocarbons closely resembling those in natural petroleum have been obtained. *Science Service* describes the product as follows: "The new method produces a pleasant smelling gasoline as clear as water and one which will not harden or become gummy on exposure. The gasoline is highly volatile and is largely made up of unsaturated compounds like olefines which impart to the gasoline valuable anti-knock properties. This enables it to be used in efficient high-compression motors without objectionable knocking and with great economy."

Since Professor Fischer's process starts with coke, bituminous coal first being converted into this substance, coal-tar is a valuable by-product of the preliminary stage. Semi-coke, of which we shall learn presently and for which a market must be created, can be used for the production of the hydrogen and carbon monoxide, which as we have seen affords the basis of this synthetic gasoline.

The process, however, has not yet emerged from the experimental into the commercial stage. Whether it can be made to compete successfully with the Bergius and other processes remains to be seen. The process seems to be much less efficient than that of the straight liquefaction of coal. According to Dr. Arthur D. Little, prominent Boston chemist, it would require by Fischer's method all of our present output of coal to meet the demand for motor fuel, for sixteen hundred pounds of coal yield but one barrel of oil. Still, remarkable transformations often occur in scientific processes. This catalytic method may yet afford the royal road to cheap and abundant gasoline.

The French have been working along similar lines and with equal progress. It is the purpose both of Germany and France to be free from dependence upon American petroleum. In the event of the early exhaustion of our wells, scientific research will be their only resource. They do well to attack the problem so vigorously. Already victory seems assured.

Another source of motor fuel is often suggested, namely, ordinary alcohol obtained by direct fermentation. The United States Navy and the United States Post Office Department have demonstrated that alcohol affords a superior airplane fuel. The best performance is obtained when alcohol is mixed with gasoline, and to make the two miscible absolute, or anhydrous, alcohol must be employed. This means alcohol free from water. Ordinary alcohol contains five per cent. water. Only a few years ago absolute alcohol sold for from ten to twenty dollars a gallon and was distributed in small glass bottles. A new chemical process now provides it in tank-car lots for plant use at less than a dollar a gallon.

The use of alcohol for motor fuel means the diversion of vast acreages for the production of starchy crops suitable for fermentation. It is possible that somewhere within the Tropics such areas might be found. Still, this avenue of approach to the solution of gasoline difficulties seems less promising than others. It has even been questioned whether the quantity of energy liberated in motor cylinders would not be less than that required in the distillation of the alcohol. The energy efficiency here is low. Alcohol possesses in high degree anti-knock properties and, as a blend for other motor fuels, it will doubtless some time find a use.

THE PROBLEM FROM ANOTHER ANGLE

We have not yet reached the end of possibilities. Like the juggler who astounds us with the quantity and variety of stuff which he draws forth from his proverbial plug hat, there seems to be no limit to the resources at the command of the research chemist. The low temperature carbonization of coal hits this problem from a different angle. By carbonization is meant the heating of bituminous coal in retorts, or ovens, out of contact with the air, thus driving off the gaseous and liquid products and leaving some sort of coke behind.

For a hundred years and more the coking process has been carried out at high temperatures, that is, at temperatures ranging from 1,000 degrees to 1,300 degrees Centigrade. By the old method of coking in the wasteful beehive ovens, a method employed in this country almost exclusively until the beginning of the Great War, millions of dollars' worth of valuable by-products, such as dyestuffs, drugs and chemicals of many kinds, besides vast quantities of fuel gas, went up in smoke each year. Today, approximately eighty per cent. of our coke is produced in the modern by-product recovery plants. By this high-temperature carbonization process, a process which by driving off the volatile constituents reduces coal to nearly pure carbon, one ton of bituminous coal is made to yield from three to four gallons of crude light oil, sixty to seventy per cent. of which is suitable for motor fuel, from ten to twelve gallons of heavy tar, and upward of ten thousand cubic feet of gas. If all of our annual output of bituminous coal were thus coked and the light oil converted into motor fuel, the quantity obtained would be sufficient to meet only about one-eighth of the demand for gasoline. Dr. Gustav Egloff, however, asserts that, if the tar were subjected to the cracking process, the resulting motor fuel would supply thirty-five per cent. of present requirements. But coke of the character produced by the high-temperature process finds little use outside of steel manufacture, and therefore it is futile to contemplate such an extension of the coking industry. Benzol, the motor fuel produced by this process, has high anti-knock properties, and, so far as it is available, it affords an excellent material for blending with straight-run gasoline.

For a quarter of a century, chemists have been turning their attention to the low-temperature carbonization of coal. This means the employment of temperatures ranging from 450 to 700 degrees Centigrade. When we consider that a Centigrade degree is equivalent to 1.8 degrees Fahrenheit, to ordinary thinking the designation of this process as one of low temperature seems a bit absurd. But it is simply a matter of relativity, an aspect of human thought which has assumed vast significance since the vogue of Einstein. In brief, this process yields from two to three times the quantity of tar obtainable by high-temperature carbonization, a semi-coke and a gas of high heat value. In addition there is a small quantity of crude motor spirits and some ammonia gas which may be converted into fertilizer. The high-temperature process also gives ammonia.

The significant thing to note here is that the tar produced by low-temperature carbonization is not only larger in quantity than that obtained by the old method but possesses a peculiar petroleum-like quality and may be cracked to a motor fuel of high anti-knock properties. Doctor Egloff asserted at the Pittsburgh Conference that, if the 1,600,000,000,000 tons of bituminous coal in this country were to be subjected to low-temperature distillation, we should obtain 800,000,000,000 barrels of tar, which upon cracking would yield 240,000,000,000 barrels of anti-knock gas. In high-compression motors, this gas would give double or more mileage per gallon than has been heretofore obtained. This supply, it is believed, would provide motor fuel for nearly a thousand years.

In order to make such a plan workable, however, it is necessary to find a market for the semi-coke produced. Much of this coke is too loose in texture and too low in density to make it suitable for the smelting of iron. Professor S. W. Parr, of the University of Illinois, the pioneer American investigator in this field, has succeeded, however, in producing by this method from what had been regarded as non-coking coals of Illinois and adjacent states "a dense, hard, strong coke." When we consider, too, that this process is still largely in the experimental stage, only just beginning to emerge into developments of commercial magnitude, it will be readily recognized that it is yet too early to set bounds to the possibilities which may lie in wait.

In one immensely important direction, this new fuel promises to be a boon to public health and domestic comfort. When pressed into briquets, it seems to afford a clean, smokeless, artificial anthracite, ideally suited to household heating. Fifty per cent. of the smoke nuisance to-day issues from domestic chimneys. A smokeless fuel, provided in abundance at a moderate price, would solve this problem and at the same time remove a serious menace to healthful living conditions.

At the Pittsburgh Conference, Mr. C. V. McIntire, of the Consolidation Coal Products Company in New York, read a paper describing an experimental plant for the production of artificial anthracite by the low-temperature process. This plant is located at Fairmont, West Virginia, and has a capacity of fifty tons a day. As the semi-coke comes from the retorts, it is ground, mixed with a coal-tar pitch to serve as a binder, and then machine-pressed into briquets. To render these briquets smokeless in their burning, they are given a second heating. The product may be shipped and handled with little breakage; it ignites readily, burns freely and retains the fire well; and it is reasonably cheap, having already sold in New England at two dollars a ton less than anthracite.

In thus going from bituminous coal to artificial anthracite, Mr. McIntire duplicates in a very short space of time a process which in Nature requires millions of years. He makes a ton of coal yield one thousand four hundred and eighty pounds of solid fuel, thirty-one gallons of tar, two gallons of light oil and three thousand cubic feet of exceptionally rich gas. As has already been pointed out, the liquid products may be largely converted into motor fuel. When fully developed, this process promises to provide an abundant potential supply of an admirable substitute for our dwindling reserves of anthracite and at the same time, by creating a large additional demand for bituminous coal, to stabilize in no small degree the chaotic conditions in the coal mining industry.

A number of other low-temperature processes are approaching the commercial stage. Among them are the McEwen-Runge process, the Green-Lauks process, the Piron process, and that of the Knowles Sole flue-oven.

That low-temperature carbonization is destined to mark a turning-point in our treatment of coal, as important as was the discovery three-quarters of a century ago of the chemical wealth hidden in black coal-tar, there is no shadow of doubt. Even now scientists are realizing that the annual combustion of a half-billion tons of raw bituminous coal in domestic and industrial furnaces with no pretense at recovering the irreplaceable by-products, is a crime against posterity which can never be effaced. When we know, too, that these by-products, now utterly wasted save for the relatively small quantity recovered in high-temperature coking plants, contain a potential supply of high-quality motor fuel, capable of replacing a large proportion of the petroleum at present required, the damage wrought appears to be not only against posterity but to ourselves as well. When we couple this waste with the self-imposed smoke nuisance which it entails, our stupidity seems to outrun comparison. But thanks to the chemist and the engineer, we are beginning to extricate ourselves from this slough of scientific and industrial iniquity. In a very real sense, succeeding generations will look back upon ours as marking emergence from the dark ages of fuel and power waste.

POWER FROM DUST

The heading of a news item in *The New York Times* of a few months ago reads, "Grain Elevator Dust Drives a Ford Engine." By making several adaptations, two engineers in the Department of Agriculture were able to make a Ford motor run on the sweepings from the floor of a grain elevator. The frightful dust explosions sometimes occurring in such elevators from an intimate mixture of dust and air set off by a lighted match or some chance spark doubtless gave the clue. The time may come when we shall drive up to a filling station and put in a plentiful supply of coal dust instead of the accustomed liquid fuel. With such possibilities in the immediate foreground, what matters the exhaustion of petroleum fields or other sources of motor fuel?

That the foregoing is not altogether a fanciful dream is evidenced by a paper read at the Pittsburgh Conference by Mr. Walter E. Trent, a New York mining and metallurgical engineer. As reported in the press at the time, he said that "the process of pulverizing coal to the consistency of talcum powder so that it becomes a fluid when heated and runs like water, will be followed by the use of the new coal oil in internal combustion engines instead of gasoline. . . . Merely heating the crushed coal to a point at which vapors are generated gives to the coal a state of great mobility. In this condition it resembles liquids and it can be made to flow, run and seek its own level."

Mr. Trent is reported to have said that pulverized

coal will compete with gasoline at six cents a gallon. The first use will be in stationary engines, then in the automobile motor and later in locomotives and ships. "Because coal can be purified," said Mr. Trent, "because it can be pulverized to minute sizes; because it can be distilled at high thermal efficiencies to produce oil, gas or carbonized powder; because it can be made to flow and to pump; because it responds to the most efficient methods for the creation of mechanical energy, the world may look forward with confidence to a new age of coal, greater and more permanent."

Certain it is that the possibilities of coal as a basic source of energy and power are only just beginning to be realized. Fortunate indeed this country is in possessing more than half of the world's total supply. With coal in abundance and the chemist as our ally, we may dismiss unceremoniously the pessimist who glibly prates of imminent disaster from the early exhaustion of power resources. Never before has it been possible to face the future with so great confidence. The prodigal waste of earlier decades must be checked. The wise utilization of what we possess in the light of all the knowledge which science provides is a duty we owe alike to posterity and to ourselves. But power in abundance the world must and will have. There is no doubt that for many centuries to come it will be provided. For this bright prospect and our salutary rescue from the headlong rush to ruin upon which we had embarked, we have in large measure to thank the chemist. Working over his test tubes and retorts, he has brought to light knowledge which shines as the noonday sun and wherein his fellows may walk in perfect confidence and security.

CHAPTER V

A GLANCE AT GASES

IMPORTANCE OF GASES IN DEVELOPING THEORIES OF CHEMICAL
SCIENCE—ILLUMINATING AND FUEL GASES—EARLY DISCOV-
ERIES—WORK OF MURDOCK, LE BON AND WINSOR—THE LIGHT-
ING OF LONDON AND PARIS—THE INTRODUCTION OF ILLUMI-
NATING GAS IN AMERICA—WATER GAS—NATURAL GAS—PRO-
DUCER GAS—COKE-OVEN GAS—WELSBACH GAS MANTLE—NEW
USES FOR GAS—ACETYLENE—OTHER GASES.

GASES have occupied a strategic position in the development of chemistry from the beginnings of the modern
era to the present moment. It was with gases that Black,
Priestley, Scheele, Cavendish and Lavoisier did their
early work. Dalton's epoch-making conception of the
Atomic Theory came as the result of experiments with
gases. The gaseous state was found to be the most
readily amenable to laboratory manipulation. It is to
this day the one state of matter about which scientists
know most. The determination of atomic weights is most
easily accomplished if the substance either is a gas or
may be made to assume a state of vapor. The spectroscopic identification of elements, either in the laboratory
or in the distant stars, depends upon the existence of the
substance in a state of incandescent vapor. Much of the
theory of chemistry has arisen from a study of gases.
One of the most prolific sources of practical knowledge

has been a generalization made nearly a century ago by Avogadro, an Italian physicist, and known ever since as Avogadro's Hypothesis. It states that *equal volumes of all gases at the same temperature and pressure contain equal numbers of molecules.* A vast amount of the most reliable experimental evidence supports the truth of this assumption. It has been particularly useful in the determination of molecular weights. And then there is Gay-Lussac's Law of Gas Volumes, which states that *whenever gases unite to form gaseous products, the volumes of the reacting gases bear the ratio of small whole numbers to each other and to the volumes of the resulting gases.* Much of the utmost practical value, both in experimental and industrial work, stands to the credit of this fundamental relationship. Our knowledge of radioactivity has been intimately associated with the gaseous disintegration products of substances exhibiting this property. Close relationships have been found to exist between the properties of gases and those of solutions. Knowledge of gases forms so large a part of the science that the whole chemical edifice would collapse, were it to be subtracted.

But it is the industrial applications of gases which we wish to discuss now. Although this is an age of electricity, were illuminating and fuel gases to drop out of the picture, industry would be tremendously handicapped and much of domestic economy, comfort and convenience would of necessity be sacrificed. And the use of gas grows with each succeeding year. It is practically double now what it was at the beginning of the World War. As we shall see, too, there are other gases of considerable economic importance.

ILLUMINATING AND FUEL GASES

The history of illuminating gases goes back for three centuries and more. Early in the seventeenth century, Van Helmont, a Dutch alchemist, did the pioneer work in this field. He described hydrogen and marsh gas and became acquainted with their combustibility. He experimented with fuels and found that when heated in closed vessels, they gave off a "spirit," which Van Helmont named "geist." In time, this word became gas. Already, Thomas Shirley, a large landowner of Lancashire, had described a spring of evil repute from which issued a vapor that burned with a flame. Dr. John Clayton, Dean of Kildare, becoming convinced that this vapor had some relation to the near-by coal mines, heated some pieces of coal in a retort, obtaining from them a "spirit" which, like the vapor from the spring, burned readily. But that this knowledge would ever be turned to account in a practical way never as much as crossed the wildest dreams of those curious investigators.

It fell to William Murdock, a Scotch mechanic in the employ of Boulton and Watt, builders of steam engines, to grasp the idea of using coal gas for illuminating purposes. His duties frequently took him to the coal mines, where he became acquainted with the gases found in them. Applying his engineering skill to the distillation of coal, he had so far succeeded that by 1792 he was lighting his own house and grounds with the gaseous product. A decade later, he lighted the interior and exterior of his employer's factory in similar fashion, producing for the times brilliant effects. Little did he realize, however, that he was laying the foundations of an industry which in its numerous ramifications was to become a bulwark of the chemical age to follow.

The next experimenters in this field were Phiilipe Le Bon of Paris and Friedrich A. Winzer, an astute German who, changing his name to Winsor, laid the scene of his commercial exploitations in London. Although Le Bon made brilliant displays in the French capital, the new form of light did not win the favor of Napoleon, who denounced the innovation as a "grand folly." Even in London, Sir Walter Scott, in ridicule of Winsor's attempts to supplant candles, wrote, "There is a madman proposing to light the streets of London—with what do you suppose—smoke!" Contrary to the favorable consideration expected from so great a scientist as Sir Humphry Davy, this beginning of a new era in the art of illumination was frowned upon.

But Winsor was not thus easily to be dissuaded. Not at all a scientist, with much of the showman about him, given to extravagant statement, and possessing the genius of a modern stock promoter, this newcomer to the British Isles appealed to the curiosity, the ignorance and the cupidity of Londoners. With lectures and demonstrations, in which he displayed much eloquence and ingenuity, Winsor sought to overcome the opposition of inborn conservatism and enlist financial support. For the first time in history, he introduced a system of public gas-lighting. In 1807, he substituted along one side of Pall Mall gas-jets for the lanterns, oil lamps and torch-bearers of that famous thoroughfare. With the publicity gained, he succeeded in organizing a company and raising fifty thousand pounds, most of which was promptly wasted in futile experiments. By 1812, Winsor had obtained a charter and organized a new company. A year later, Westminster Bridge was lighted throughout its length with gas. In the person of Samuel Clegg, a competent engineer, was found the genius capable of putting the manufacture and sale of gas upon a sound commercial basis. He invented the gas-meter and the gas-holder, and so quickly did he dissipate popular prejudice that by 1816 gas-lighting had become a commonplace in the British metropolis. It followed in Paris four years later.

In America, as early as 1806, David Melville of Newport, Rhode Island, duplicated the stunt of Murdock in England by lighting his house and grounds with gas of his own manufacture. The American counterpart of Winsor appeared in Charles Wilson Peale, an artist who established a "Museum" in Baltimore, which he lighted with gas and in which he demonstrated the possibilities of the new illuminant. Early in 1817, public gas-lighting had become a reality in the Maryland city. Boston and New York followed in 1821 and 1823, respectively. Not until 1841 did Philadelphia fall into line.

Although wood was first employed as a source of gas in America, coal was soon substituted. In iron retorts, bituminous coal was heated to a temperature of seven or eight hundred degrees Fahrenheit to drive off the volatile constituents. In the early days, little attempt was made at purification, save to remove the bulk of the harmful sulfur, and none of the coal-tar or ammonia was recovered. This was ordinary *coal gas* and similar to the coke-oven gas of to-day except that from the latter we now recover the valuable by-products.

In the early seventies of the last century, Professor

Thaddeus S. C. Lowe, of Baltimore, and a Frenchman, Tessie Du Motay, independently of each other, demonstrated the commercial possibilities of producing combustible gases by passing steam over hot carbon in the form of coke or anthracite coal. The product is known as *water gas* and consists of a mixture of hydrogen and carbon monoxide. The hot carbon decomposes the steam, uniting

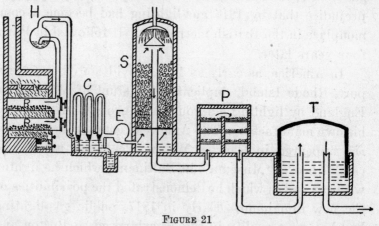

FIGURE 21

Diagram of coal gas plant. Bituminous coal is heated in the retorts, R and R, from which the gas passes to the hydraulic main, H, in which part of the coal-tar is removed. In the condenser, C, the bulk of the ammonia and the remaining coal-tar are extracted. An exhauster, E, keeps the gas moving, forcing it through the scrubber, S, in which a spray of water thoroughly washes it. In the purifier, P, layers of lime, or sometimes lime and iron oxide, remove the sulfur compounds and carbon dioxide. From the purifier, the gas goes to the storage tank, T.

with the oxygen and leaving the hydrogen. Of course, the blowing of steam through a white-hot bed of coke or coal quickly lowers the temperature and if continued would cool it entirely. After three or four minutes, the steam is turned off and air is blown through the bed to bring back the temperature necessary for the reaction. This is again followed by a blast of steam. Water gas thus prepared burns with a blue, non-luminous flame.

For lighting purposes, and originally that was practically the only use for gas of any kind, water gas has to
be enriched by spraying into it finely atomized oil, which
in a superheater is permanently combined with the gas.
This addition, too, increases the heat-producing capacity
of the gas. Water gas soon became a large factor in

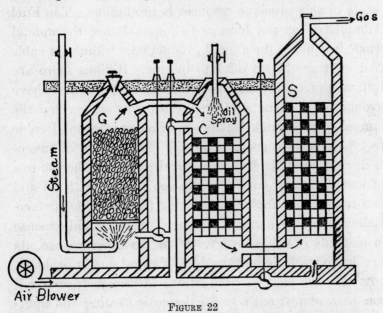

FIGURE 22

Water gas plant. A blast of air blown through the bed of coke or
coal in the generator, G, brings the temperature to a white heat. Then the
air is shut off and steam is blown through for several minutes. The hot
carbon in the generator decomposes the steam, forming a mixture of hydrogen and carbon monoxide. This mixture passes to the carburetor, C, where
the gas is enriched by a spray of oil, after which it enters the superheater,
S. There a perfect gaseous blend of oil and gas is made.

municipal lighting and domestic heating. Its importance
has continued to the present day.

Natural gas, first used for lighting at Fredonia, New
York, in 1821, constitutes by far the larger proportion of
illuminating and fuel gases in the United States. In

Europe, however, these gases are chiefly manufactured from coal, oil and water. As the huge reservoirs of natural gas in this country become exhausted—as they are being at a very rapid rate—manufactured gas will here too assume the ascendency. One-tenth of all the cook-stoves in this country burn natural gas, and yet the waste of this precious resource is prodigious. The Fuel Administration not long ago estimated that the annual waste is equal to the annual production. Billions of cubic feet of it are blown off into the air. Billions more are left underground, and protection against leakage above ground is inadequate. One authority estimates that the annual loss through leakage is nineteen thousand cubic feet per house served. The wasteful method of manufacturing lamp-black from natural gas is another source of loss. Natural gas occurs in conjunction with oil and is a tremendous factor in bringing the oil to the surface. Exhaustion of gas means increased difficulty and expense in methods of oil recovery. If for no other reason, its profligate waste is inexcusable. Natural gas is probably now near the peak of production. Although formerly it was used almost entirely for domestic heating and lighting, three-fourths of the output is now burned in industrial plants. The gasoline extracted from natural gas in 1924 reached nearly a billion gallons, or about one-tenth of the country's motor fuel requirement.

When coal, usually anthracite, or coke is burned in an insufficient supply of air, carbon monoxide, a highly combustible gas, known as *producer gas,* is formed. Sometimes a little steam is also blown through the coke or coal with the air. All the carbon in the fuel employed may thus be converted into gas, which issues from the gas producer in a highly heated condition. If this gas is used directly, the heat contained is not wasted but is utilized in a highly efficient manner. Engineers have

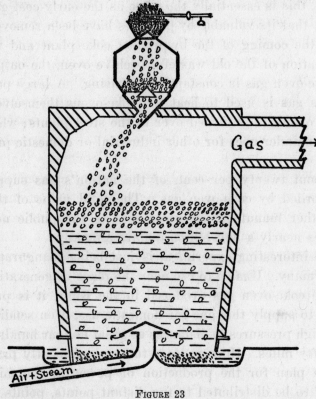

FIGURE 23

Gas producer. Through a bed of hot coke or anthracite, air in just the right proportion, together with a little steam, is blown. The resulting gas is chiefly carbon monoxide. Fresh fuel is fed in at the top and ashes are removed from the bottom.

learned that for many purposes it is far more economical of heat and fuel to convert coal into gas, using the gas either for heat or power, than it is to burn the coal directly. Thus in the open-hearth process of manufacturing steel vast quantities of producer gas are used. So also in the making of glass and pottery. Considerable quantities of producer gas are used in gas engines.

Coke-oven gas has been mentioned. As already stated, this is essentially the same as the early coal gas, except that its valuable by-products have been removed. With the coming of the by-product coke plant and the elimination of the old wasteful beehive oven, the output of coke-oven gas is constantly increasing. A large part of this gas is used to heat the coke-ovens themselves; about one-third is turned over to the steel plants; while the remainder goes for other industrial or domestic purposes.

About twenty per cent. of the nation's gas supply is afforded by coke-oven gas. The total value of this and other manufactured gases sold to the public now reaches nearly a half-billion dollars annually.

An interesting experiment is just being inaugurated in Germany. Unable to use near the place of generation all the coke-oven gas produced in the Ruhr, it is proposed to supply this gas for domestic use, even sending it at high pressures to distances as great as four hundred and fifty miles. Here appears to be an eminently practicable plan for the production of power at the mine mouth to be distributed to far distant points, points as remote as could be economically reached by electric transmission. The great difficulty with the mine-mouth development of electric power is the immense quantities of condensing water required. In few localities is the supply sufficient. But, in the generation of gas, no condensing water is necessary. Should the German plan succeed, and there seems to be no reason why it should not, the whole nation may be supplied with gas from the

Ruhr. Local companies would then become mere retailers of gas from central plants.

If Germany can succeed in this undertaking, other countries, and the United States in particular, can too. Already a four hundred and fifty-mile pipe line carries gas from the Texas Panhandle to Kansas City, and two lines, each three hundred miles long, convey the natural gas of West Virginia to points in Ohio. Even in the case of manufactured gas, it would appear to be much more economical to generate it at the mine mouth and pipe the gas than to haul the coal from the mine to the city. In this way, too, many places en route could be supplied from a single main line and its branches. Revolutionary changes in fuel production and control may be at hand. Time will tell, and the time may be short.

At the Centennial in 1876, an exhibition of gas for cooking purposes was given. This was the first time that gas had been so used. Theretofore, its only use had been for illumination. Soon, however, the coming of electricity was apparently to sound the death knell of gas as an illuminant and with that it seemed that the entire industry was threatened with extinction. Two circumstances saved the day. Dr. Carl Auer, a young Austrian chemist, invented the Welsbach gas mantle, and a multitude of new uses were found for gas.

Doctor Auer, working in the Bunsen laboratory at the University of Heidelberg, was investigating that interesting group of elements known as the "rare earths." It was work upon this same group which led in 1926 to the discovery, told elsewhere, of the only element ever to have been isolated by an American chemist. The story of how Auer conferred upon the gas industry a new lease of life has frequently been told. The quantity of material with which he was compelled to work was exceedingly limited. In his efforts to identify the elements present in the mixture, he was making use of that marvelous instrument the spectroscope. In order to use his available material to better advantage, he put it into solution and, saturating small pieces of cotton cloth, held them in the flame of a Bunsen burner. Auer had arrived at one of the rare moments of chemical discovery. Behold, a light of dazzling brilliancy glowed before his eyes. The cotton fibers were consumed, but in their place, magiclike, had been woven a delicate fretwork, consisting of the oxides of these rare earth metals. As the flame played over this framework, exquisite as frost upon a window-pane, a brilliant incandescence shed around a flood of light. From a problem of purely scientific interest had arisen a vision of vast commercial possibilities. To their development, Auer turned with eager interest. His first experiments indicated that the oxide of the rare element thorium was responsible for the light-giving properties. It *was* to the extent of ninety-nine per cent. Not, however, until he had done much more research and had met with bitter disappointment did he discover that the thorium must be adulterated with one per cent. of cerium, another rare earth, to give its magic glow. Then, too, there were the development of the gas mantle ''stocking'' and the quest for an adequate supply of the precious elements whose utilization promised the rehabilitation of an industry which was nearing the breakers. But no obstacle proved too great. Gas-lighting entered upon a new era of progress, and in recognition of his triumph, the Austrian Government conferred upon Doctor Auer the title of Count of Welsbach.

In addition, industry came to the rescue of gas manufacture. Uses multiplied. The number of applications of gas in trade processes grew from a few score to a thousand, then to five thousand, and now it is announced that no less than twenty-one thousand needs of industry are served either with natural or manufactured gas. In 1925, the use of gas for all purposes established a record of 421 billion cubic feet. This represented an increase of 16 billion cubic feet over the previous year and a growth of 100 billion in the preceding five years. No one longer talks of the disappearance of gas from industry, and, as a matter of domestic convenience and economy in household cooking and heating in our cities, gas grows in importance each succeeding year.

In acetylene, the gas industry found a recruit which has done valiant service in the production of heat and light. Although this gas had been known for a number of decades and much work upon its chemistry had been done by the French chemist Berthelot, it was not until 1892 that researches of Thomas L. Willson in this country led to an appreciation of its commercial possibilities. In an effort to obtain metallic calcium, Willson heated together in an electric furnace a mixture of lime and coal. The immediate result was a dark-colored mass of material, which, when thrown into water, generated a gas with an exceedingly offensive odor and burned with a soft white light of great brilliancy. It was further discovered that the combustion of the gas produced intense heat. The substance obtained from heating the mixture of lime and coal was calcium carbide, familiar to every user of an acetylene lighting plant and whose manufacture on a large scale was shortly after inaugurated at Niagara Falls. The use of acetylene as an illuminant and the process of oxyacetylene welding and cutting of iron and steel are too well known to need repeating here. Ethylene, a gas obtained by eliminating the elements of water from ordinary alcohol, is now replacing acetylene to some extent in the welding and cutting of metals. Acetylene affords a capital example of the modern practise of putting museum curiosities to work.

OTHER GASES

The use of other gases in industry is rapidly coming to the fore. These are chiefly supplied in condensed form. In 1923, the market value of such gases was placed at $54,000,000, a more than fivefold increase in ten years. Of this, oxygen accounted for $23,382,000, a twelvefold increase in this period, and the gain in the use of this fundamental gas is still growing. Plants for the preparation of commercial oxygen are now to be found in all large industrial regions. Its sources are from the liquefaction of air and the electrolysis of water. This increased production, too, has resulted in a steady decline in cost, present prices being approximately sixty per cent. of the pre-war level. Oxygen has always occupied a strategic position in the realm of Nature. Its rôle in industry is no less important.

The commercial use of hydrogen, too, is on the gain. Hydrogen was the earliest known combustible gas, but despite the inroads of numerous competitors, it has not been displaced. Large quantities are used in the inflation

of balloons and dirigibles. The oxyhydrogen torch, long
the acme of high temperature research, is still used in
glass-working, in lead-burning, in the cutting of metals
and in the manufacture of artificial rubies and sap-
phires. Its largest industrial application is found in
the hydrogenation of oils, discussed elsewhere. Exclusive of the hydrogen contained in illuminating and
fuel gases, this country alone uses more than 300
million cubic feet a year.

The spectacular rise of helium from a substance rarer
than diamonds to a strategic resource of peace and war
forms a quite recent chapter in the romance of chemistry.
Elsewhere the spectroscopic discovery of this gas in the
atmosphere of the sun by Sir Norman Lockyer and its
subsequent isolation by Sir William Ramsay as one of
the rare gases of the earth's atmosphere have been discussed. We are familiar with the intimate relationship
of this gas to the phenomena of radioactivity. And the
general reader knows that within recent years helium has
been found to the extent of about five-tenths per cent. as a
constituent of certain natural gases of our Southwest.
During the war, this country produced approximately
two hundred thousand cubic feet of this gas for use in
dirigibles. Still, the continued production of helium is
by no means a certainty. Already, the natural gas from
the Petrolia, Texas, field, which has afforded the supply
to date, is playing out. However, it is thought that the
Nocona field, near Fort Worth, will produce from ten
to twelve million cubic feet per year for a period of about
fifteen years. The future supply, like that of petroleum,
depends upon new discoveries. Quite recently an important use of helium has been found in the preparation

of a "synthetic atmosphere" to be breathed by deep-sea divers upon coming to the surface. When compelled as they are at these depths to breathe air of several times its normal density, some of the air becomes dissolved in the blood. As the pressure is removed from the body, this air tends to form bubbles which bring great distress and often death. To avoid the difficulty the diver must remain in a decompression chamber sometimes for more than two hours, in which time the pressure is gradually brought to normal. However, the breathing by a diver of a mixture of oxygen and helium, in which the latter takes the place of nitrogen normally in the atmosphere, reduces this decompression period by seventy-five per cent.

Argon, another of the rare gases of the atmosphere obtained from liquid air, is important in the gas-filled lamp. Together with nitrogen it makes possible a much higher temperature of the tungsten filament with a consequent increase in candle-power and efficiency. Its existence in the atmosphere to the extent of nearly one per cent. assures a continuous supply. Neon, too, a much rarer member of this coterie of gases, has found its niche. When an electric discharge is passed through a tube filled with this gas at low pressure, the tube glows, the intensity of the glow depending upon the strength of the discharge. Such a tube forms an essential unit in the system of electrical devices which has made possible the recent triumph of television.

In the field of refrigerants chemically prepared gases reign supreme. The public has long been familiar with the use of liquid ammonia in the manufacture of artificial ice and in cold storage plants. And now comes carbon dioxide in the form of "dry ice" as well as refrigeration systems employing sulfur dioxide, ethyl chloride, ethane, ethylene, propane, propylene and similar gaseous compounds.

We have just mentioned sulfur dioxide and carbon dioxide as refrigerants. Their other uses are numerous. Sulfur dioxide is an important bleaching agent and disinfectant. It is also finding new fields, particularly in medicine. As to carbon dioxide, in a recent year fifty-one million pounds of this gas in compressed form valued at five million dollars were manufactured for use by the soda-fountain trade and the bottlers of soft drinks. For many years, it has been important as a fire-extinguisher, and now it is finding a place in the manufacture of automobile tires and in the spraying of paint.

Without the strong germicidal properties of chlorine, many large cities would be seriously handicapped in their purification of drinking water. Shipped in car-load lots in the form of liquid chlorine contained in steel cylinders, this gas is extensively used as a bleaching agent in the pulp and paper industry and in the manufacture of textiles. In 1923, one hundred and twenty-five million pounds of this gas were manufactured. Ozone, a highly concentrated form of oxygen existing in what is known as the allotropic state, is also important in the purification of water and of air in ventilating systems. The poisonous gas cyanogen is being put to use in the extermination of rats on ships and rodents in ground burrows. The use of poison gases in warfare is discussed in another chapter. So also is the synthesis of nitrogen compounds for fertilizers and explosives.

The production of nitrous oxide for use as an anesthetic is now greater than ever, this country alone affording a market for nearly fifty million gallons a year. Its combination for this purpose with oxygen of high purity has stimulated its use.

This brief discussion by no means exhausts the subject of gases. Numerous other applications of scientific and practical importance will be noted throughout the pages of this book. Like every other branch of the science, knowledge of the chemistry of gases grows with each succeeding year. Vital to the fundamental processes of respiration, combustion, growth and decay, as well as indispensable to a host of commercial processes,—gases bulk large in any chemical view of life and industry.

CHAPTER VI

AGRICULTURE AND WAR

AGRICULTURE AND WAR HAVE MUCH IN COMMON—NITRO IN
WEST VIRGINIA AND OLD HICKORY IN TENNESSEE—CHILE SALT-
PETER—LIEBIG AND FERTILIZERS—WARNING OF SIR WILLIAM
CROOKES—RESULTS—FIXATION OF ATMOSPHERIC NITROGEN—
EARLY DISCOVERIES—BRADLEY AND LOVEJOY—BIRKELAND AND
EYDE PROCESS—CYANAMIDE PROCESS—GERMANY INVENTS A
SYNTHETIC PROCESS—RELATION OF PROCESS TO WAR—DESCRIP-
TION OF PROCESS—PROGRESS IN UNITED STATES—MUSCLE
SHOALS—FIXED NITROGEN RESEARCH LABORATORY—FIXED
NITROGEN FROM COAL—SYNTHETIC NITRATES AT HOPEWELL,
VIRGINIA—REMOVAL OF A NATURAL MONOPOLY—POTASH IN
PEACE AND WAR—SOURCES IN UNITED STATES DURING WAR—
POTASH FROM SEARLES LAKE—WHAT THE INDIANS TAUGHT
THE EARLY SETTLERS—UNITED STATES WORLD'S SOURCE OF
PHOSPHATE ROCK—PLANTS NEED MANGANESE—ETHYLENE
GAS—BABCOCK MILK TEST—FARMER'S DEPENDENCE UPON
CHEMISTRY—WAR ON INSECTS—WAR AND POISONOUS GAS.

AGRICULTURE and war,—what have they in common?
Much. Chemistry links them with an inseparable bond.
Long centuries before chemistry was born, too, the
comparative wealth and economic supremacy attendant
upon agricultural life offered incentives to the warlike
instincts of men. Time and again, quiet pastoral scenes,
grazing herds of cattle and flocks of goats and sheep,
cultivated lands, and fertile fields of ripening grain have

213

aroused in less successful neighbors the spirit of envy and invited the forward march of conquest. Pressure of growing populations, realization that subsistence must come from the soil, the irrepressible instinct of self-preservation, unbounded faith in the star of national destiny, and the consequent determination of a people to carve for itself a place in the sun have to-day more than ever brought the pursuit of agriculture into intimate relationship with the grim business of war. At innumerable points, they touch, and each is dependent for its highest efficiency upon a knowledge and control of chemical processes. Indeed, the chemical processes of the one are closely associated with those of the other. Both, in their modern aspects, are children of chemical industry. The growing of foodstuffs and the production of military explosives have become the Siamese twins of the modern world.

Let us visit in succession Nitro, in West Virginia, and Old Hickory, in Tennessee. It is February and March of 1918. We find ourselves in each case hundreds of miles from the seaboard, beyond great mountain ranges, in the midst of fertile agricultural regions, well protected by river barriers and encircling hills, and densely populated with rural loving folk. Already, these peaceful farms are planted with corn and sown to grain. But the exigencies of war with its iron hand are about to touch them. Hundreds of thousands of soldiers are in camp. Agricultural products in prodigious quantities are needed, and so are explosives. Yes, the whole western front of that European battle-field is consuming explosives at a terrific rate. The very atmosphere is aquiver with the chemical reactions of billions of detonating molecules. Civilization seems to hang in the balance. Explosives and yet more explosives is the never-ending cry of roaring cannon, bursting bombs and the crackling of machine-guns. The Allies look to America. The supply must be forthcoming. Military experts have been quick to perceive the ideal qualifications of these secluded spots in West Virginia and Tennessee for munitions plants,—isolation, within easy reach of raw materials, excellent transportation facilities, abundant power resources, adequate reservoirs of water, and a dependable labor supply. The decision has been made. The word has gone forth. There is no alternative. Large-scale action begins,—not next week or next month, but immediately. Between seedtime and harvest, we see these peaceful farms, far from the voice of the city, transformed into great industrial communities, pulsating with life, vibrant with energy, swarming with thousands of workers, and studded with immense plants turning out hundreds of thousands of pounds of smokeless powder a day. Three of the fundamental raw materials are cotton linters, a product of the southern plantation, sodium nitrate, an important fertilizer, and alcohol, a product of agricultural starch. And every process, from the production of the raw materials to their conversion into high explosives, has been a chemical one. Thus do agriculture and war, through the medium of chemistry, meet on the battle-field.

And again, just at the beginning of the Great War, we see German cruisers stationed off the coast of Chile. These have escaped the British blockade, and their commanders know the strategic importance of Chile saltpeter as a war-making material. Without the nitric acid to be obtained from it, explosives are impossible. Germany has imported during the previous year a million tons. She now seeks to prevent her enemies from obtaining the accustomed supply, while her armies in Belgium and France smash their way through to a speedy victory. Britain sends a fleet to the Pacific, but it is defeated. Then she sends a stronger one, and on December eighth overwhelms the German ships. But for nearly four months, a period in which its need has been the most urgent, the allied world has been cut off from Chile saltpeter.

For nearly a century, Chile saltpeter has been a large factor in the agricultural prosperity of the world, and therein agriculture and war meet once more. To keep the record straight, let us go into a little ancient history. It was in 1830 that exports of Chile saltpeter began, ten years before Justus von Liebig proposed his revolutionizing theory of soil fertility. Liebig asserted with all the vigor of his impetuous soul that only the mineral constituents of the soil are necessary for plant growth. These minerals enable the plant to build its organic matter from the nitrogen and carbon dioxide of the air. Simple experiments seemed to justify his conclusions, and soil analysis soon showed that the three elements which plants take from the soil are nitrogen, potassium and phosphorus. Therefore, the matter of fertilizing the soil was reduced to simplicity itself. It became necessary only to know by analysis what element or elements the soil seemed to lack and to supply the deficiency. To a large extent this is true, but the problem has proved to be vastly more complex. Nevertheless, the three elements named have remained the essential constituents of artificial fertilizers. And until yesterday, so to speak, Chile saltpeter, in its immense nitrate beds covering thousands of square miles of the South American Desert, has afforded the world's supply of nitrogen both for fertilizers and explosives. The exact origin of those deposits is still a geologic mystery.

In 1898, Sir William Crookes, in his presidential address before the British Association for the Advancement of Science, warned the world of the approaching exhaustion of the Chile saltpeter deposits and proclaimed the impending peril of racial starvation, if some new means of obtaining nitrogen compounds were not discovered. Although he did not do so, Sir William might equally well have announced the banishment of war by modern methods, for the war-maker too drew upon these same nitrate beds for the most essential ingredient of explosive manufacture. It is difficult to say which of the two prospective calamities proved the greater incentive to the chemist in his work of discovery and invention.

It is interesting to know that, while 1921 was the year Crookes set for the commercial exhaustion of Chile saltpeter, the event is still in the distant future. Even the one small area of deposits which has so far been exploited will continue to supply the present rate of export for more than a century to come, and there are large tracts yet to be explored. The recent application of scientific research in the Chile saltpeter industry and the adoption of better methods of mining and extraction promise to effect large economies in production and greatly to prolong the life of the deposits. Thus, like many another prophecy, this forecast of dire calamity would have failed of fulfilment, though no scientific research had followed. The world would not have starved, but it is reasonably certain that the World War would have been impossible. Thus did a voice of despair in the name of agriculture provide the sinews of war for the greatest conflict in history. Let us see how it happened.

FIXATION OF ATMOSPHERIC NITROGEN

And so the present century opened with a chemical problem of the first magnitude thrust into the foreground. In grim earnestness, chemists accepted the challenge. For long it had been known that growing and thriving upon the roots of leguminous plants, of which beans, peas, alfalfa and clover are examples, are nitrogen-fixing bacteria, which are able to take the nitrogen of the air and build it into the tissue of the plant. Other kinds of plants are unable to effect this important chemical transformation. Here was what has come to be called natural "fixation" of atmospheric nitrogen. It gave the chemist his clue. If he could discover some relatively cheap and practicable commercial process for artificially fixing the nitrogen of the atmosphere in chemical compounds suitable for industrial use, he could nicely bridge the yawning chasm of racial starvation, and the Chile saltpeter beds might go glimmering.

Nature also provided the chemist with another clue. The discharge of lightning through the air causes a small quantity of oxygen and nitrogen to combine to form oxides, which are washed down by the rain, thus adding, it is estimated, about five pounds of fixed nitrogen to each acre of ground per year. If lightning will do this, why not imitate the process with a high voltage discharge of electricity through air in a confined space. As early as 1781, Sir Henry Cavendish had observed the formation of nitric acid when hydrogen was burned in the air. And Sir Humphry Davy, in 1800, had formed an oxide of nitrogen by passing air over a wire heated with an electric current. In 1865, the French chemist Deville obtained ammonia, a compound of nitrogen and hydrogen, by passing a mixture of the two gases through a porcelain tube heated to 1,300 degrees Centigrade, but the amount was very small.

This was the state of knowledge when the chemist started out a quarter of a century ago to solve the problem of producing synthetic nitrogen compounds. Of raw material, there was an inexhaustible supply. Resting upon every square mile of the earth's surface are approximately twenty million tons of atmospheric nitrogen. But the difficulty lay in the chemical inactivity of the element itself. It does not easily enter into combination with other elements, and when it has done so the resulting compounds are unstable. The atoms of nitrogen manifest a strong tendency to break loose from their associations with the disruption of the molecules and the liberation of large quantities of energy. Therein lies the utility of nitrogen compounds in explosives. But it proved to be a most formidable obstacle to the chemist in his effort to bring the element into amicable relations with other elements. Still, the necessities of agriculture and the demands of war had to be met.

In 1902, two American chemists, Bradley and Lovejoy, in imitation of Nature, set up at Niagara Falls the first apparatus designed for the commercial fixation of atmospheric nitrogen. Through the intense heat of an electric arc, they forced air, actually burning a small quantity of it to oxides of nitrogen, which they absorbed in water to form a dilute solution of nitric acid. They demonstrated the feasibility of the process and blazed the way. But these pioneers could not interest American capitalists. The yield of acid was exceedingly small, the quantity of energy required prodigious, and many technical difficulties remained to be solved.

Still, in the very next year, Birkeland and Eyde, two Norwegian chemists, put this process upon a successful commercial basis, utilizing the cheap and abundant water-power of which Norway is the fortunate possessor. A chief difficulty of this process lies in the rapid decomposition of the oxides of nitrogen, if they are not immediately cooled. In other words, these compounds must be cooled so quickly that they do not have time to decompose. A special system of refrigeration did the trick. I never think of this accomplishment without recalling the story of the farmer who asserted that a sudden drop in temperature one night froze the water in his pond so suddenly that frogs were left with their heads protruding through the ice.

The arc process is confined chiefly to Norway. It could be carried out only where immense quantities of water-power are available and the cost is small. Less than two per cent. of the electrical energy consumed is utilized in the chemical product. The waste is prodigious. And only about one and a half per cent. of the nitrogen in the air is fixed by this method. To-day, less than ten per cent. of the fixed nitrogen of world production is obtained by this process.

The way had now been opened. Chemists were at

work, and by 1908 another process, the cyanamide, had
appeared. It, too, was established at Niagara Falls, but
on the Canadian side and under the auspices of the
American Cynanamide Company of New York. Again,
electric power was the source of energy, but the quantity
required was only a quarter of that consumed by the arc
process. Therein lay its great advantage. Calcium
cyanamide, the end-product, is a compound of the elements calcium, carbon and nitrogen. The raw materials
for the first stage are ordinary lime and coke. These are
melted together in an electric furnace. The intermediate
product thus formed is calcium carbide, the substance
which with water yields acetylene gas. After crushing
to a fine powder, the carbide is brought to a red heat and
over it is passed pure nitrogen obtained from liquid air.
The result is calcium cyanamide, which, under certain
restrictions, may be used directly as a fertilizer, but it is
objectionable in some mixtures and has not come into
favor with American agriculturalists. It has found its
chief use for the production of ammonia gas by heating
with steam under pressure. The ammonia may be either
quickly converted into ammonium fertilizers by absorption in acids or oxidized to nitric acid for use in the
manufacture of explosives, dyestuffs and many other
products. An important fertilizer and one which is
bound to become of constantly increasing significance
is ammonium phosphate, combining both nitrogen and
phosphorus, two of the essential elements of plant foods,
in a single compound. The requirement seems to be a
cheap method of providing phosphoric acid, but the solution of the problem will doubtless soon be forthcoming.
Another nitrogen fertilizer growing in favor, which may

be made from calcium cyanamide and also from ammonia and carbon dioxide, is urea. It will be recalled that this was the first organic compound to be synthesized in the laboratory, the achievement having been accomplished in 1828 by Wöhler.

The cyanamide process was of tremendous importance during the war, but it is passing into disfavor now. Although large quantities of cyanamide are still used, particularly in Europe, the industry is not growing. A better method is taking its place. In the developmental stages of nitrogen fixation it was a dependable process and could be counted upon to work when others failed, for which the world will always be grateful.

Great strides had been taken. Only ten years had passed since the gloomy prophecy of Crookes, and the vision of nitrogen starvation was already beginning to fade, like the mirage above the shimmering sands of desert wastes. Although but one per cent. of the world's need for fixed nitrogen was being met by the synthetic processes, that one per cent. was evidence supreme of vast latent possibilities. Little did the world realize that six short years would see the success of synthetic nitrogen compounds, a bulwark of agriculture and war alike.

In the meantime, Germany had seen the handwriting on the wall. Her chemists had not been asleep. Indeed, they were the busiest of any. If any people were to starve from lack of nitrogen fertilizers, they were determined that it should not be the German people, and, as for war, fixed nitrogen in abundance was indispensable in their business. Despite her vastly smaller area, consumption of nitrogen compounds in Germany has always exceeded that in the United States. The intensive agriculture practised there of necessity compels the liberal use of fertilizers. Germany's extensive chemical industry, too, requires vast quantities of nitric acid. The prophecy of Crookes hit the German nation in a vulnerable spot, and her chemists, already at work upon the problem of the artificial fixation of nitrogen, redoubled their efforts.

What of the result? Just before the Great War, success perched upon the German banner in the shape of a synthetic process, differing from either of those already described and the one which to-day seems certain to displace all others. It is known as the Haber, or sometimes the Haber-Bosch, process, for Professor Fritz Haber is the chemist whose researches brought about the production of synthetic ammonia as a commercial proposition.

Never was a great scientific triumph more timely. Without it, the farms of the Central Powers during the Great War would have been unable to produce sufficient food to maintain their populations, and the exhaustion of their supply of explosives and the wherewithal to provide more would have ended the war within six months from lack of ammunition. Indeed, there are those so ungenerous as to assert that there was a close connection between the German discovery and the inauguration of the conflict. But, be that as it may, when Germany realized that the war was to be something more than a military parade ending quickly with a successful dash on Paris, and the enormous consumption of explosives in battering her way through Belgium rapidly depleted her large initial supply, German chemists and engineers in feverish haste began to enlarge the fixed nitrogen plants. Upon their perfect functioning and vast quantity production depended the sinews of war. The fate of millions hung in the balance.

Again, what of the result? Before the end of the first year of war, Germany had an annual production of two hundred thousand tons of fixed nitrogen, an amount greater than the total consumption of nitrates by the United States in 1913. At the close of the war, German tonnage had risen to three hundred thousand, and in 1925 her production of fixed nitrogen had reached 447,828 tons. Of this, 73,150 tons were supplied by the ammonia from by-product coke and gas works, but the present plan is to enlarge the plants at Oppau and Merseburg to a total of a half-million tons of artificially fixed nitrogen per year, exclusive of that from other sources. In 1925, too, Germany exported 83,511 tons of nitrogen compounds and laid them down in the markets of the world at prices competing successfully with the natural product of the Chile saltpeter beds. Indeed, she recently created a near-panic among Chilean producers by discharging at a Peruvian port two hundred tons of German synthetic nitrate bound for Bolivia. When we consider that in 1910 the total production of artificial nitrates in Germany amounted to only 4,108 tons we gain some idea of the magnitude of this chemical triumph. Still more closely did it cement the bonds between agriculture and war.

EXPLANATION OF CATALYTIC PROCESS

Now, for an idea of the German process itself. Professor Haber made use of the principle of catalytic action, which, as we have seen, is rapidly becoming of vast importance in the chemical world. Why use such enormous quantities of electric energy to compel nitrogen to enter into peaceable union with other elements, if these modest servants known as catalysts will overcome the nitrogen antipathies with a fraction of the expenditure? Haber proceeded to prepare ammonia gas by the direct union of the two constituent gases, nitrogen and hydrogen. He compressed a mixture of three volumes of nitrogen to one volume of hydrogen to a pressure of many atmospheres and passed the gases over a heated catalyst. Many catalysts have been tried. In Haber's first success, he employed uranium metal. The catalyst which has been found most effective is iron reduced from magnetic iron oxide and containing about three per cent. of alumina and one per cent. of potash. These latter substances are known as promoters, and have a wonderful influence in increasing the efficiency of the action. Only a part of the gases are made to combine in the first passage over the catalyst. The ammonia is removed either by absorption in water or by condensation to a liquid and the remaining gases are passed again over the catalyst. By successive passages, a large percentage yield may be obtained. The temperature required for the process is relatively low, ranging from 450 to 600 degrees Centigrade.

In the development of the process, a number of difficulties had to be overcome. In the first place, the catalyst becomes easily poisoned by any impurities in the gases and refuses to bring about this easy chemical union of the elements. Therefore, the production of hydrogen and nitrogen of great purity became the chief problem. Although there are a number of processes for obtaining these gases, the one most widely employed passes air and

steam over glowing coke. The oxygen of the air and
also that of the steam combines with the coke to form
the combustible gas carbon monoxide, thus leaving nitrogen from the air and hydrogen from the water. Next

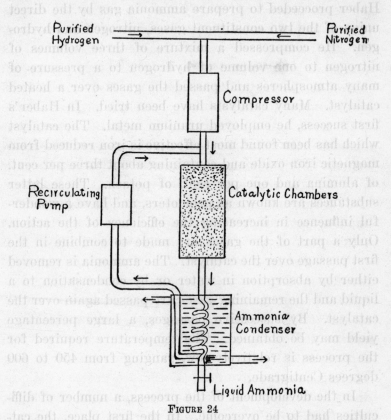

FIGURE 24

Diagram illustrating the catalytic process for the synthesis of
ammonia.

begins a most rigorous chemical treatment to remove the
last traces of such substances as the oxides of carbon, or
compounds of sulfur and phosphorus. Even in minute
quantity, they are ruinous to the sensitive catalyst. With

purification accomplished, the catalytic synthesis is ready to begin.

Although there are four distinct modifications of the synthetic ammonia process, the fundamental principle is the same in each. The tremendous advantage in this process over the arc and cyanamide processes consists in the small quantity of energy required, it being only a quarter as great as that of the latter and only a sixteenth that of the former. During the war, however, not much was known of the details of the catalytic process outside of Germany. As a matter of fact, very little atmospheric nitrogen was fixed in this period among the Allied nations. With command of the seas and access to Chile saltpeter, the need was not so great. And yet the intensive submarine campaign and the excessive burden imposed upon shipping stimulated all nations to seek an artificial supply.

With the artificial production of ammonia, the chief problem of fixation was solved. This gas can by neutralization, or union, with various acids be directly converted into fertilizers, such as the nitrate, chloride, sulfate and phosphate. Still, for the manufacture of explosives, nitric acid and not ammonia must be had. Therein lies the advantage of the arc process. It produces nitric acid directly, and this, too, may be changed into fertilizers by union with various bases. But to obtain nitric acid from ammonia, a second step was required. Without it Germany's triumph would have been only half complete. She might have saved her people from starving, but she could not have provided her armies with munitions of war. However, this difficulty had been met. Ostwald had already developed another catalytic process by which ammonia may be oxidized to nitric acid. By passing oxygen and ammonia together over heated platinum gauze, the synthesis is effected. And so Germany's double-barreled gun, a product of some of the most crucial researches in the history of science, was ready for action.

Thus did the exigencies of war and agriculture forge processes of incalculable value to industry.

PROGRESS IN THE UNITED STATES

As we have seen, the first attempt at nitrogen fixation was made at Niagara Falls in 1902 by two American chemists. In 1909, a similar start was made in South Carolina, but soon abandoned. We have noted the beginning of the cyanamide process in 1910. In 1917, at La Grande, Washington, another small arc plant was established. It is still in operation, having produced in 1926 three hundred tons of fixed nitrogen. Then came the nation's entrance into the war, and with it the fixation of nitrogen compounds became a matter of great military importance. What had before been the concern of peaceful agricultural and chemical industries only, now became the necessity of war.

Out of investigations of government representatives in 1917 grew a nitrogen fixation program. Two plants were built at Muscle Shoals. Plant No. 1 was to employ the synthetic ammonia process of the Germans, while Plant No. 2 was to utilize the more familiar cyanamide process already established at Niagara Falls. In addition two other plants were started in Ohio. When the Armistice came, the cyanamide plant, costing $70,000,000, was just ready for operation. It was at that time given a test run and found to operate successfully. Since then, the plant has remained idle. Its capacity is forty thousand tons of fixed nitrogen a year, the largest cyanamide plant in the world. However, with the passing of this process into eclipse, the huge investment becomes a war loss, for it is exceedingly doubtful that the plant will ever be operated either as a government or private enterprise. Not enough was then known by American chemists regarding the synthetic ammonia process to permit the successful operation of Plant No. 1. The total production of fixed nitrogen from the atmosphere in this country had reached only two hundred and seventy-six tons in 1919.

Following the war, the War Department established in Washington the Fixed Nitrogen Research Laboratory. In evidence of the intimate relation between the chemistry of war and agriculture this laboratory was transferred in 1921 to the Department of Agriculture. Its staff of research chemists, under the direction of Dr. Frederick G. Cottrell, is still engaged upon fundamental problems in this field. Much has already been accomplished. Fixation of nitrogen has been studied from every angle, and our chemists are now in possession of all the technical knowledge essential to the building and successful operation of such plants. In 1925, the output in this country of fixed atmospheric nitrogen products amounted to 13,050 tons. In that same year, our total consumption of nitrogen compounds was 325,566 tons. Thus we may see how relatively small the nitrogen fixation industry even yet is. At the close of 1926, it was estimated that the seven plants now operating in the

United States have a total output of about seventy tons of ammonia a day.

When, however, we consider the world as a whole, the picture is different. Whereas in 1910 Chile was supplying 65 per cent. of the inorganic nitrogen consumed and the artificial processes but 1.4 per cent., Chile nitrate now furnishes but 31 per cent., while the synthetic production has climbed to 45 per cent. The remainder comes from a source of which we shall speak presently.

The gloom shed abroad by the foreboding of Crookes has now, thanks to the world's chemists, been completely dissipated. Despite the world catastrophe resulting from the researches which this prophecy stimulated, the sun shines once more. Never again need we fear starvation from the exhaustion of nitrogen fertilizers. It is by no means certain, however, that their twin brothers, the giant explosives of modern warfare, may not again disturb the peace of nations.

ANOTHER SOURCE OF FIXED NITROGEN

Ever since the beginning of the distillation of bituminous coal in closed ovens out of contact with the air, first for the production of illuminating gas and later coke, there has been an available source of nitrogen compounds of large potential value. Until the coming of the synthetic ammonia process, all the ammonia of commerce was derived from this heating of coal. And that was but yesterday. In the United States to-day, this is still practically the only source. Every ton of bituminous coal contains from thirty to forty pounds of nitrogen combined with other elements. In the heat of the coking retort, these atoms break loose from their associations and, when they recover their equilibrium after having been driven from the retort, a large number of the nitrogen atoms find themselves in partnership with atoms of hydrogen in the ratio of one atom of nitrogen to three of hydrogen. In this way about four or five pounds of the nitrogen in each ton of coal gets converted into ammonia. It has been estimated that, were all the bituminous coal in the United States to be coked and the nitrogen thus recovered, it would result in more than a trillion tons.

Along with this ammonia is condensed out coal-tar, that vast treasure-house of chemical wealth of which you have heard so much in recent years. And you know, too, how that before the war Germany was the only nation making a business of recovering these by-products. The distillation of coal in the United States was carried out chiefly for the production of coke for the steel industry. It did not pay to bother with the recovery of the ammonia, coal-tar and gas. Our coal-tar products were costing us but a mere bagatelle of nine million dollars a year. It was cheaper and far easier to allow Germany to make these for us. The fact that coal-tar is the source of such high explosives as picric acid and the famous T. N. T. did not enter into the picture. We were a peace loving people. We had no designs on other nations. The idea of national preparedness had not been born.

Then, almost overnight, the rude awakening came. I do not need to repeat the story. Enough to say that, whereas in 1910 but seventeen per cent. of the coke in this country was produced in by-product ovens for the recovery of these substances, in 1925, seventy-nine per cent. was being thus prepared. Not only agriculture and war, but a host of industries found themselves dependent in a thousand ways upon these products of the coke oven.

About ninety per cent. of the ammonia thus obtained is passed into sulfuric acid to form ammonium sulfate, an important fertilizer. Part of the remainder is dissolved in water to supply the common household ammonia of trade, while the rest is employed for refrigeration purposes. The by-product ammonia produced in this country in 1925 amounted to 123,600 tons. With the adoption of the low temperature carbonization of all the bituminous coal used for domestic purposes, the supply of ammonia would be vastly increased. It is entirely conceivable that this source would then meet every need of industry and war without the importation of Chile saltpeter or the artificial fixation of atmospheric nitrogen. Still, that achievement is a long distance in the future.

A report just come to my attention states that one of the biggest chemical manufacturing companies in this country, after five years of research and the expenditure of $4,500,000, is to build at Hopewell, Virginia, the largest factory in the world for the production of synthetic nitrates. Beyond doubt, this will practically destroy the Chile saltpeter trade with this country, which has already declined steadily since the beginning of 1926. It will, unless the group of American business men and engineers who are now attempting to rehabilitate the inefficient and old-fashioned South American industry can effect economies which will put it once more on the map. As an indication of what synthetic nitrates have done to a "natural monopoly," the stock quotations on the London Exchange tell an illuminating story. On

Removing caliche—the crude ore from which Chilean nitrate of soda is refined. For three-quarters of a century, Chile was the world's only source of nitrates

Ammonia catalyst fusion pot used in research on the fixation of atmospheric nitrogen

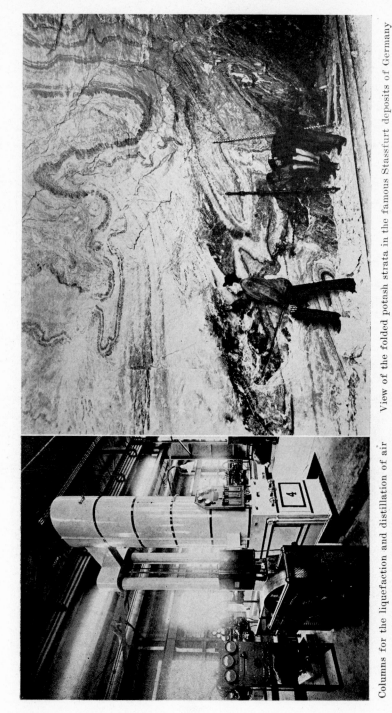

Columns for the liquefaction and distillation of air   View of the folded potash strata in the famous Stassfurt deposits of Germany

Plant No. 2, Muscle Shoals, for the fixation of atmospheric nitrogen by the cyanamide process, a process which is now falling into disuse

January 1, 1926, the aggregate value of the shares of five great Chile nitrate companies was £3,578,000. On December 31, 1926, this value had fallen to £1,634,000. No small tribute, this, to the scepter of power which chemistry wields.

Dr. Charles L. Parsons, Secretary of the American Chemical Society, in a paper appearing in the July, 1927, issue of *Industrial and Engineering Chemistry,* said: "Nitric acid produced by the oxidation of ammonia can now be made in any concentration, including fixed charges on plant, for at least thirty dollars per ton less than it can be made from Chilean nitrate even figured on the basis of two cents a pound. Nitrogen in the form of ammonia is now obtainable for less than half the price of nitrogen in Chilean nitrate. This, together with other important developments in the last ten years, points to early obsolescence of plants producing nitric acid by the old processes, in America as well as in Europe." Once more a time-honored industry bows before the supremacy of him who controls the forces of chemical action.

Nitrogen compounds, the world must have, and the chemists have made sure an inexhaustible supply. It has been asserted that the nitrogen consumption of a nation is to-day a measure of its prosperity. Even explosives are essential to the pursuits of peace. In this country alone, a half billion pounds are consumed annually in mining, quarrying, road-building, and clearing land for cultivation.

POTASH IN PEACE AND WAR

When Germany was bottled up by the British blockading fleet in 1914, this country was receiving from the famous Stassfurt deposits one million tons of potash a year. This strategic combination of potassium compounds has a multitude of uses, chief of which is as a fertilizer for worn-out soils. It is also important in the manufacture of soap, glass and matches. Some of you will remember the old-fashioned leach in which water was poured over wood ashes to obtain lye, which, heated with the fat scraps from the kitchen, formed soft soap, the only soap known in the early days. Wood ashes contain potash, and this original source of supply accounts for the name. An abandoned, worn-out farm, having been allowed to grow up to brush and small trees, was occasionally burned over and tilled again. To the pleasant surprise of the early settlers, the soil was found to have recovered largely its lost fertility. During the intervening years, the hardy second-growth had been able to appropriate the scanty supply of available potash in the soil and store it for future use. Gradually, as the fundamental importance of potash as a fertilizer became known, the chemist and the soil expert taught the American farmer to use it in large quantities. The only known supply of water-soluble potash in the world at that time was the vast deposits at Stassfurt, Germany, and in Alsace-Lorraine. To promote trade in this large source of German revenue, the German Kali Works spent fifty thousand dollars a year in propaganda work among American farmers.

Then came the call to battle, the hurried tramp of armies, and the naval command of the seas. Almost overnight, the price of potash shot from forty dollars a ton to four hundred dollars, and even at that price it was not to be had. In two years, our annual supply had been reduced to ten thousand tons. Once more agriculture and war had been brought into conflict.

Still, potassium compounds are abundant. The clays and many of the rocks contain this element, but the chemical combination is so strong that the roots of plants are unable to break it. Furthermore, large quantities of energy are required to set it free from its original partnerships with other elements, so much so that its profitable production in industrial plants has largely been an impossibility. And yet, a certain amount of potash was essential. The glass for gunsights, periscopes, range finders and binoculars must have it. At least, it had always been thought so. Soap manufacturers and farmers might do without it for a time, but the necessities of war must be met. You remember how it was done. The natural brines of certain lakes in Nebraska and California supplied some. Sea-weed, blast furnace slag, the dust from cement mills, the refuse from sugar-beet factories, and distillery wastes accounted for more. In 1919, we were producing all told 207,000 tons of potash a year, about twenty per cent. of our pre-war supply.

Out of this war-time experience has grown one of the greatest triumphs of American chemistry. During those eventful years, at Searles Lake, California, was discovered a source of potash salts which is proving to be of vast importance. Over an area of something like twelve square miles of this old geologic lake and to a depth of seventy feet is a crust of salt, the brine of which yields about four per cent. of potassium chloride. The salt, however, is contaminated with large quantities of borax, and the chemical problem became to separate the two successfully and cheaply. The American Trona Corporation undertook the task, but progress was slow. In 1919, only twenty tons of potash salt were being produced a day and costs were exceeding the revenue. Then, Doctor John E. Teeple, a consulting chemical engineer of New York, was put in charge of the plant. As the result of much research, splendid staff team-work, the solution of a multitude of chemical and engineering problems, and the liberal expenditure of money, the Searles Lake works to-day are producing more potash than any single mine of Germany or France. It is estimated that the 1927 output of potassium chloride will be 90,000 tons, and in addition there will be 45,000 tons of borax, enough to meet more than half of the world's requirements. This is the largest borax refinery in the world. Further, this achievement has been accomplished without the aid of a protective tariff, for potash is on the free list. In recognition of this splendid service, Doctor Teeple was awarded the Perkin Medal on January 14, 1927.

Of course, the Searles Lake deposits are not inexhaustible. Their life will be relatively short. But it is comforting to know that there is little likelihood of our ever again being compelled to depend upon a foreign supply. What seem to be vast deposits of potash, comparable in extent to those of Stassfurt, have recently been located by the United States Geological Survey in western Texas and southeastern New Mexico. In drilling for oil, potash salts have been brought up from depths ranging from 700 to 2,200 feet, and the estimated area of the deposits embraces 70,000 square miles. The minerals known as polyhalite, kainite and sylvinite, characteristic of the European beds, have been found and in addition a different salt named langbeinite. The potash content, that is potassium in terms of its oxide, has been shown by analysis of many samples to run from 1.5 per cent. to 18.5. Some of these minerals are so rich in potash that they will need only grinding as they come from the mine to make them suitable for agricultural use in near-by territory. For long-distance shipment, chemical plants for concentration, so as to reduce freight costs, will doubtless be required. To be sure, many problems remain to be solved, but war or peace, our potash future seems to be assured.

Our importation of potash for 1925 was a little more than a half-million tons, by mutual agreement seventy per cent. of it coming from Germany and thirty per cent. from France. Through the fortunes of war, France has gained the potash mines of Alsace-Lorraine and thereby an agricultural resource of vast importance. Poland, too, has recently discovered potash deposits. Her output for 1925 was 143,000 metric tons, a metric ton being equal approximately to an English long ton. No longer does Germany monopolize the world potash supply, and for the breaking of this monopoly the war was chiefly responsible.

Another process for the production of potash from New Jersey greensand has been started on a small scale. It consists in treating the greensand with sulfuric acid. This changes the iron, aluminum and potash present into sulfates. Continued heating converts the iron and aluminum sulfates into soluble oxides, after which the potassium sulfate may be leached out with water and crystallized. The recovery of a large part of the sulfuric acid used together with the oxides of iron and aluminum as by-products give promise of a commercially profitable industry.

AGRICULTURAL ASPECTS, WARLIKE AND OTHERWISE

The Indians taught the early settlers to plant a fish in each hill of corn. Neither the Indians nor the settlers knew the "why" of it, but they did observe that this practise, particularly on old soils, resulted in a more luxuriant growth of stalk and ear. The chemist has long since learned that the fish supplies two essential plant foods. From the fleshy parts comes nitrogen and from the bones phosphorus. The phosphorus, however, is largely in a form unavailable for plants until it has been acted upon at a fertilizer works with sulfuric acid. To-day, the conversion of phosphate rock into soluble fertilizer, known as superphosphate, is an immense industry and constitutes one of the greatest uses of sulfuric acid, a foremost raw material of chemical manufacture.

Although lacking supplies of nitrates and potash, the United States has been the world's source of phosphate rock, of which Florida, Georgia, Tennessee and the Carolinas possess large deposits. During the war, however, the farms of Europe starved for lack of phosphorus. Shipping could not be spared to transport the rock overseas. Once more the necessities of war collided with the needs of peaceful agriculture.

Now, let us look at an aspect of agriculture which, happily, can have no warlike significance. Until quite recently, the old idea prevailed that only ten elements are useful in plant growth, namely, carbon, hydrogen, oxygen, nitrogen, phosphorus, potassium, calcium, magnesium, sulfur and iron. As we have seen, nitrogen, phosphorus and potassium are the only ones heretofore added to the soil in commercial fertilizers. Researches carried out at the Agricultural Experiment Station, at Lexington, Kentucky, however, show that small amounts of manganese, copper, zinc, boron, barium, strontium, iodine and arsenic are essential to the plants growing in the fertile soils of the Blue-Grass State. In particular, manganese seems to be absolutely required. Many experiments were carried out in growing plants with and without this element in the soil, and the results were unmistakable. As long ago as 1774, Scheele, the discoverer of manganese, showed that it is assimilated by plants. It is now known that this element, which is as widely distributed in the soils as iron, though less abundantly, is necessary for the plant's synthesis of green chlorophyll and the assimilation of carbon. It is believed that the luxuriant growth and deep green color of Kentucky blue-grass, as well as its superior nutritious value as fodder, are due largely to the presence of manganese in Kentucky soils. This, too, may have been no small factor in producing those breeds of horses and live stock for which Kentucky is justly famous. Here is a field for further research. It may be that manganese salts will become an increasingly important ingredient of commercial fertilizers.

In the next chapter, we shall learn of the use of ethylene gas, a compound of hydrogen and carbon, as an anesthetic. During the war large quantities of it were used in the manufacture of mustard gas. The gas is also highly combustible and, mixed with air, explosive. Its flame is even more useful than that of acetylene in the cutting and welding of iron and steel. For some years it has been used for changing the green coloring of citrus fruits yellow. At a recent meeting of the American Chemical Society announcement was made of the discovery that ethylene will ripen in a few hours fruit which would require days or even weeks to ripen in the sunshine on the trees. A very small quantity of the gas released in the air will ripen a chamber full of green fruit. The ripening action consists in reducing the acidity of the fruit and in increasing its sugar content. Through this discovery it will be possible for the fruit grower to spread the ripening and marketing of his crop over a considerable period without being compelled to dump it on the market all at once, temporarily producing an over-supply and depressing prices. Experiments have also been carried out with celery. The gas bleaches green celery quickly and gives to it a delicious flavor as well as leaving the stalks freer from stringiness than are those bleached by the usual methods.

Some years ago, I wandered into a chemical laboratory of the Agricultural College of the University of Wisconsin. An elderly gentleman with white beard and kindly face and voice asked if I were a stranger and would wish to be shown about. I gratefully accepted his offer, and, when I left him at the end of a pleasant half-hour, I learned to my surprise and pleasure that my host had been no other than Dr. Stephen Moulton Babcock, the inventor of the Babcock milk test, used throughout the world for the determination of butter-fat in milk. In speaking of this contribution, Secretary Jardine recently said: "One of the most brilliant examples of the benefits which have been conferred by chemistry upon agriculture is the Babcock test for determining the butter-fat content of milk. It won grand prizes at both the Paris and St. Louis Expositions. Babcock's invention, from the effect which it had in improving dairy herds, in securing the payment for milk and cream upon a fat percentage basis, in controlling the processes of manufacturing dairy products, and in regulating milk supplies, has been of inestimable value to the American people, although he himself, by generously dedicating his process to the public, has had no share in the vast financial benefits which others have acquired.''

In a still larger way, chemistry promises to increase the value of the annual milk production of the farmer. Until quite recently, skim-milk has been regarded largely as waste. Only the fat, constituting less than four per cent. of the milk, has been utilized. The casein, milk sugar and albumin, together more than double the quantity of fat, have gone the "primrose way" of many another by-product of a country rich in natural resources. But the chemist is changing the picture, and the future is big with promise. From the twenty-two and a half billion pounds of skim-milk available annually in this country fourteen and a half million pounds of casein were extracted in a recent year. Still, in that same year we imported 26,489,992 pounds, and the manifold uses of this newcomer in the field of industrial chemistry have only begun to be developed.

Casein is a colloidal substance, a form of matter of which we shall learn more in a later chapter, held in semi-solution in the milk. It may be coagulated by the simple souring of the milk, the addition of dilute mineral acids, or by treatment with rennet, an enzyme (exciter of chemical action) obtained from the lining of calves' stomachs. Practical processes of separation are built upon all three methods. Of course, casein has been utilized in the making of cheese for many centuries. However, only a small portion of the milk supply has been converted into this product. Ignorance of the many uses to which casein may be put and the absence of chemical knowledge regarding it combined to relegate this substance to the realm of sheer wastes.

Casein is not a distinct compound but appears to be a mixture of several. Its properties differ according to the method by which it has been prepared. It is largely replacing animal glue as a binder for the pigment in mixtures for coating paper. Casein-prepared coatings are unaffected by moisture and the ink effects obtained with them are of wonderful detail and sharpness. For many other purposes, casein glues are proving superior to those of animal origin. Unaffected by moisture, of great strength, small cost and ease of preparation for use, casein glues have an assured future. In the preparation of "cold-water" paints, that is paints consisting chiefly of a pigment, water and a binder, casein is finding an important application. But it is as a basis for the manufacture of plastics that casein is proving most useful. The process depends fundamentally upon the chemical reaction of casein with formaldehyde. The product is a tough, hornlike substance, tasteless, odorless, noninflammable, and capable of taking a high polish. It takes dyes well, producing a great variety of color effects. Casein plastics are used in the manufacture of umbrella handles, billiard balls, knife handles, buttons, fountain pens, pencils, beads, buckles and numerous novelties.

Casein, too, is finding use in the preparation of massage creams and skin lotions. With special treatment it forms an easily digested food. Casein mixed with limewater gives an excellent lining coat for the interiors of oil containers. It is also useful as a sizing for walls preparatory to papering.

The industrial field for casein products is practically unlimited. Doubtless many more uses are yet to be discovered. If all the casein in the skim-milk of this country were utilized each year, there would be available approximately three-quarters of a billion pounds for industrial use. Here is a large resource of potential wealth. As yet, only a beginning has been made. The quantity of sugar, too, in this skim-milk, now almost entirely waste, exceeds in quantity the casein. Both this and the albumin must be recovered and turned to account. To do so will be the work of the research chemist, and the results achieved will accrue to the benefit, not only of agriculture, but of many other industries. In the war, casein glue proved to be the only glue capable of meeting the exacting requirements for cementing ply wood in airplane construction. And thus this product of the farm became a resource of war.

And we might multiply these examples of the service which chemistry has rendered to agriculture. The industrial application of the laboratory discovery of the hydrogenation of liquid vegetable oils to form solid fats has added millions of dollars to the value of the annual cotton crop of the United States. In the warfare upon insects and fungous growths, the chemist has provided the farmer with a whole arsenal of poisonous compounds, here uniting the interests of agriculture and war in a common cause. And what would the farmer do without tools of tempered steel, cement for concrete, gasoline for his automobile and tractor, oil for his machinery, paint for his buildings, wire for his fences, bricks for his silo, medicines for his stock, and explosives with which to clear his land,—all the products of chemical industry? Chemistry has revolutionized the production and refining of sugar. In the miracle of modern transportation systems, in no small measure the product of chemical research, the isolation of the farm has been banished. Even in the farmer's war upon crows and woodchucks, he is indebted to the chemist for the steel of his gun and the powder and shot of his charge.

In providing chemical poisons, insecticides and fungicides, with which to combat the ever restless hordes of crop pests and to cure the diseases of sick plants, the chemist has made himself the most serviceable ally the farmer has. Paris-green, employed for several decades, kills the potato bug. So does calcium arsenate, a cheap substitute provided by the chemist for the more expensive lead arsenate. Both are used in making war upon the boll-weevil, which plays such havoc with the cotton crop. The nicotine, extracted by the chemist from tobacco, is a deadly insecticide and rapid in its action. Scale insects succumb to lime-sulfur, a mixture prepared by boiling together lime, sulfur and water. Ethyl acetate, carbon tetrachloride (ordinary Pyrene) and carbon disulfide will kill the insects which attack stored grain. The exceedingly poisonous gas known as hydrocyanic, or Prussic, acid is employed in greenhouses. Seeds treated with formaldehyde or corrosive sublimate before planting will kill fungous spores. The most famous fungicide is Bordeaux mixture, used particularly upon grape-vines. Originated at Bordeaux, France, it consists of a mixture of lime and copper sulfate, or blue vitriol.

It is thought that as large a proportion as one-fifth of the world's crops is destroyed each year by insects and fungous growths. Estimates place the amount of money spent by the farmers of the United States in 1925 in the war upon insects and grubs at more than a billion and a half dollars. Were this war to cease, the people of this country would soon face starvation. Thus, every one benefits from the work of the chemist, and war and agriculture meet once more.

Yes, chemistry in a thousand ways is the bond servant of agriculture and war alike, and from time immemorial agriculture and war have been locked in intimate partnership. As to war, from the explosives and poisonous gases of the battle-field and the steel of big guns and armor-plate to the production of foodstuffs and the healing drugs of the hospital, it is all a matter of chemistry. But, assuredly, it can be no reproach to chemistry that its discoveries become the chief reliance of the most peaceful of industries and at the same time the bulwark of war.

CHEMISTRY AND WAR

And now one more word about war. Appalling and frightful as was the last great conflict, it is exceedingly doubtful whether the world has yet learned its lesson. The "war to end war" may still be in the future. And when that war arrives, regardless of all conventions of disarmament conferences to the contrary, nations will employ chemical warfare as the chief weapon of offense and defense. As has been so many times pointed out, from the first use of gunpowder to the present moment war has been chemical in its work of destruction. That needs no argument. It is patent to all. These later, and to some more frightful, methods of chemical warfare are simply more refined and scientific applications of the art. That is all.

Let us be frank. The business of war is to kill and destroy. So long as war is recognized, what difference does it make whether an individual is blown to bits by an exploding bomb, drowned on a torpedoed ship, or dies from poisonous gas? In each instance the agency of death is chemical in origin. It is idle to talk of humane warfare. War can never be humane. Nevertheless, the American Legion, the Association of Military Surgeons, the Military Order of the World and the Reserve Officers' Association assert that the use of poisonous gas is more humane, less destructive of human life, and less productive of suffering than are other methods of warfare.

The only way to outlaw war is to make it as hideous as possible. Unmask it. Rob it of its respectability. Strip it of its gold braid and of the pomp and glory of military display. Take away from it its professional status. Let it stand forth in all its nakedness. Appraise it for what it is,—the science of death and destruction. If war can be made frightful enough, it may give to those responsible for its inauguration pause before they plunge.

Of course, a chief objection to the use of poisonous gas is the ease with which it may be used upon non-combatant populations. Still, we have only to consider what war does to such populations whenever it can be carried into the enemy country to know that in principle gas warfare is no different from any other form of legalized destruction. The time honored way has been for an invading force to lay waste to the country, destroy its resources, and by thus withdrawing its support weaken the main fighting force. The result may be death by starvation or from deprivation and exposure. The lives of large numbers may be placed in jeopardy,— women, children and old men. Still, that is legitimate. It is in accordance with the rules of the game. But suppose a fleet of enemy airplanes fly over a country and let loose poison gas, by dropping bombs which explode among the civilian population. The defenders of "humane" methods of taking life and working hardship and suffering raise their hands in horror. This is fiendish. It never has been done. It must be outlawed and every nation that participates in such barbarous tactics must be regarded as a degenerate outcast among the inhabitants of this planet. Still, does any one doubt that poisonous gas has come to stay? Will governments, knowing the tremendous destructive power which this new weapon confers, allow it to remain idle? Will not the nation which cherishes such a delusion and does not keep abreast of the latest developments in this field of chemical research find itself hopelessly outclassed, should it suddenly be called upon to make defense against an enemy armed with every weapon of modern science? International conferences may talk of outlawing poisonous gas. It will never be done.

Another objection to poisonous gas comes from those who make war their profession. Chemical warfare will render obsolete large armies with their swollen retinues of officers. All the old-time glory of war will have gone. The appeal to the imagination, the chivalry, the heroism and the glamour surrounding this business of war, as flowers which soften the grim spectacle of death, will take their places in the mausoleum of lost arts. The tramp of armies will be heard no more. Vast aggregations of fighting forces, the cannon fodder of previous wars, will no longer be needed. Indeed, it would be criminal folly to make them easy targets of these new weapons of chemical warfare. Airplanes and poisonous gases, more deadly than any yet used, will drive the pageantry of this greatest game of the ages from the theater of action as effectually as gunpowder displaced the armor and the lance of medieval times. We can not stay the rising tide. Defenders of things as they were—military leaders, statesmen and sentimentalists—may make gestures of opposition, but they will be as futile as was the command of King Canute to the ocean waves. We stand at the beginning of a new day in warfare. Its very terribleness is at once its stigma and its crown of redemption.

When men know that war is no longer a contest to be fought at a distance, that it may be carried with the utmost expedition to every man, woman and child of any country, that war means something more than sending armies to the front with opportunities to make huge fortunes from the lucrative business of providing them with munitions, food and supplies,—in short when it is impossible for any one from the highest to the lowest to escape the risks and penalties of war, when the lives of large numbers may indiscriminately be snuffed out by poisonous gas or mayhap with germs of disease, then and not until then will statesmen and military leaders outlaw war in earnest. Bring a lively consciousness of the possibility of death home to every citizen, and no large groups will be found in any country who will sponsor this unintelligent method of settling international disputes. Safeguard it with standardized rules of the game, and this legitimitized agent of death and ruin will stalk in our midst for generations yet to come.

At a meeting of the New York Section of the American Chemical Society just following the Great War, I saw in sealed glass tubes samples of something over thirty poisonous gases used in the trenches. As is well known, this new era in modern warfare began on April 22, 1915, at Ypres, when the Germans let loose against the British lines a cloud of chlorine gas. Startlingly successful in the easy conquest it made, had the Germans been prepared to follow up their advantage, the terms of surrender might have been dictated by the Central Powers in Paris or London at a much earlier date than 1918, instead of by the Allies.

Gas masks against chlorine were soon devised, and the Germans turned from chlorine to more deadly and insidious gases. One of the first was phosgene, so effective that one part in ten thousand parts of air may be fatal. It is made by the chemical union of chlorine and carbon monoxide. An advantageous characteristic from the standpoint of the user is an inoffensive odor, which fails to arouse suspicion until the damage has been done. The ease with which it may be liquefied and stored in steel cylinders facilitates its distribution. Inhaled, it attacks the heart action and renders the victim especially susceptible to death from slight exertion.

Chloropicrin, made from picric acid by the action of chlorine, was another of the later compounds used. It was mixed in a shell or bomb with tin chloride, which forms dense white clouds of vapor capable of penetrating the gas masks and carrying with it the volatile chloropicrin. Highly poisonous in itself, chloropicrin induces nausea and vomiting, thereby causing the victim to remove his mask and rendering him an easy prey to other lethal gases.

Of what might be termed the "big four" combination of poisonous compounds used in the war, mustard gas proved to be the most persistent and treacherous. A liquid, slowly evaporating and comparatively stable, this substance would linger for days in the trenches, penetrating the clothing, blistering the skin, and producing serious burns and ugly ulcers. Attacking the throat, nose and lungs, it led to bronchial affections and frequently pneumonia. Mustard gas, the common name for the compound known to the chemist as di-chlor-di-ethyl-sulfide, is prepared from chlorine, alcohol and sulfur. The alcohol is converted into ethylene while the action of chlorine upon melted sulfur gives sulfur monochloride. The combination of the latter with ethylene produces mustard gas.

In addition to the foregoing gas-producing compounds, other poisonous substances were used. Arsenic, bromine and cyanogen were the starting-points in the preparation of a number. Some of these were known as tear gases and sneeze gases. They are highly effective in temporarily putting out of commission a fighting force. A most legitimate use of these weapons is in dispersing a mob, or quelling a riot of prisoners. A golden opportunity to have employed tear gas was in putting down the recent disturbances in China. It results in no fatal casualties, but its physical and psychological effects are immensely salutary. Upon humanitarian grounds alone, tear gas must become a strategic weapon of the future.

No one familiar with the situation felt that more than a beginning in the use of poisonous gas was made in the late war. More than well-founded rumors assert that the Germans surrendered just in time. A new gas, devised by American chemists and more deadly than any yet used, was about to be let loose in quantity against the Central Powers. Indeed, it is said that knowledge of this discovery was a factor in hastening surrender. Whatever of truth there may be in the foregoing statements, certain it is that gas warfare is only in its infancy. The stocking of the arsenal of poisonous gases has only begun. There can be little doubt that gases so violently effective as to be able to snuff out large units of population at a single stroke are within easy grasp of chemical research. Such weapons coupled with mastery of the air will render armies obsolete and bring military success to any nation that commands them. To cherish the thought that with a knowledge of the practical utility of power so overwhelming, men will not invoke it in time of war is to discredit the record of the past and to indulge in utopian visions impossible of present realization. But this cloud is not without its silver lining. The spread of this knowledge will do more to discourage the war-making proclivities of interested groups than any other

circumstance. When warfare becomes simply the wholesale extermination of large numbers, stripped of all its
former glory and romance, men will find peaceful ways
of settling their disputes. The will to war will disappear.

So long as war is a possibility, no nation, and in particular the United States, can afford to neglect the
chemical warfare branch of the service. Oceans are no
longer effective barriers. They do not afford protective
isolation. War could be quickly carried into our very
midst. We must fight fire with fire. We must command
the air and be prepared to meet the chemical offensive of
the enemy with a superior defense in kind. As in times
past but still more in the future, chemistry will constitute
the bulwark of the nation's defense. To neglect to provide it with every means for adequate development with
respect to war is national folly, little short of criminal.
The future security of the peaceful agricultural and
other industrial interests of the land demands that the
fullest measure of protection be taken. To do less is to
invite disaster. It is to create for ourselves a fools'
paradise.

CHAPTER VII

CHEMISTRY AND DISEASE

PREVENTION THE KEYNOTE OF MODERN MEDICAL PRACTISE—
CHEMISTRY ESSENTIAL TO CONQUEST OF DISEASE—REIGN OF
THE ALCHEMIST—FIRST GREAT MEDICAL TRIUMPH—COMING
OF ETHER—CHEMISTRY AND MEDICINE SLOW TO COOPERATE—
WORK OF PASTEUR AND LISTER—PAUL EHRLICH AND "606"—
THE SEARCH FOR SPECIFICS—DISCOVERIES OF NEW ANTISEPTIC
DRUGS—THE USE OF DYES—HEXYL-RESORCINOL—IDEAL ANTI-
SEPTIC—"BAYER 205"—THE DUCTLESS GLANDS—ADRE-
NALIN—THYROXIN—PARATHYROIDS AND THEIR FUNCTIONS—
MEANING OF INSULIN—PITUITARY GLAND AND HUMAN
MONSTROSITIES—SEX GLANDS—VITAMINS—VITAMIN D AND
RICKETS—VITAMINS AND ULTRAVIOLET RAYS—RECENT DIS-
COVERIES—UNSOLVED PROBLEMS—PROBLEMS FOR THE CHEM-
IST—CHEMIST CAN NOT WORK ALONE.

"To CURE is the voice of the past; to prevent is the
divine inspiration of to-day. In times past, when the
Cape Breton fisherman pricked his finger with a dirty
fish-hook, he offered a votive prayer to the Virgin Mary.
Now he cleanses his hand and applies an antiseptic."
Thus did the late President Eliot, of Harvard, enunciate
the gospel of preventive medicine, a gospel of which the
immortal Pasteur and Lord Lister were the first great
apostles in a line which numbers such giants as Koch,
Roux, Behring, Ross, de Grassi, Bruce, Reed, Osler, and
others little less known to fame. True, prevention is the

keynote of modern medical practise, but to be able to cure is often the physician's only alternative to the death of his patient. In both fields of medical endeavor, chemistry plays a leading rôle. Life itself is dependent upon a series of nicely balanced and intimately related chemical processes. From the air we breathe, the food we eat, and the water we drink to the clothes we wear and the curative and preventive drugs of medicine, chemistry is our servant in a host of ways. From the days of Paracelsus, who asserted that the object of chemistry is "not to make gold but to prepare medicines," the conquest of disease has very largely gone hand in hand with advances in chemical science. Even the antiseptic with which the Cape Breton fisherman destroys the microbes which might infect his blood is a product of the laboratory. It is in a knowledge of the chemistry of the living cell, the irreducible unit of all life, that science must look for an understanding and control of vital processes. In the hidden laboratory of the cell of living protoplasm, the fundamental reactions of life originate and take place. Vast continents of unexplored truth beckon to the investigator in his battle with disease. Let us consider some past and present accomplishments, that we may better appreciate future problems.

The reign of the alchemist marked the heroic age of chemistry in its relation to medical science. This was particularly true from the time of Paracelsus to the dawn of modern chemistry. Every apothecary shop in Europe was a research laboratory in which the mysterious concoctions brewed in pots and retorts became the immediate resource of those gentry who aspired to wield the healing wand of curative medicine. The art was wholly empirical, that is, experimental. Indeed, even to this day, it is more so than scientists wish. But we have grown wiser. We no longer recklessly experiment upon a human being with some untested drug of doubtful effect. Armies of guinea pigs, mice and rabbits have been impressed into the service. Their bodies become living laboratories, in which the scientist makes discoveries of the utmost moment. And these discoveries hinge upon chemical changes in the organism, often little understood, and yet holding in the balance the issue of life or death.

The first great triumph of medical science was Jenner's discovery of vaccination against smallpox in 1796. And yet this was not the work of chemistry. True, the changes effected in the blood of the patient are chemical, but neither their nature nor the composition of the active principle is understood. Such is also true of the vaccines and antitoxins developed in more recent years. Here is a vast field for research in which the chemist must work hand in hand with the pharmacologist, who determines the effects of drugs upon living organisms, and with the practising physician. In times past, there has been little cooperation between the chemist and those who administer the products of the laboratory in the alleviation of human suffering. Even to-day this lack is all too manifest. Davy discovered the anesthetic properties of nitrous oxide, or "laughing gas," in the first years of the last century, but nearly four decades passed before Dr. Horace Wells, a dentist, of Hartford, Connecticut, utilized its beneficent properties as a destroyer of pain in the extraction of teeth. Five centuries elapsed between the discovery of ether and the coming of that never-to-be-forgotten October 16, 1846, when a young man in the Massachusetts General Hospital, awaking from a deep sleep, in which he had undergone what would formerly have been an excruciatingly painful surgical operation, exclaimed, "I have felt no pain." No wonder Doctor Bigelow, who witnessed this miracle of medical science, said, "I have seen something to-day that will go round the world." *The Future Independence and Progress of American Medicine in the Age of Chemistry* says, "Magnesium sulphate was well known to chemists in 1694, but two hundred years elapsed before it was learned what great relief it gave in lockjaw, burns and strychnine poisoning. Twenty-three years elapsed between the discovery of amyl nitrite by the chemist and the discovery of its medicinal properties by the physician; during this period tens of thousands of human beings suffered the tortures of agina pectoris because the chemist, pharmacologist and physician were not working together." Other examples might be cited. Coal-tar dyes had been known and thousands of them artificially prepared for half a century and more before the antiseptic properties of some of them were discovered and utilized. Indeed, the chemist and physician are just beginning to realize what a fruitful pathway of investigation this discovery has opened. Doubtless, concealed within drugs already well known to chemistry, lurks the death sentence of many an insidious foe to human health. Chemistry as never before is becoming the handmaid of medical progress.

In the seventies of the last century, the great Pasteur caught the vision of preventive medicine. "Perhaps," he said, "I can save more lives than were lost in the

Franco-Prussian War.'' Already, Lord Lister, the real father of antiseptic surgery, had won great triumphs in the hospitals across the Channel. For the first time, he employed drugs to cleanse a wound and keep it free from the entrance of infectious germs. Chemistry and medical practise, under the direction of intelligent leadership, were at last joining hands. And now Pasteur, acknowledged master in the field of chemistry, entered the French hospitals and, snatching the instruments from the hands of the attending surgeons, passed them through the sterilizing flame. Aghast at the faddish notions of this crazy old paralytic, the physicians of France opposed his innovations. But he would not be thrust aside. The appalling loss of life must cease. Gangrene, caused as he believed by air-borne germs, must no longer be permitted to entail such enormous sacrifices. In the antiseptic drugs of chemistry, he saw the means of relieving untold suffering and saving thousands of precious lives. He forced the use of sterilized bandages and with all the energy of his passionate soul strove to overcome the skepticism of the medical profession. How well he succeeded, every hospital in the world now testifies. It was the most signal and sweeping triumph of chemical knowledge deliberately applied to the redemption of mankind from disease and pain that men had ever seen. Even in his pioneer work in combating anthrax and rabies, it was his training in the chemical laboratory that made possible his conquests. These victories inspired the more recent achievements in checking the ravages of such maladies as cholera, tetanus, diphtheria, typhoid, yellow fever, malaria, bubonic plague, leprosy, scarlet fever and other ills.

Thus did Pasteur, the chemist, found the new branch of medicine known as serum-therapy by which antitoxins are developed in the blood of animals for inoculation against disease. To-day, no less than yesterday, the world needs his message: "Take interest, I implore you, in those sacred dwellings which one designates by the expressive term: Laboratories. Demand that they be multiplied, that they be adorned; these are the temples of the future—temples of well-being and of happiness. There it is that humanity grows greater, stronger, better."

THE HUNT FOR A SPECIFIC

In the whole history of medical science but two absolute specifics have ever been found. They are quinine for malaria and the famous "606," better known as salvarsan, which makes war on the trypanasomes responsible for African sleeping sickness and in particular annihilates the insidious microbe which produces the loathsome disease of syphilis. A specific is a drug which delivers a knockout blow to the species of microbe causing some particular disease of the human family. Let us see how Paul Ehrlich came upon the second of these and in so doing opened up avenues of discovery which are only just beginning to be followed.

No more picturesque figure has ever appeared among research workers than this German physician and chemist, walking encyclopedia of scientific information, possessed of a notion so absurd that some called him crazy, searching for a remedy with which to slaughter a microbe which he did not know existed, and almost by accident stumbling upon the greatest chemico-medical discovery made in half a century. Yet, this was Paul Ehrlich, who for two decades followed a trail which at nearly every step of the way seemed like a blind alley.

One day in the eighties of the last century, this German doctor, for Ehrlich was a physician by profession, conceived the idea of injecting a dyestuff into the blood-stream of a living animal. Into the ear vein of a rabbit, he shot a little of his favorite dye, methylene blue. To his amazement, the dye coursed through the blood of the creature, staining nothing but the ends of the nerve fibers. It was this selective action of the dye in staining just one tissue out of hundreds which started Ehrlich on his great quest. And yet the idea was at first vague and ill-defined. "Suppose," he mused, "I could find a dye which would select for death the microbes in the human system, but leave the tissues unharmed." Could he bring this dream to pass, he would have the specific of the ages, something approaching in potency the Philosopher's Stone of the alchemists. From the enchantment of that idea, he never escaped, and step by step it led him to his great triumph.

For a time, he worked in the laboratory of Robert Koch, famed for his discovery of the tubercular bacillus, but it was always with dyes,—dyes and mice. Yes, and guinea pigs too. Droves of these martyrs in the conquest of disease marched to their deaths that Ehrlich might learn the ways of microbes and mayhap hit upon the magic that would pronounce their doom. Books, he read without end, whole libraries of them, and he forgot nothing. One day, he read of the work of the French scientist, Alphones Laveran, upon trypanasomes. Just why this particular microbe, so beautifully adapted to the accomplishment of his final victory, should have fired his imagination, it is impossible to say. We may call it the hand of destiny or a happy stroke of fate. However that may be, Ehrlich proceeded to import from Paris an afflicted guinea pig and to transfer drops of its blood, swarming with trypanasomes, to the veins of healthy mice. Then, he injected into the blood of the mice dyes, scores of them. He watched them as the little beasts turned first one color and then another. But they always died, every mouse, with the most perfect regularity. Upon Ehrlich's gay colors, the trypanasomes seemed to thrive. Apparently, he was getting nowhere.

Then, this German doctor began to alter his dyes, to change their chemical architecture. At length, he hit upon Trypan Red and, injecting it into the blood of a mouse sick with trypanasomes, slew the microbes and saved the mouse. Ehrlich believed himself on the flood-tide of success. But his hope was of short duration. Trypan Red was not a specific. Some mice got worse. Others recovered for a time, but the trypanasomes eventually got the best of them. Victory still refused to perch upon the banner of this indefatigable searcher for a selective microbe poison.

And now Frau Speyer, of Frankfort, builds for Ehrlich a large laboratory, equips it with all that money can provide, and surrounds him with a small army of chemists. Never was a scientist engaged in a great search more favorably situated. And he set his chemists to altering old dyes and making new ones. The idea of a specific dye for a specific microbe never left him. One day, he read of a new drug known as "Atoxyl." Ehrlich learned that already it had been tried on men and mice afflicted with sleeping sickness. In some way he became possessed with the passionate belief that this compound might be so altered as to yield the long-sought specific for trypanasomes. His whole army of chemists was directed to this end. Two years passed, and six hundred and five alterations of atoxyl had been made. Six hundred and five derivatives of this arsenic compound, for arsenic is the strategic element in atoxyl, had been tried on sick mice. Some it cured, only to bring on a worse malady or to afflict the little beasts with an insane propensity to dance. And at length the trypanasomes seemed to become immune to the treatment. Failure, utter and ignominious, seemed to stalk in that laboratory. More than twenty years had passed since Ehrlich received his great idea, and success was still in the future.

Then, in 1909, after six hundred and five compounds of arsenic made in the new laboratory had proved failures, "606" was born. It killed trypanasomes in mice with the utmost expedition, and it left no trace of after effects. The immediate purpose of his quest had been achieved, but a larger one thrust itself into the foreground. Ehrlich had read of Schaudinn's discovery that trypanasomes are closely related to spirochetes, the microbes which cause syphilis. The cure of this loathsome malady had been utterly foreign to his thought, but the possibility of accomplishing so great a miracle of applied chemistry now set the brain of this great researcher in a fresh whirl. In August, 1909, he inoculated with his new remedy chickens and rabbits whose blood swarmed with the spirochete microbes. The results were seemingly miraculous. Within twenty-four hours every microbe had met its death. Not a one survived in the blood of these animals.

Ehrlich stood on the threshold of a great victory. Still he hesitated. Would a specific fatal to microbes in the blood of animals prove the same in men? Human life was precious, but there could be no turning back. Ehrlich took the chance, and, as all the world knows, won,—yes won gloriously. In arsphenamine, or salvarsan, he had found a specific for the most insidious foe of humankind. It has been estimated that there are over ten million cases of this disease, in its various forms, in the United States alone, and in 1925 there were manufactured and sold here about two million doses of the specific, valued at a million and a half dollars.

And so the hunt for a specific came to an end. At last Ehrlich had found a chemical compound, or rather fashioned one, which, injected into the blood-stream, would course through the veins, meting out death to a particular species of microbes which prey upon human health, and yet doing no injury to the tissues. Cures were immediate and of such astounding character as to appear to be miraculous. Why, this selective property of the drug is a mystery. And why it will destroy one tribe of microbes and have no effect upon all others is also a mystery. But scientists can be content to remain in ignorance upon these points, if the specific will deliver the knockout blow to these microscopic enemies of men, and salvarsan does this in almost one hundred per cent. of the cases. Occasionally, occurs the exception that proves the rule. Again, no one knows why.

This search for specifics is one of the chief goals of chemistry in the field of medicine. We have vaccines, antitoxins, and near-specifics, which accomplish marvels in combating infectious diseases, but the drug which proves to be a specific remedy for a specific brand of microbes is known in only the two cases mentioned. That chemistry can and will find or prepare others, there can be no shadow of doubt.

A NEW TRAIL TO FOLLOW

The work of Paul Ehrlich, who, though beaten on a score of battle-fields, refused to surrender and thereby won a noble triumph for himself and suffering mortals, opened new avenues of research, which are only just beginning to bear fruit. This use of aniline dyes as powerful antiseptics and selective poisons for infectious microbes has presented chemistry with a fresh method of attack. Indeed, this brilliant therapeutic discovery of salvarsan founded a new science.

The astounding success of Ehrlich's achievement painted rainbow visions of possibilities in this field. To Ehrlich the problem reduced itself to marvelously simple terms. It became only a matter of preparing a chemical substance, death-dealing to a particular brand of invading microbes, but harmless to the body tissues. As we have seen, his plan of operations was to start with some compound whose properties appeared promising and then to alter the architecture of the molecule of this substance, step by step, until the desired result was attained. It may be that no other chemist has had the perseverance of Ehrlich, but certain it is that no other typical specific has been prepared by this method. And yet brilliant results have already been achieved.

Research in this field has brought to light the highly antiseptic properties of a number of drugs. Chief among these are mercurochrome, acriflavine, brilliant green, gentian violet, and acriviolet. In mercurochrome, the chemist sought to combine mercury, a powerful but weakly penetrating antiseptic, with fluorescein, a highly penetrating and non-irritating dye. The result was a notable success. The combination has proved to be wonderfully efficient, owing to its strong germicidal powers, to the ease with which it penetrates the tissues, and its absence of irritating qualities. It has found wide use in the treatment of infections of the mucous membranes of the eye, of the bladder, and of the pelvis of the kidney. Encouraged by these results, the drug began to be used in the more difficult treatment of cases of blood poisoning, injected directly into the veins. In commenting upon this use, Young and Hill, of the Johns Hopkins Medical School, say: "The mercurochrome cases include two cases of septicemia (blood poisoning)—both desperate cases—in which cure was effected and the blood sterilized by intravenous injection of mercurochrome. The results were almost miraculous, the patients being verily snatched from the jaws of death." Although these workers with the new antiseptic report five other cases equally convincing, they warn the medical profession that much more will need to be accomplished before physicians and surgeons may proceed with certainty in the use of the drug. Still, there can be no question that the chemist has scored a genuine victory which promises much for the future.

Gentian violet, another of the five dyes mentioned above, has much to its credit. Dr. John W. Churchman, of the Cornell University Medical College, who discovered the antiseptic properties of the dye, reports its use upon a boy, brought to the hospital two weeks after an elevator accident which had left him with "a dirty granulating wound near the left knee cap, a knee joint full of pus, and a comminuted fracture of the patella." Without being able to remove the infection from the knee joint, it would be impossible to suture (unite) the fractured patella, thus leaving a permanent deformity. At least, it would be impossible to attempt to do so without great risk. Thanks, however, to gentian violet, the surgeons were able to open up the joint and sterilize it before suturing. The result was a perfect union and a normal leg. Gentian violet has also been used in other similar cases with equal success. In army hospitals, it was used to paint amputation stumps, thus preventing infection from diphtheria bacilli. Young and Hill give this added testimony: "The five cases treated by gentian violet comprise just as desperate cases as some of those treated by mercurochrome, and gave just as brilliant results."

Acriflavine proved to be a boon to thousands of sufferers from suppurating wounds in both armies during the Great War. It possesses remarkable antiseptic properties and is non-irritating to the tissues, besides being even more effective in the presence of a serum than in its absence. It in no way interferes with the healing action of the white blood corpuscles, and experimentation is now going on regarding its internal use. It has found use, too, in the treatment of gonorrhea.

Rivanol, a newer dye developed in foreign laboratories, has accomplished much as an antiseptic for internal use. In nine late cases of appendicitis reported by the German surgeon Katzenstein, after the operation and surgical cleansing, a solution of the dye was introduced into the peritoneum and the wound closed. Every patient recovered, whereas in similar cases without the use of the dye death invariably ensued. This dye so effectively destroys the action of the armies of invading germs that the white corpuscles, the body's own soldiers against infection, are given a chance to vanquish the enemy.

We must not forget that these blessings to hosts of sufferers are the products of the chemist and the laboratory. They are organic compounds, prepared from black, foul-smelling coal-tar as a result of the fundamental researches in this field of such chemists as Perkin, Kekulé and van't Hoff. These men took the uncertainty out of molecular architecture and made possible the altering of old compounds and the invention of new ones. Without this exact science, the preparation of healing remedies would still be largely the hit-and-miss guesswork of the alchemistic laboratory.

The preparation by Professor Treat B. Johnson, of Yale University, of hexyl-resorcinol, an antiseptic fifty times more powerful than carbolic acid, is a notable triumph of modern medicine and a capital example of applied chemistry deliberately directed toward the accomplishment of a definite purpose. Professor Johnson began the search in 1913 and brought it to a successful conclusion a dozen years later. His method was the perfectly logical one of the trained chemist. Carbolic acid, known to the chemist as phenol, and resorcinol, a dyestuff, are both derivatives of benzene, the compound consisting chiefly of a ring of six carbon atoms, whose formula Kekulé worked out a half-century ago. Now, Professor Johnson wished to build an antiseptic which might be taken internally, destroying the insidious microscopic foes of the human organism and yet doing so without injury to the body. He began by attaching a side chain of carbon atoms to one of the carbon atoms of the benzene ring, which forms the central feature of resorcinol and of carbolic acid alike. He continued to lengthen this chain by the addition of successive carbon atoms, each time obtaining a new compound, the antiseptic properties of which he tested and compared with those of carbolic acid. When six atoms had been added, he obtained a very powerful antiseptic. With additional atoms, its effectiveness fell off. Since the new compound was a derivative of resorcinol and contained in the side chain six carbon atoms, its logical name became hexyl-resorcinol. Fifty times as powerful as phenol and yet entirely harmless to the body tissues, this new antiseptic may be taken through the mouth, thence it passes out through the kidneys, thus sterilizing portions of the body difficult of access to earlier antiseptic agents. A by-product of this investigation was butyl-resorcinol, a derivative with four atoms in the side chain and about half as powerful.

In speaking of the ideal antiseptic, one which may be used either for surface infections or injected directly into the blood-stream, of deep penetrating power and yet without injury to body cells as well as being quickly eliminated when its work is done, Dr. John W. Churchman says, "It would, of course, be fatuous to hope and rash to predict that any one substance will ever be found combining all these desirable qualities. Yet the fact that investigation has actually succeeded in overcoming some of the apparently insuperable difficulties, and in providing substances which in some respects begin to approach our ideal, justifies a certain optimism as to the remaining obstacles." To overcome these obstacles must be the work of the research chemist.

Supplementing salvarsan and neo-arsphenamine, the original arsenic compounds prepared by Ehrlich and his fellow-workers, tryparsamide and sulpharsphenamine, two additional drugs for treatment of late cases of syphilis, have been prepared in this country, the one at the Rockefeller Institute and the other at the Hygienic Laboratory. Tryparsamide, too, has been found to be an effective agent in the treatment of African sleeping sickness. "Bayer 205," prepared as its name indicates after the fashion of Ehrlich's "606," in its annihilation of the trypanasomes responsible for this dread malady of tropical Africa, comes near to being a specific. What this means in making possible the opening up of large areas of the Dark Continent to colonization by white men is a measure in some degree of the debt the world owes to chemistry for this discovery.

And so this hunt of Paul Ehrlich for a specific microbe killer has carried the world a long way forward in its conquest of disease. But science has only entered upon the trail which he blazed. Many main thoroughfares and innumerable side paths remain to be explored. In particular chemistry must find means of combating the plant-like bacteria which infect the human system, as it has done the protozoic, or animal-like, microbes causing such diseases as malaria, syphilis and African sleeping sickness.

Louis Pasteur

Dr. F. G. Banting

Together with a student assistant, Mr. C. H. Best, Dr. Banting first obtained insulin in sufficient purity for use in cases of human diabetes

Dr. J. J. R. MacLeod and Dr. G. H. A. Cowes

In the laboratory of Dr. MacLeod, of Toronto University, and with the aid of his advice, Dr. Banting and Mr. Best worked. Under the direction of Dr. Clowes, of Eli Lilly and Company, the first commercially available insulin in the United States was prepared

Dr. John J. Abel, of Johns Hopkins University

Dr. Abel has been foremost in the isolation and purification of the active principles of the endocrine (ductless) glands. In 1927 the American Chemical Society awarded him the Willard Gibbs Medal in recognition of his recent work in preparing for the first time

CHEMICAL LABORATORIES OF THE DUCTLESS GLANDS

The average individual never suspects that he is a walking chemical plant, the vital functioning of which depends upon the manufacture of certain active principles in the chemical laboratories of the ductless glands, scattered here and there throughout the body and pouring their life-controlling secretions directly into the blood-stream without making use of the tube-like ducts of other glands. Most people do not know that they have any ductless glands. Even the physician did not suspect their existence until a little more than a half-century ago, while a knowledge of their tremendous importance to normal health is a matter of yesterday and to-day. These obscure but vastly significant members of the human organism include the thyroid, parathyroid, thymus, gonads, pineal, pituitary and adrenals, besides the pancreas, which, like the gonads, has duct as well as ductless functions. The secretions of these glands are known as *hormones,* which means exciters, and they are chemical in nature, being poisonous drugs of the most remarkable potency.

We have all read of the deadly poison with which the natives of the Upper Amazon tip their arrows, a poison so violent that the slightest scratch will kill the largest animal in a few minutes. This poison is adrenalin, obtained from the glands of a certain toad. In man, the adrenals, or suprarenal bodies, located one just above either kidney, secrete this chemical and pour it into the blood in the proportion of one part to a billion parts of arterial blood. Its larger secretion in times of emergency stimulates the whole system to action. It excites the nerv-

ous system, releases energy, steels the muscles, stops the
secretion of saliva and other digestive juices, quickens
the heart beat, dilates the eyes, opens the sweat glands,
and makes the hair stand on end. It bucks us up and
makes us ready for a fight. Under its influence, brave
men rise to lofty heights and cowards take on the qualities of heroes. It is a potent factor in producing the
psychology of the mob. The adrenals have been rightly
named "glands of fear and courage."

Now the chemist comes upon the scene. In 1897, Dr.
John J. Abel, of Johns Hopkins University, succeeded in
isolating the active principle of these glands, adrenalin,
in the form of a derivative. The Japanese chemist
J. Takamine later obtained the principle itself in pure
crystal form. As a result, it is now an article of manufacture and may be purchased at any pharmacy. Let us
see what some of the benefits of these discoveries have
been to suffering men and women.

Injected directly into the blood in extremely dilute
solution, adrenalin produces much the same effects as
does its natural production in times of emergency combat. Applied externally to a bleeding wound, it stops the
hemorrhage instantly, thus enabling the surgeon to perform bloodless operations. Mixed with a local anesthetic,
it constricts the blood-vessels, preventing loss of the
anesthetic and making possible the use of a smaller quantity with less danger of poisoning effects. It stimulates
and strengthens the heart action, thus making it invaluable in the treatment of pneumonia and in preparing
greatly weakened or aged patients to withstand the
shock of an operation. One of its greatest blessings is to
be found in its power to check almost immediately the

spasms of acute bronchial asthma. And yet, it was not until 1855 that Dr. Thomas Addison, first among physicians, suspected any influence whatever of the adrenal glands upon the human organism. Without the chemist, the blessings arising from the artificial administration of their secretion would be wholly unknown.

Under-activity of the thyroid gland from birth results in a form of inherited idiocy known as cretinism. When the thyroid gland of an adult goes on strike, a corresponding malady known as myxedema converts an otherwise normal individual into what Sir William Osler has described as a "poor, feeble-minded, toad-like caricature of humanity." The secretion of this gland "regulates the speed of living" and spells the difference between a hideous form of imbecility and a sane and normal life.

Until quite recently such conditions were incurable. These miserably unfortunate members of society slowly and painfully followed their forlorn pathways to the welcome grave. But to-day, the chemist has largely changed the picture. In 1918, Dr. E. C. Kendall, of the Mayo Foundation, isolated thyroxin, the active principle of the thyroid gland, a crystalline substance so exceedingly energetic that the occasional administration of a dose of a minute fraction of a grain will cure cases of cretinism and myxedema. Even before this, thyroid extract had been used with similar results. In 1920, the first patient treated for myxedema died. For twenty-nine years, daily doses of the extract had stood between him and a living death. In his darkened brain the light of reason had been made to shine once more and a coarse, stupid "caricature of humanity" had been restored to his birthright. Many similar miracles have been wrought.

Word now comes from England that synthetic thyroxin is an accomplished fact. Dr. C. R. Huntington, of the University College Hospital, London, and Professor George Barger, of Edinburgh, using coal-tar products and iodine as starting points, have prepared a substance said to be fully as effective upon human beings as the thyroxin obtained from the gland. A half ounce of thyroxin will keep a man who has no thyroid gland normal for seventy-five years, but because of its great scarcity heretofore the drug has been more precious than diamonds. Now, we may be sure this will all be changed. This reward comes after ten years of search by organic chemists throughout the world.

The active element in thyroxin seems to be iodine. A deficiency of iodine in the diet is thought to give rise to an enlargement of the thyroid gland known as simple goiter. In many instances, the artificial administration of iodine compounds has been found to correct this disturbance. However, the dose is exceedingly minute and it should always be taken under the direction of a competent physician.

In pairs, located on each side of the thyroid, are minute, seemingly unimportant structures, but little larger than grains of wheat. They are the parathyroids. In the beginnings of modern surgery, these glands were occasionally removed by accident. But the unfortunate victim always died, a martyr to science, and death was accompanied by a form of convulsions known as tetany.

Rickety children are subject to a form of tetany, owing to a deficiency of lime, or calcium, in the system. It may usually be relieved by injecting a solution of a calcium compound into the blood-stream. These facts make it probable that the parathyroids govern the calcium content of the blood. In any case, the active principle manufactured in this quartet of chemical laboratories is absolutely essential to life.

In 1925, Dr. J. D. Collip, of Alberta, Canada, succeeded in obtaining from the parathyroids an extract containing parathyrin, the hormone of these glands. The determination of its composition and the discovery of a method of artificial preparation are the next steps. Already, the administration of the extract has been found to relieve convulsions both in adults and in children. Dogs whose parathyroids have been removed may be kept alive almost indefinitely with the aid of the drug.

The parathyroid hormone, too, seems to have something to do with the coagulation of the blood. Underactivity of these glands and therefore an insufficiency of calcium in the blood prevents quick coagulation and in case of operation or accident may result in death from bleeding. Actual experiments indicate that the use of the extract will relieve these unfortunates from a very real menace to life.

Other disturbances may be traced to parathyroid deficiency. Their correction waits upon the chemical preparation and purification of the active hormone for general administration.

What has the discovery of insulin meant? In the United States alone, a half-million sufferers from the inactivity of the ductless portion of the pancreas can tell a wonderful story. These diabetic victims, condemned to an innutritious and unpalatable diet, robbed of much of the joy of living, subject to progressive physical weakness, and with an insidious form of death ever lurking in the foreground, have been removed of all their disabilities through the magic of this product of the laboratory. True, they can not escape the use of the drug. As yet science has found no way of stimulating into renewed activity the "Islands of Langerhans," the ductless portion of the pancreas, in which insulin is naturally produced in the body. Still, as compared with the original sentence, the commuted form seems like a heavenly dispensation.

For many years, it has been known that sugar and similar chemical compounds called carbohydrates are converted by the normal activity of the liver into glycogen, or animal starch, which is stored there for future use. When need arises this starch is reconverted into sugar and released to the blood to supply through oxidation the energy needed by the human system, for sugar is one of the finest and most essential forms of bodily fuel. But how does the liver know when to make the change from starch back to sugar? It must receive some stimulus, and it does. The controlled liberation of the starch in the form of sugar is due to the secretion of the hormone of insulin by the ductless portion of the pancreatic gland. When the amount of insulin is insufficient or absent, there is no control, and the liver gives up the sugar so rapidly that the tissues can neither store it nor oxidize it. The result is that the sugar unutilized passes off through the kidneys as waste, and the body is deprived of the energy it should receive from its most nourishing and vital form of food. The physical effects of this condition constitute diabetes.

In 1922, word went round the world that two physicians, Banting and Best, working in the laboratory of

Doctor MacLeod, of the University of Toronto, had isolated the active hormone of the islands of Langerhans, an accomplishment which many of the best members of the medical profession had been seeking for years. Some had almost reached the goal. At the time the investigation was begun, no one was sure that such a hormone exists. It was purely hypothetical. But in the pancreatic glands of normal dogs it was found. In 1926, Dr. John J. Abel announced that he had succeeded in taking the next essential step, that of preparing the hormone in pure crystal form. Now comes the word from Germany that three workers in the clinic of Minkowski, one of the early investigators in this field, have obtained a synthetic chemical substance, named synthalin, which possesses the essential properties of insulin. Once more chemistry has come to the fore with important advances in medical science. And there was no element of luck or chance in these triumphs. They were wholly the result of definite and deliberate efforts directed toward specific ends.

To-day, thousands of diabetic patients administer insulin to themselves, under competent medical direction. And what are the results? It reduces the sugar in the blood and excretions to the normal quantity; it permits these patients to eat freely of the hitherto prohibited kinds of food and the system to assimilate it, thus supplying that fund of abundant energy essential to healthful existence; it restores to normal the physical and mental activity; and it removes entirely every trace of the dread acidosis characteristic of the later stages of the disease with its resulting coma and death. Still, insulin is not a cure. The patient is a slave, albeit a willing one, to its use. The goal now is to restore to normal activity in these sufferers the ductless portion of the pancreas. But, though it never be attained, chemistry has already brought new tenure of life to countless thousands under sentence of death, a victory which must give the world pause.

Hidden away at the base of the skull, in a little bony receptacle, is the pituitary gland, which, despite its diminutive proportions, is responsible alike for the giant of the side-show at the circus and the typical fat boy,—of infantile sexual development, large of size, flabby-muscled, and fat-chested,—so well depicted in Joe of Dickens' *Pickwick Papers.* Divided into two portions, the over-activity of the anterior lobe results in such monstrosities of physical growth as have filled the long line of the world's famous giants, while the misfunctioning of the posterior lobe interferes with the normal development of the sex organs and impairs the action of vital processes. From the latter, Abel and Rouiller have isolated an extract so powerful that, when diluted with twenty billion parts of water, the active hormone contained in it will cause muscle suspended in the solution to contract. They have carried the chemical purification of the hormone so far that their product is twelve hundred and fifty times as powerful as the drug used as a standard of comparison. It is of especial value in overcoming lack of muscular tonicity and the accompanying hemorrhage following childbirth. It stimulates muscular action of the intestines after abdominal operations and increases the blood pressure in cases of shock. Inhaled in dilute solution through the nostrils, it has an antidiuretic action upon the kidneys. But in all cases the dose is exceedingly minute. Among other distressing effects of the misbehavior of this gland is a form of epileptic fits. However, the administration of artificially prepared pituitary substances has been found to give great relief, as well as reinvigorating the whole system. The isolation and synthesis of other hormones of this gland are tasks awaiting the chemical researcher. When that day arrives, it is safe to predict that many a human derelict amid the flotsam and jetsam of the social stream may be redeemed for a life of useful service.

Probably the most important of the secretions of the ductless glands are those of the gonads, or sex glands. One of the immediate problems of chemical investigation is their isolation and artificial preparation. Already, some success has been reported in this field by Doctors Allen and Doisy, of St. Louis. The isolation and purification of the female hormone is said to be nearing completion. It is believed that the administration of these purified principles by the skilled practitioner will have a profound influence in preserving the physical and mental vigor of the race. There is no hope of prolonging the natural period of life, but it is thought that this discovery will lengthen the span of years within which men and women will remain fit for active service in business and intellectual pursuits. Old age will be held in abeyance. When it does come, however, one's decline will be rapid and abrupt to the setting of life's sun. In commenting upon this phase of chemical research, Dr. Julius Stieglitz, of Chicago University, said: "There is not the least doubt scientifically that there are chemical principles of the gonads which find their way into the blood and which have an extraordinary effect on the working power, the fighting ability, the vitality of the mind of the

individual, secondary effects of these powerful hormones, developed naturally enough in the course of
evolution.'' If, through their isolation, the chemist can
supply the means of prolonging by a decade the active
period of productivity of a genius, the gain to society
will be incalculable. Let us hope that this may be one of
the early triumphs to the credit of chemistry in this
field.

The other ductless glands present equally fertile
fields for research. Indeed, the harvest only waits the
coming of the skilled reaper.

VITAMINS

In the dictionaries of little more than a decade ago,
the term vitamin is wholly wanting. Our grandfathers
were vaguely aware that certain diseases such as scurvy
and beri-beri were in some way related to a deficiency in
the diet, but it was all a baffling mystery. They did not
know that normal growth and often life itself hinges
upon the presence in the food of certain minute but all-
important chemical principles, which science to-day
designates as vitamins. But, although we recognize the
vital activity of these principles and have named four of
them vitamins A, B, C and D, the mode of their functioning is still largely veiled in mystery, as is also their
true chemical nature. A is the growth-promoting
vitamin; B prevents beri-beri; lack of vitamin C causes
scurvy; and D is intimately associated with the lime and
phosphorus assimilation of the system and a chief factor
in the cause and cure of rickets. Although present in a
well-balanced diet in exceedingly small quantities, the

vitamins are as essential to health as ignition is to a gasoline motor.

Probably more is known regarding the action of vitamin D than of any of the others. This vitamin is found abundantly in cod-liver oil, in certain other fats and in green vegetables. The facts regarding it were ascertained through a study of the cause and prevention of rickets in young children. As has been known for generations, this disease is due to the inability of the system to appropriate the calcium and phosphorus in the blood for the building of bone. Since eighty-five per cent. of the mineral matter of bone is calcium phosphate, this inability manifests itself in bones which are soft and pliable, thus frequently resulting in such deformities as knock-knee, bow leg, hunch back, and curvature of the spine. In chickens it produces "weak legs" and in pigs "rheumatism," which is simply a mineral deficiency in the bones.

Now it was well known that there might be an abundance of calcium and phosphorus in the diet, and still rickets would appear. The vital something essential to the bodily assimilation of these elements was lacking. Investigation did not seem to warrant the assumption that the disease is an inherited one. Even though it were, that would not explain its cause. Gradually, certain facts became apparent: rickets is more prevalent in winter than in summer; the shut-in children of the cities are more susceptible to it than those in the country; the children of savages are free from the disease, as are also those of Eskimos; and sunlight and cod-liver oil will cure it.

Early in the present century, Hess and Unger, of

Columbia University, proved experimentally that sunlight, that is, sunlight in the open air, unfiltered by passage through glass, will cure rickets. It is now known that it is the ultraviolet rays of the light which effect the cure. Irradiation of rachitic children by the ultraviolet rays of the quartz mercury-vapor lamp will produce equally beneficial results. In passing, let it be said that while ordinary glass is opaque to these rays, quartz glass, one of the notable triumphs of recent chemical research, is transparent to them. Thus this victory in the treatment of a long-standing disease is dependent upon an important chemical factor.

It was also found that certain foods have a curative effect upon rickets. Chief of these is cod-liver oil. Later investigation disclosed that this oil is rich in vitamins A and D. For a time, it was thought that but one vitamin was present in the oil. However, Dr. E. A. Park and his associates at Johns Hopkins found it possible by partial oxidation to destroy the growth-promoting properties of the oil without lessening its efficiency in curing rickets. That proved the presence of the second vitamin, and now an extract containing both is upon the market.

Dr. W. T. Bovie recently carried out elaborate experiments upon two hundred and twenty-five chickens at the Biophysics Laboratory of Harvard University. A rickets-producing diet was fed to all of them. This was followed with three different treatments. To one group was fed cod-liver oil, mixed with the food. The second group was given constant access to the outdoors and sunlight, while the third group was irradiated for fifteen minutes each day with ultraviolet rays from a mercury vapor quartz lamp. In each case the rickets was cured, although the chickens fed on the distasteful cod-liver oil ate less food and did not thrive so well. Similar experiments made by Dr. Harriette Chick, of England, upon babies in Vienna following the Great War produced equally striking results.

Miller, Eddy and Seidell have obtained extracts from yeast products rich in vitamins B and D. These extracts are given the general name of "bios," and in one instance the chemical composition, formula and melting point have been determined. An exceedingly small daily dose of this substance fed to rats whose food was lacking in vitamin B resulted in improved growth. Here is a rich field for chemical research. Investigation has only begun. These vitamins in every instance must be isolated and prepared artificially for administration by the medical profession. When the chemist has solved these problems and made the vitamins universally available, ailments now little understood will become readily amenable to treatment.

Observations of the last year have shown that while sunlight or ultraviolet rays are essential to the formation of vitamin B, they destroy vitamin A, but have no effect upon vitamin D.

Mention has already been made of the close relation between the activity of the parathyroid glands and the assimilation of calcium and phosphorus in the system. Still, administration of parathyroid extract will not cure rickets. Vitamin D and ultraviolet rays hold the key to this citadel of bodily "metabolism." But just how they work is still a mystery, another obscure process upon which chemistry must shed the light of knowledge.

SOME RECENT ACHIEVEMENTS

The loss for several seasons in succession of large quantities of carnations shipped into Chicago and kept in greenhouses has led to the discovery of a new anesthetic for modern surgery. The faint odor of illuminating gas in one of the greenhouses led a florist to suspect that this might have something to do with the wholesale killing of buds and the causing of open flowers to "go to sleep." The removal of a leaky pipe solved the difficulty. In the meantime Doctors Knight and Crocker, plant physiologists of Chicago University, had become interested in the problem. They soon traced the poisoning effects to the presence of minute quantities of ethylene, a gas which has been known since 1795. So small a quantity as one part in two million parts of air was found to cause carnations to close in twelve hours. At this point, Luckhardt and Carter, two animal physiologists, determined to discover the effect of the gas upon animals. In small amounts it had no effect, but mixed with oxygen in proportions of eighty to eighty-five per cent., it proved to be a wonderful anesthetic. A summary of its physiological action states: "It lacks, or has in only low degree, the bad qualities of ether, chloroform and nitrous oxide. It has no lethal action, does not induce sweating, and produces little nausea or gas pains; one recovers quickly, so quickly, indeed, that incision pains are often still felt. It promises to displace the older anesthetics for many types of surgical operations." Already it has been used in upward of fifty thousand operations in this country alone.

A new anesthetic has just been reported from Berlin.

Its name is "107," which indicates that it is one of those synthetic products arrived at after a large number of deliberate attempts. A press despatch in the *New York Times* states, "The invention is a bromine preparation which is introduced into the intestines through an enema in the form of a solution which produces complete anesthesia in a very short time. . . . Patients treated with the new anesthetic fall into a deep sleep, while the heart, pulse action and blood pressure remain normal. The most important advantage of the discovery Dr. Ernst Unruh stated is the fact that the new anesthetic does not endanger the heart, lungs and nerves, and makes operations possible even in severe cases of pneumonia and advanced tuberculosis." In three hundred tests, it has already proved entirely successful.

Doctors Henderson and Haggard, of Yale, have discovered that the mixture of a few per cent. of carbon dioxide gas with oxygen affords an invaluable means of saving life in the first stages of asphyxiation from carbon monoxide poisoning. In the steel mills, the Henderson-Haggard mixture is proving to be a godsend to these victims of modern industrial practise.

In 1926, there came from Germany the announcement of a new synthetic drug, plasmochin, far more effective than quinine as a specific for malaria. For centuries, quinine has been the standard remedy for this mosquito-borne disease and, until the coming of salvarsan, the only genuine specific known to medical science. Still, some persons are wholly impervious to quinine treatment. While the drug is quickly fatal to certain species of malarial parasites, too, others resist its action. But plasmochin, it is claimed, lets no guilty microbe escape. With its use it is hoped to be able to exterminate every type of malaria germ as effectively as were the fossil animals of early geologic ages. And plasmochin was not an accidental discovery. It is the product of deliberate attempts by German chemists to invent a sure-fire remedy for this scourge of human kind. A progressive campaign directed first against one type of the disease and then another advanced step by step until an artificial specific completely effective, according to German reports, in curing the malaria characteristic of the human species was discovered.

In this connection it is interesting to recall that a few years ago the discovery was made that paresis, a form of progressive paralysis, up to that time regarded as incurable, could be checked by infecting the patient with malaria. The two kinds of microbes could not live side by side in the same blood-stream. Now, plasmochin can be used to rid the system completely of malaria parasites after the other host has been vanquished.

This discovery brings up anew the whole subject of specifics. Why should one drug prove wholly murderous to one form of microbes and perfectly harmless to another? Why should each be so finicky as to require his pet brand of poison? But, that being the case, chemistry must find the fifty-seven favored brands and place them at the disposal of medical science.

For many years, chaulmoogra oil, an "irritating, nauseating natural product," has been used in the Orient in the treatment of leprosy. Chemistry has isolated from this oil pure acids, the essential healing constituents, and combined them with ethyl alcohol to form a new drug, which may be introduced directly into the blood of these unfortunate victims of a loathsome disease. Already, great progress has been made in combating the malady. And now, at the University of Illinois, Dr. Roger Adams has succeeded in synthesizing compounds similar to those in chaulmoogra oil, which are proving to be effective germicides in the treatment of leprosy. Only one who has been literally snatched from a living death by such a scientific triumph can appreciate to the full the debt which society owes to chemical and medical research.

Recently, announcement has come from Dr. Antenor Machado of a new treatment for leprosy, the oil of a Brazilian tree, commonly known as the sapucainha. It is said to be less painful than chaulmoogra oil and to give quite satisfactory results. Undoubtedly, the chemist will be able to improve upon the natural product.

During 1926, Dr. James B. Sumner, assistant professor of biological chemistry at the Cornell Medical College, for the first time isolated an enzyme, obtaining it in pure form as minute octahedral crystals. Now an enzyme, let me hasten to say, is a highly important accelerator of chemical action. Of many different types, enzymes are produced by plants, animals, or microorganisms. An enzyme is a catalyst, which means that it is a substance which will hasten or retard a chemical change without itself being used up. For instance, it is enzymes in yeast which change sugar by fermentation into alcohol and carbon dioxide. Rennin, obtained from the stomachs of calves, affords the stimulus for the chemical change which results in converting milk to cheese. Thrombin is essential to the coagulation of blood. And pepsin, an enzyme of the gastric juice, speeds up the digestion of food, but just why or how it acts, no scientist knows. It is this very ignorance which makes Doctor Sumner's isolation of urease, an enzyme of the jack-bean, so highly important. It gives promise that chemistry may soon be able to prepare artificially these speed regulators of vital bodily functions. Here is a large field for chemical research. The opening wedge has now been driven. The attainment of the goal will reduce to a science the operation of health-determining processes which are now obscured by the shadows of incomplete knowledge.

Chemists took to pieces the molecule of cocaine, consisting of forty-three atoms, and, after determining just which groups are beneficial in producing local anesthesia, they proceeded to build new compounds having all the pain-destroying properties of the original drug without its poisonous effects. Thus, surgery now has at its command procaine, beta-eucaine, apothesine, benzyl alcohol, and similar substances. Chemistry has likewise converted morphine into codeine and dionine, two drugs having the God-given sedative effects of the original but shorn of the curse of its habit-forming properties. In the place of such dangerous sleep-producing compounds as chloral and the sulphonals, chemistry has given us barbital, luminal, adalin and similar hypnotics, safer and less disturbing to the physical system. Luminal, too, is said to be a near-specific in attacks of epilepsy. In combating hookworm, which claims millions of victims throughout the world, chemistry has provided thymol and chenopodium. Cinchopen, an artificial chemical product, has proved its efficiency in the treatment of gout. Theophyllin, another remedy from the chemical laboratory, is a valuable diuretic in kidney troubles.

And so one might proceed, for chemistry is proving to be the very foundation of medical progress. From its constantly growing arsenal of remedies, germicides, and anesthetics, the physician and the surgeon draw the weapons essential to victory in the ages-old battle with disease. A later chapter contains a discussion of synthetic medicinals.

SOME UNSOLVED PROBLEMS

While the spectacular conquest of infectious diseases has meant much to the race and the average expectation of life has been prolonged by fifteen years during the last generation, vast areas of human disaffections remain to be subdued. Dr. Alexis Carrel, of the Rockefeller Institute, in speaking of this situation, not long ago said: "Although the adult individual has much fewer chances of dying from smallpox, cholera, tuberculosis or typhoid fever than fifty years ago, his expectation of reaching the age of seventy-five or eighty has not markedly increased. But he surely has more prospect of being tortured by some form of cancer, afflicted with slow diseases of the kidneys, the circulatory apparatus, the endocrine (ductless) glands, of becoming insane, suffering from nervous diseases, or of making himself miserable by his lack of judgment and his vices. Modern medicine protects him against infections which kill rapidly, but leaves him exposed to the slower and more cruel diseases and to brain deterioration."

Despite this somewhat pessimistic note and the existence of many unsolved problems, progress is sure and certain and it gains momentum with each succeeding decade. Of the great scourges still unconquered, probably all will agree that pneumonia, tuberculosis, cancer, influenza, and the common cold are the most baffling and insidious and take the largest toll of life. The greatest blessing which chemistry could confer upon the race would be the discovery of specifics for all of these. That it may do so, and sooner than we dare predict, is entirely within the range of possibilities.

What do we know about pneumonia? In the first place, science has determined that there is not only one, but four distinct types of this fateful malady. The disease is contagious and spreads from person to person and by contact just as does a cold in the head. The so-called turning-point in a case is signaled by the appearance in the blood of antibodies, or certain immune substances, that is, substances immune to the pneumococci microbes which set free the pneumonia toxin. When a sufficient number of these have formed, the pneumococci can not remain in the blood. In some way these substances make it possible for the white corpuscles, the blood's own soldiers against microbes, to vanquish the invading germs. But each type of pneumonia produces its own species of immune substances.

Now, the logical mode of attack was to prepare in the blood-streams of living animals sera, just as has been done in the cases of other infectious diseases, for injection into the blood of the patient. This has been done, and the serum in any particular case contains immune bodies capable of wrestling with the toxins of more than one kind of pneumonia. The disadvantage in the use of a serum, however, is the difficulty of administering enough, without shock to the patient, to supply sufficient immune substance to turn the tide of battle. And it is right here that chemistry comes in to play its part. It is the problem of the chemist to work out a method of preparing these immune substances artificially in the laboratory, so that in purified and concentrated form they may be administered by the physician with absolute precision and certainty of result. When that time arrives, pneumonia will become as much a conquered disease as are smallpox, diphtheria and scarlet fever now. Much progress has already been made and the future is bright with hope.

By providing an abundance of pure oxygen, chemistry has already made it possible to administer this life-giving gas artificially to pneumonia patients, thus bringing the oxygen concentration of the blood approximately to normal and thereby greatly enhancing the chances of recovery.

During 1926, Dr. Florence B. Seibert, of Chicago University, discovered the chemical compound in tuberculin which is responsible for the skin reaction in persons suffering from tuberculosis. This is probably the most important step yet taken toward an understanding of the chemistry of the great white plague. The preparation of a specific which shall kill the tuberculosis germ without poisoning the tissues of the body is the unattained goal of chemistry in this field. Dr. Albert Calmette, of the Pasteur Institute in Paris, believes that he has developed in ''BCG'' a vaccine which will give immunity to this disease. Should this rainbow of hope be found actually to have its bag of gold at the end, it will become the duty of the chemist to isolate and purify the chemical substance conferring this boon upon mankind, so that it may be universally available for the emancipation of people everywhere from the ravages of this scourge.

To date, the basis for recovery from tuberculosis has been: rest, sunshine, fresh air, nourishing food and the will to live. Just now, a campaign has been launched for the conquest of the disease. As summarized in the *Science News Letter* for January 22, 1927, the objectives of the attack are: "First, knowledge of the chemistry of the tubercule bacillus itself; second, information with respect to the chemistry of the cells of the body that take part in the formation of the tubercules; third, study of the anatomy of the different animals subject to tuberculosis; fourth, precise standards in the X-ray pictures of tuberculosis lesions." Thus, chemistry is to play an important part in the conquest which there is every reason for believing will eventually be made. Economically, tuberculosis presents the most serious disease problem of this planet.

When we come to cancer, probably the most dreaded of human scourges, the three recognized methods of treatment are radium, the X-ray and the surgeon's knife. Another remedy, however, is coming to the fore. Dr. Francis Carter Wood, Director of the Institute of Cancer Research, Columbia University, says, "Only recently another treatment has been devised which adds to the possibility of our occasionally controlling cancer when it is past the skill of the surgeon, and that is the use of lead, a method devised by Professor Blair Bell, of Liverpool. There is no more dramatic scene possible than to see in Professor Bell's clinic well and happy people, now leading useful, active lives, who, without his discovery, would have been, in the normal course of events, dead some years ago. . . . The important thing about lead is not so much that it can cure a few patients now as that it opens up a vast field for future investigation. It is likely that some chemist will invent a compound in which the poisonous quality of the lead, which now makes its use difficult and dangerous, may be concealed behind some harmless chemical with which it is united, thus protecting the body from the dangerous effects while permitting this new chemical to poison the tumor." Again, medicine looks to the chemist, and it is his dream, of course, to discover the long-sought specific.

It should be said in passing that early diagnosis is the most important factor in the treatment of cancer.

Influenza is a wholly unconquered scourge. The microbe causing it has not yet been isolated, and no vaccine nor specific treatment has been discovered. That the discovery of this microbe, however, will be made and that the chemical poison exactly suited to his extermination either is already among the compounds known to the chemist or will be prepared to order when the time arrives, there can be little doubt.

Already, the Chemical Foundation is making war on the common cold. Its purpose is to discover the cause and cure of a disease which exacts a larger toll in time lost among the working population of the United States than does any other malady. The larger portion of the nation's annual drug bill of a half-billion dollars goes for cold remedies.

Most of the approximately fifty thousand drug items on the market are supposed to be weapons against the cold or its effects. In this beneficent research, in which every branch of science is to serve, chemistry will play a leading rôle.

In one important field of medical research, chemistry holds the key to future progress. The chemist must isolate the pure principles of the antitoxins and vaccines used in combating infectious diseases, determine their compositions and learn to prepare them artificially in the laboratory. Then, the perfect precision with which the physician may administer these conquerors of invading germs will take the uncertainty out of much of medical practise. To obtain a certain effect, it will no longer be necessary to cumber the blood-stream with large quantities of undesirable serum or other harmful media of the vital, curative principles required. Results will then be immediate and sure. And this work must be followed by an exhaustive study of the chemistry of the tissues themselves and of the cell of living protoplasm. Every branch of chemistry must be made available in this quest for the cause and cure of disease.

But the chemist can not work alone. The physician, pharmacologist, bacteriologist, pathologist and chemist must pool their knowledge and unite their efforts. And with it all must be money,—money to provide the sinews of war and that freedom for research necessary to throw the search-light of truth into the dark and hidden recesses in which lurk the secrets of the conquests of human disease and suffering.

CHAPTER VIII

Rubber: Yesterday and To-morrow

WHEN PLANTATION RUBBER CAME INTO ITS OWN—UNITED
STATES CENTER OF RUBBER MANUFACTURING—RUBBER PROD-
UCTS—STORY OF GOODYEAR—RUBBER AND THE BICYCLE—
SOURCES OF RUBBER—BRAZIL—BEGINNING OF RUBBER PLANT-
ING IN THE EAST—TAPPING THE RUBBER TREE—BRITISH
RESTRICTIONS—RUBBER INDEPENDENCE FOR AMERICA—THE
GUAYULE SHRUB—RUBBER AND THE CHEMIST—SYNTHETIC
RUBBER—GERMANY'S ACHIEVEMENT—OTHER GOALS THAN
SYNTHETIC RUBBER.

BEFORE me lies a picture. Under it I read, "Brokers
in Front of the Rubber Exchange, in Mincing Lane,
London." In imagination, I behold the frenzied scenes
which occurred there in 1910, when plantation rubber for
the first time came into its own and the world, particularly the British portion of it, went rubber mad, in the
wild speculation, bringing the price to $3.12 a pound and
sending stocks skyrocketing to a premium of five thousand per cent. More than a decade later, I see the rubber market once again ride the whirlwind and the price
mount to $1.21 a pound. And I recall that here in the
United States, where three-fourths of all the rubber
goods used in the world is manufactured, we have more
than a billion and a quarter dollars invested in what has
come to be a basic industry of the nation. The output of

293

tires in 1925 was 59,000,000 and the total value of our rubber products a billion and a half dollars. Our petroleum, automobile and rubber industries, all of them intimately related to bountiful supplies of this raw material of the modern world, represent a combined capitalization of fourteen billion dollars. Our annual gasoline bill is close to two billion dollars, and crude rubber at a value of a half-billion is our largest single import. The consumption of rubber in the United States rose from approximately 100,000 tons in 1913 to about 500,000 tons in 1925, and in the same time the manufacture of automobiles increased from a few hundred thousand a year to three and a half million. During this same period, too, the dealer's cost of a tire dropped from $21.30 to $9.90, and the quality of the tire was twice as good. Confronted with a tremendous world demand for a new commodity, capital and science entered into partnership to meet it. Foremost in bringing about the meteoric progress of the last two decades in this field has been chemistry. When, if ever, synthetic rubber becomes a necessity, the chemist will provide it.

Rubber touches life at innumerable points. More than fifty thousand articles made wholly or in part of rubber are in common use. Not long ago, one of the large rubber companies of this country was working up one hundred and seventy-five tons of rubber a day, and the quantity is doubtless now still larger. From this great mountain of plastic material came fifteen miles of rubber hose, sixty thousand pairs of rubber heels, fifteen thousand pairs of boots and shoes, four thousand water-bottles, eighteen thousand battery jars, eleven thousand golf balls, seven thousand bulbs, twenty thousand tires, nearly a ton of rubber bands, covering for sixty miles of insulated wire, besides thirty thousand other articles. Every year the figures grow. New uses are constantly being discovered. What it means to be without adequate supplies of rubber was keenly brought home to the German nation during the war, when it was cut off from the outside world. Rubber independence has become a factor of vast significance in international politics and in the maintenance of world peace. Without ample supplies of rubber, a nation's place in the sun is insecure. Of its own rubber supply, which is seventy per cent. of world production, the United States produces less than three per cent. The havoc wrought in Germany from lack of rubber was mild in comparison with the distress certain to accompany a rubber famine in America.

MAKING RUBBER USEFUL

No one can ponder the subject of rubber long without allowing his thought to drift back to that memorable day in 1839 when Charles Goodyear wrenched loose from its long-sought hiding-place the secret of vulcanization. Beset by poverty, his footsteps dogged by misfortune, hampered time and again by unjust imprisonment, often baffled but never defeated, Goodyear with an extra large measure of Yankee perseverance pursued his goal until he was able to give to the world the knowledge without which rubber would have remained the useless, sticky and ungovernable mass which he found it.

Even as a lad Goodyear had been interested in rubber, and he was a born inventor. In his father's shop, at New Haven, Connecticut, he learned the fundamentals of mechanics. He once said, "I long to make poor, clumsy things better. They seem to cry out to be improved. I should want to do it even if I did not have to earn a living." When repeatedly imprisoned for debt, he had his bench and tools brought to the jail that he might both earn to support his destitute family and satisfy his bent for invention.

His interest in rubber began with a chance visit to the New York warerooms of the Roxbury Rubber Company. He learned there of the difficulties experienced with rubber goods in hot and cold weather. Rubber softened with the heat of summer and stiffened with the cold of winter. The manager of the company appealed to Goodyear for a remedy. From that moment the thought of rubber crowded every other interest from his mind.

Goodyear followed a dozen trails. Time and again, he seemed on the verge of success, only to be plunged once more into the depths of apparent defeat. Benefiting from the spinning and weaving of his wife, borrowing money from his friends and relatives, pawning his furniture, at one time selling the schoolbooks of his children, Goodyear managed to continue his experiments, working all day and far into the night. With the acid-gas process he seemed almost to have the secret, but the business panic of 1836 swept away the fortune of William Ballard with whom he had formed a partnership, and nothing came of the venture.

Then, Nathaniel Hayward, of Woburn, Massachusetts, taught Goodyear to put sulfur with rubber gum and expose the mixture to the rays of the sun. The process promised to work, but his rubber products were soon up to their old tricks. A batch of mail bags made for the Government became a mass of ruins on the floor of his shop. Undaunted, he worked on. Finally in the winter of 1839 came the lucky accident. One day he brought a mixture of rubber and sulfur in contact with the hot stove of the kitchen, which in his poverty he was using for a workshop. To his surprise, it did not melt but charred like leather. Surely, here was an interesting discovery. He heated another mixture to a high temperature and nailed the stuff to the outside of the door in the intense cold of winter. We may imagine the joy with which he found on the following morning that the rubber had not stiffened. It was still soft and pliable. And it did not melt with heat. Goodyear christened the process vulcanization, and it has been the controlling factor in rubber manufacture from that day to this.

Gradually, the discovery of Goodyear revolutionized the rubber industry, but growth was slow. Up until 1890, the chief products were footwear, water-proof coats, garden hose, and articles of domestic use. Then came the bicycle. Those were the days when this old earth, without knowing it, hovered between two worlds. Horses were still supreme upon the city street and country highway. Men and women had not caught the fever of the twentieth century. They did not have their feet upon the speed accelerator. Distances were still great. Space had not been annihilated. The old-time craftsman still found pride in his work. The wayside motor hospital had not made the country blacksmith shop almost as obsolete as a dinosaur. The divorce courts were less active than now, and possibly the happiness of a quiet life not quite so much at a premium as it seems to-day.

But, as we were saying, the bicycle era came and with it a new demand for rubber. It marked the second stage in the expansion of the rubber industry. The bicycle mania swept the country. Everybody rode the two-wheel "safety,"—young and old, big men, fat men, little men, sedate spinsters in bloomers and sailor hats, boys and girls. This was the brief preliminary to that wild delight in joy-riding which still holds the race in its grasp. For the first time, the manufacture and distribution of tires became a factor in the commercial life of the nation, but it was hardly a foretaste of what was to follow. In 1907, began the meteoric rise of the motor-car and with it came the development of plantation rubber. In that year, the total output of automobile tires in this country was something less than three-quarters of a million. In 1925, it had reached nearly sixty million.

SOURCES OF RUBBER

Until 1910, the world's supply of rubber came chiefly from the jungles bordering the Amazon River of South America. For a time, the Belgian Congo, infamous for the atrocities committed against the rubber gatherers, supplied a portion. But the fine Para rubber, so-called from its port of shipment, dominated the market, and Brazil for many years enjoyed a monopoly of the rubber trade.

Back in the dense, humid, almost impenetrable thickets of the Amazon region grow two trees, the Hevea and Castilloa. Rising at four o'clock in the morning, the native tapper of these trees, braving the snakes and poisonous insects which beset his pathway, goes forth into the forest, carrying a small hatchet and a supply of tin cups. On the first of his two daily trips, he cuts long gashes, or wounds, in the bark of the rubber trees and sets a tin cup beneath the gash to catch the juice, or latex, as it is called. On the second trip, he gathers the juice in a bucket and returns to camp. In a day, he will tap and collect the juice from seventy to one hundred trees.

Building a fire from wood and palm nuts, with which to obtain a dense smoke, the native begins the main part of his work, which consists in thickening, or coagulating, the milk of the rubber tree. This must be done immediately after collection to keep the juice from spoiling. Dipping a wooden paddle into the latex, he slowly rotates it in the smudge of smoke. This evaporates the water and leaves the rubber in a solid mass. Over and over he repeats the process, and, when the ball becomes too large and heavy for easy handling, he rests the ends of the paddle on supports on either side of the fire and slowly turns it, at the same time applying more juice. When, bitten by mosquitoes and insects and with sore eyes and inflamed face from the smoke of the fire, the native finishes the day, he finds himself in possession of a ball of raw rubber of considerable weight as the reward for his labor.

Until the coming of the automobile, wild rubber met practically the entire needs of science and industry. At the beginning of the century, it was in full possession of world markets. However, the closing quarter of the preceding century had seen the initiation of a movement which was destined to pronounce its doom. The famous Para, although still to remain the standard of quality, was largely to disappear from market-place and factory.

It was in 1876 that a far-sighted Englishman, named
H. A. Wickham, succeeded in obtaining from the upper
waters of the Amazon seventy thousand seeds of rubber
trees and secretly transferred them to England, where
they were planted in the royal gardens at Kew. Some
of the two thousand eight hundred seedlings which
sprouted were sent to Ceylon and Singapore. In 1881,
seeds from these were distributed to Java, the Malay
States, and India. Thus began the rubber industry of
the Middle East, which now numbers in its seven thousand square miles of plantations approximately three-
quarters of a billion trees.

So completely has plantation rubber gained the
ascendency, that, whereas during the first five years of
the century its output was negligible, it now supplies
ninety-four per cent. of the world trade. Although
botanists are acquainted with upward of one hundred
plants yielding rubber forming juices, ninety-eight per
cent. of all natural rubber produced is obtained from the
celebrated Hevea tree. Ninety per cent. of the world's
rubber supply is obtained from plantations located in
Dutch and British possessions, chiefly in British.

A well-managed rubber plantation will have from one
hundred to one hundred and twenty-five trees per acre.
Still, the proper number has not yet been determined
with certainty. In the early days, too many were set out.
Tapping is on alternate days. With a tool resembling a
carpenter's gouge, a narrow strip of bark about four
inches wide is cut out. The cutting begins at a height of
approximately four feet from the ground and proceeds
diagonally downward about one-third the way around
the tree. Through a metal spout at the bottom, the latex

oozes at the rate of about two drops per second into a small porcelain cup. In something like an hour the flow stops. At the second tapping, a thin strip of bark is cut from the channel, thus exposing a new surface from which the latex flows. Immediately following these cuts, Nature begins to replace the bark. By the time the tapping cuts have reached the ground, the first cuts made have been so recovered with new bark that tapping can begin again. This results in a four-year cycle of tapping, and trees are known which are still yielding latex after thirty years of continuous tapping.

Each tapping yields about one fluid ounce of latex per tree, and this contains one-third of an ounce of dry rubber. This represents an annual production of about three pounds of rubber for each tree. Put in another way, an acre will yield about one pound per day. When we consider the quantity of rubber required for an average automobile tire, to say nothing of other uses, nearly eight hundred million plantation trees do not seem at all large to meet the need. Professor Roger Adams, of the University of Illinois, states that "it requires the output from two full grown trees for a whole year to supply the rubber for one 29x4 (Ford size) cord tire." What a vast plantation is necessary to provide the rubber for the tires on all the Ford cars built in a year!

The latex is placed in large stoneware or tile tanks, where it is immediately coagulated with dilute acetic acid. Here the process differs from that followed with the wild rubber of the Amazon region. Contrary to a once prevailing impression, smoking, although an efficient means of coagulation, confers no special virtues. The product from the coagulating tanks is machine processed, washed and hung up to dry, sometimes in an atmosphere laden with smoke from a slow-burning wood fire.

As is readily apparent, the United States is almost entirely dependent upon foreign sources for its supply of crude rubber. The operation of the Stevenson restriction act, adopted by Great Britain, has already demonstrated the unhealthfulness of such a situation. That we may understand the origin of this bit of legislation in restraint of the natural operation of the law of supply and demand, let it be recalled that the era of plantation rubber began in earnest with the spectacular boom in rubber stocks of 1910. Then, English and Dutch planters began to set out large areas to rubber trees. It takes about seven years for a rubber tree to begin to produce, and it does not come into full production until ten years. The result of the intensive planting just mentioned was an overproduction of rubber in 1920 and the years immediately following. The price in this country fell to sixteen and one-half cents a pound in 1921. The planters of the Far East faced financial ruin. In desperation, they appealed to their Government for legislative relief. An investment of $700,000,000 and a great national asset were at stake. Accordingly, the Stevenson Act, which sought to stabilize the price at thirty-six cents a pound, was passed. To accomplish its purpose, rubber exports of all planters were limited to sixty per cent. of the normal production with provision for a gradual increase as the price rose. The plan worked. Although the price did not rise much above the minimum fair-price set until 1925, in July of that year it touched one dollar and twenty-one cents, the highest point since 1910.

The immediate effect of the price decline of 1920 was

a decided falling off in new acreage planted to rubber trees. Whereas in 1918 plantings totaled four hundred thousand acres, in 1923 they had dropped to one-tenth that. Consequently there will be little gain in production between 1926 and 1930, with consumption expected to exceed production in 1928 and to result in a shortage of sixty thousand tons in the latter year. Not until 1934 will anything approaching normal conditions be restored. The increase in prices recently established has stimulated planting. Relief will follow in due course.

Let it be said that England has been entirely within her rights in passing restrictive legislation. Through the foresight and daring of her men of capital and business initiative, she insured the world's rubber supply and made possible the mass production of American motorcars. She is not required to suffer loss that American profits may be swollen.

AVENUES OF ESCAPE

What can the United States do to obtain rubber independence? Manifestly, we are just two decades behind time in getting started. The amount of American produced rubber is negligible. Still, as long ago as 1903, the United States Rubber Company made a start. To-day it owns one hundred and twenty-four thousand acres of plantation lands in the Far East, which produced ten thousand tons of rubber in 1925. A decade ago, the Goodyear Company began with a nucleus of twenty thousand acres, and now the Firestone Plantations Company is opening up Liberia to rubber cultivation. Indeed, private initiative is making a beginning, but it is pathetically small in view of the need.

One of the most obvious solutions of the difficulty is to develop rubber plantations in the Philippines under American control. Colonel Carmi A. Thompson, special representative of President Coolidge to those provinces, but recently asserted that these islands can be made to supply all our needs. Climate, soil and labor conditions are all propitious. The chief obstacle seems to be the land laws, which limit ownership to two thousand five hundred acres. When we compare this unit with rubber plantations in the British and Dutch possessions of more than one hundred thousand acres each, it is too small to attract American capital. This difficulty, however, should not be insurmountable.

Again, we may turn to economic concessions in Mexico, and in Central and South America. In time of war the ocean lanes to these parts could much more easily be kept open than those overseas. Most anywhere within a belt measuring about fourteen degrees on either side of the equator rubber trees will grow. It is estimated that this belt makes available approximately seven million square miles of suitable territory, only a thousandth of which has yet been utilized. It would seem that there should never be a shortage of crude rubber, much less that the United States should allow other countries to control the output and price of this basic material. Even though we should produce rubber to meet but a quarter of our needs, it would prevent the domination of a foreign monopoly.

Still, this country has one more avenue of escape, one which looms large on the horizon of possibilities, and it is at our very door. I refer to the Guayule shrub, native to certain parts of Mexico and to the Big Bend counties

Gathering latex, an emulsion issuing from the rubber tree and containing
about one-third its weight of rubber

Six months old Guayule plants on a plantation in California

This shrub may become an important factor in rendering the United States independent of a foreign rubber supply

Malayan women sorting crude rubber for shipment

Scene in a rubber factory

of southern Texas. This shrub, the only commercial shrub known, yields a large percentage of rubber. The presence of rubber was accidentally discovered many years ago by a Mexican who chewed some of the bark. The Guayule shrub grows to a height of only two feet and, like the rubber tree, requires seven years to mature.

For long, it seemed impossible to extract the rubber from the shrub. Then, toward the close of the last century, an Italian chemist, William Prampolini, worked out a practical chemical process and succeeded in enlisting the financial support of the late Senator Nelson W. Aldrich and Thomas F. Ryan. In 1903, as the result of research work by William A. Lawrence, assisted by his daughter, Clara Louise, a purely mechanical process was perfected and patented. Guayule rubber has now become an article of commerce. In 1925, something over four thousand tons were produced. Its properties are excellent and for some purposes superior to rubber from the East.

Furthermore, it has been found that the shrub will grow readily in California, Arizona and South Carolina. The annual rubber requirements of this country are now approximately a half-million tons. Suppose we were to supply one-quarter of this need through the cultivation of the Guayule shrub. It is estimated that the required acreage would be six hundred and forty thousand, or one thousand square miles. This by no means seems beyond our ability to provide. And while this acreage would require six hundred thousand laborers in the Far East, the machine methods of handling to which the Guayule shrub is amenable would reduce the number to forty thousand. Guayule requires very little care and no daily tapping. When the shrub is cut, Nature renews the supply. The industry is barely in its infancy.

That the United States may control its rubber future, there is no doubt. The way has been made plain. Private initiative and capital together with government encouragement should give us early independence. The underlying factors of rubber production have long since been established.

RUBBER AND THE CHEMIST

So far, the chemist has not seemed to figure largely in the picture that has been sketched. But, from the time Goodyear discovered the process of vulcanization to the present moment, he has been at work. We simply have not talked about him, that is all. The chemist has shared with the botanist and the plant pathologist the work of transforming the growing of plantation rubber from the rule-of-thumb methods prevailing in the beginning to the more scientific procedure of to-day. He has contributed to the conquering of rubber-tree diseases. He has provided fungicides and solved important problems related to the quality of soils and their fertilization. The matter of coagulation of the latex has been the subject of chemical investigation for half a century, and many substances have been tried. In the manufacture of rubber, it has been the chemist in the laboratory who has discovered just what mixtures of ingredients are best for each different kind of rubber.

Goodyear soon learned that the process of vulcanization could be greatly hastened by mixing with the rubber and sulfur chemicals such as lime, magnesia, white lead, red lead and litharge. These substances, too, were found to have certain other useful effects. However, it was not until 1906 that real chemical work was begun on the influence of these "accelerators" of vulcanization. In that year, George Oenslager, a chemist in the employ of the Diamond Rubber Company, began to experiment with aniline oil. This was the first time that an organic substance had been tried. The results were so promising that other organic compounds were used. Hundreds are now in use, not only to hasten vulcanization but also for the properties which they impart. There are few rubber compositions which do not contain them. Since 1902, the time of vulcanization has been reduced by two-thirds. The resulting saving in time and in investment in machinery has been large. William C. Geer, an expert of the rubber industry, says, "I assume that this discovery alone has been the means of saving to investors clearly $200,000,000; and due to accelerators alone the consumer of rubber goods gains an improved quality worth over $200,000,000 per year." No small gains are these to the credit of the chemist. It is estimated that the cost of automobile tires in the United States alone is $50,000,000 a year less than it would be without the use of organic accelerators.

An evil property of rubber has been the ease and rapidity with which it would age. The chemist has discovered that oxidation is one of the chief factors in this aging process. Better still, he has found certain organic substances, known as "antioxidants," which, mixed with the rubber in process of manufacture, will prevent or materially delay this deterioration. The discovery has been a large factor in the increased life of tires. At the beginning of the century, a tire under favorable circumstances might run three or four thousand miles. Tires now give the consumer an average of twelve thousand and more miles, no small gift of the chemist to the motor public.

Within the memories of many now active in the fire departments of our cities, fire hose was a source of peril. In time of direst need, it might unceremoniously burst. Millions of dollars have been lost from aged and decaying hose lines. The chemist has changed all this. Fire hose is as dependable as the water supply and often more so. Conveyor belts for handling coal and ores formerly wore out quickly. Now, after carrying thousands of tons, they show little wear. Ernest Hopkinson, of the United States Rubber Company, has recently developed a process of spray drying the liquid latex, whereby crude rubber of excellent quality is produced. By this process is accomplished in a few moments results which formerly required, by older processes, hours or days for the coagulation, separation and curing of the rubber. In 1899, a young chemist, Arthur H. Marks, working in a Boston laboratory, began experimenting on a process for improving the quality of reclaimed rubber. He succeeded marvelously. The "shoddy" of the earlier years of the industry is now a thing of the past. The Marks process dominates the situation, and reclaimed rubber superior to any previously known has become a big factor in rubber manufacture. While not the equal of new rubber, it is indispensable for many purposes. In 1925, 140,000 tons were used in the United States. Representing, as it does at the present time,

approximately thirty-five per cent. of the crude rubber
employed, reclaimed rubber is a large factor in stabilizing the price of crude. Dr. Harry L. Fisher, working
in the laboratories of the Goodyear Company, has succeeded in transforming the rubber molecule into compounds resembling in properties gutta percha. These
new substances will adhere to metals and therefore may
be used for protective coatings. A notable recent
achievement of S. E. Sheppard, of the Eastman Kodak
Company, and Doctor Klein, of Budapest, is the deposition of rubber by means of the electric current. In this
case, the particles of rubber are deposited upon the
anode, or positive pole of the bath, just as in ordinary
electroplating metals are deposited upon the cathode.
The high quality of the rubber deposited gives promise
of important future developments.

And in all this advance in the knowledge of rubber
chemistry, processes have by no means been reduced to
mere mechanical routine. The chemist is still the high
priest of the compounding room. He it is who must
choose from the wealth of available accelerators, antioxidants, and reinforcing pigments, just the ones and
the right proportions best suited to give the desired
quality of product. He knows, too, the particular benefits to be obtained from any of these substances. No
longer are they regarded simply as "fillers." He has
learned, for instance, that the tread of an automobile
tire will soon wear out if it does not contain zinc oxide
and carbon black. While it is true that the manufacture
of rubber involves a multitude of mechanical processes,
chemical control still dominates and guides it, and a
host of problems remains for the chemist to solve.

SYNTHETIC RUBBER

I know it is synthetic rubber about which you have been waiting to hear. What is the present status of the problem? What are the prospects of being able to duplicate or possibly to outstrip the handiwork of Mother Nature? These processes for preparing artificially in the laboratory and chemical plant natural products of great usefulness hold a wonderful fascination both for the chemist and the layman. The synthesis of rubber, however, embodying all the manifold qualities of that obtained from the latex of the rubber tree, has proved to be a difficult problem. Still, much progress has been made. In the presence of a great emergency, synthetic rubber might come with a bang.

There are those who contend that rubber is a substance which should not be made artificially. Here is one of the few examples of the utilization of the energy in the direct rays of the sun in the production of a basic material of the first importance. Why, in an age of diminishing resources, seek to substitute for a natural process of high efficiency one which needlessly consumes raw materials and energy supplies needed for other purposes? Would it not be better to endeavor by the process of artificial selection and improved methods of cultivation to increase the yield of the rubber tree, just as the sugar content of the beet has been brought from less than five per cent. to eighteen per cent.?

There is much logic in the foregoing contentions. However, this line of action availed Germany nothing in the Great War. With the ocean lanes closed between a nation and the Tropics, artificial rubber is the only answer in the hour of need. And then, too, the knowledge that synthetic rubber is an accomplished fact would afford a wonderful stabilizing influence to the rubber market as well as providing a powerful deterrent against the establishment of a monopoly. Fortunately for the United States, the cultivation of the Guayule shrub offers potential independence of Tropical rubber. And still, Guayule rubber can not be had overnight. It requires seven years to bring the shrub to yielding. Vast acreages, too, would be needed to meet the full rubber demand. It is quite doubtful whether we shall for many years, if ever, produce domestic rubber in sufficient quantity. Therefore, the only certain hope of being able to ward off a possible national crisis is through the achievement of artificial rubber. Let us see how bright are the synthetic skies.

It has long been known that isoprene, the fundamental hydrocarbon in the composition of rubber, may be obtained from turpentine, petroleum, starch and coal-tar. Methyl-isoprene, a cousin of the foregoing hydrocarbon and also a starting-point for the synthesis of rubber, can be built up from acetone, a substance which may be manufactured from coal, but which is now obtained in quantity as a by-product of the direct fermentation of the crude starch of cereals. It soon became apparent how utterly futile it is to tap one tree to obtain a substance from which to prepare an inferior imitation of the product of another tree. This together with the insufficient supply eliminated turpentine. Although petroleum might afford a source, its future is already mortgaged to another phase of the motor industry. Thus one of the chief obstacles to the attainment of synthetic rubber is a cheap and abundant raw material. Still, were the prospective financial returns sufficiently high, the raw material would be forthcoming. Starch could doubtless be had in sufficient quantity. And then again, as in times of national peril, price is not the controlling consideration. It has been estimated that plantation rubber can be produced at a profit at thirty cents a pound. That being true, in ordinary circumstances synthetic rubber must meet that price competition.

It was in 1909, in the laboratories of the Bayer Company, in Elberfeld, Germany, that the first synthetic rubber as the result of direct technical development was produced. This was under the direction of Fritz Hofmann, and the product is said to have met various rubber tests successfully. Others had obtained synthetic rubber earlier, but usually the "polymerization" process, by which large aggregations of the rubber molecule are built up, had been brought about by accident, and no one had been able to duplicate the procedure with any degree of success. In England, Tilden and Perkin, son of Sir William Perkin of coal-tar fame, had done important work in this field, and there were others. But, independently of Hofmann, only Harries of Germany had obtained a product which could be vulcanized. In 1912, at the Eighth International Congress of Applied Chemistry, at the College of the City of New York, Carl Duisberg, official representative of the German Emperor, exhibited a set of automobile tires made of synthetic rubber, which were said to have run some four thousand miles. In speaking of this achievement, Doctor Duisberg said: "The difficulties which have been overcome were great indeed and those which still remain to be surmounted in order to produce a substance equal to Para caoutchouc in quality and capable of competing with cheap plantation rubber costing only two marks per kilo are still greater. But such difficulties do not intimidate the chemist and manufacturer; on the contrary they spur them on to further efforts. The stone is rolling and we will see to it that it reaches its destination."

Then came the Great War, and German chemists were called upon in grim earnest to make good their prophecy. Rubber was urgently needed for tires, cables, storage battery cases for submarines and for a host of other purposes. What should the raw material be? The synthesis from acetone was determined upon, but how could the acetone be obtained? The fermentation of the starch of grain or potatoes to form first alcohol and then acetic acid, from which acetone might be made, was out of the question, for grain and potatoes were important foodstuffs. But coal could be used. Heated with lime, coal yields calcium carbide, which, as is well known, with water produces acetylene gas. Acetylene, through a series of changes, gives a compound known as acetaldehyde, then acetic acid, and finally acetone. Reduction of acetone with aluminum ends with methyl-isoprene, better known as dimethylbutadiene, a barbarous name, but one which has a perfectly definite meaning to the chemist. The next step, and one of the most difficult, was polymerization. As already stated, this means causing the primary molecules of the intermediate rubberlike substance to combine into large units, approaching in properties and quality of product the characteristics of the aggregations of molecules in the latex of the rubber tree. Two processes were employed,—one with heat and the other in the cold. The two products obtained were known respectively as "W" rubber and "H" rubber.

Next came the problem of vulcanization. It was not an easy one to solve. Conditions differed from those of natural rubber. Many accelerators and stabilizers were tried. Intensive research was the order of the day. Scores of patents were taken out. Finally, artificial rubber emerged. In describing it, C. C. Burgdorf says, "As a general rule it can be said that the vulcanized product obtained from artificial rubber was good enough for the average technical use of soft rubber, although not so good as the product obtained from natural rubber. For hard rubber our polymerization gave excellent results. By vulcanization, goods of high elasticity and of excellent dielectric (non-conducting) behavior were obtained, which for certain purposes were no doubt superior to those obtained from the natural product. Artificial rubber as a chemically pure hydrocarbon is free from ash and other impurities, and for electrical purposes is more uniform and reliable. For dental work it was preferred to natural rubber."

It is as a substitute for hard rubber that the artificial product has thus far scored its chief success. In the cold, it becomes hard and brittle and loses its elasticity. It was necessary in cold weather to jack up all standing automobiles provided with full sets of tires made from synthetic rubber. The total quantity produced during the war was 2,350 tons, which is, of course, but a drop in the bucket compared with world consumption. This does not matter, however. The big thing is that commercial synthetic rubber has been brought immeasurably nearer by these researches carried out under the spur of necessity. Doctor Burgdorf estimates that the capital required for a plant having a capacity of three thousand tons of artificial rubber per year would be between ten and fifteen million dollars, exclusive of equipment necessary to provide the acetone with which to start. This would mean a high cost for a product as yet inferior.

From petroleum, through the cracking process, chemists are able to obtain hydrocarbons similar in composition to isoprene, notably butadienes. Professor Roger Adams, of the University of Illinois, has estimated that, could these rubberlike compounds be converted without loss into synthetic rubber, fifty-two million barrels of petroleum would be sufficient for the production of four billion pounds. Were it not for the imminent exhaustion of American petroleum fields, it would seem that out of an annual production of approximately three-quarters of a billion barrels this quantity might be spared for rubber purposes. Still, there is a long road yet to travel.

W. C. Geer, already quoted, says, "The world has little to expect, and the planters nothing to fear, from synthetic rubber; and in the inevitable cost competition which would arise, were synthetic rubber to be produced, the planter would be able to deliver crude rubber on board ship at a profit to himself, and at a price to which synthetic rubber could not be brought."

The X-ray, so useful in the diagnosis of the underlying nature of properties of metals, gives promise of assisting in the solution of the problem of synthetic rubber. At the Institute of Chemistry, held under the auspices of the American Chemical Society, during the summer of 1927, Professor George L. Clark, of the University of Illinois, said: "X-ray photographs show the amorphous pattern for unstretched rubber, and the fibre-crystal structure of stretched rubber. That this is due to the rubber hydrocarbon is demonstrated in new work on very pure soluble rubber. The most interesting feature at present is that no sample of synthetic rubber has been found to produce this sharply fibre diagram. It is possible that this is the criterion of the successful artificial reproduction of rubber.'' It is only a matter of time till the rubber molecules yield their secrets and lend themselves to artificial synthesis as readily as a host of other molecules have done.

Many believe that a more legitimate goal of chemistry in this field is not the achievement of synthetic rubber itself, equal in qualities to natural rubber, but artificial substitutes which for many purposes shall be superior to the products obtained from the latex of the rubber trees. Rubber now has uses for which it is not ideal. Flexible glass would be better for electric insulation. For steam hose, a material more resistant to heat could doubtless be synthesized. Rubber shoes do not permit ventilation. A synthetic material, permeable to perspiration and yet reasonably water-proof, would possess decided advantages. Inner tubes for tires deteriorate rapidly with exposure to sunlight. The chemist may be able to provide a better material. Other examples might be cited.

Scientific achievement travels so rapidly these days and so much has already been accomplished that it would be rash for any one to write ''impossible'' upon the door leading to the synthesis of commercial rubber. If for no other reason than that of national preparedness, synthetic rubber on a large scale, if need be, must be translated from the land of dreams to the world of actuality.

CHAPTER IX

The Twilight Realm of Matter

EXAMPLES FROM ASTRONOMY—THE COLLOIDAL STATE—
SUSPENSIONS, TRUE SOLUTIONS, AND COLLOIDAL SOLU-
TIONS—DISCOVERIES OF GRAHAM—TYNDALL-FARADAY EFFECT—
ULTRAMICROSCOPE—BROWNIAN MOVEMENT—SOLS AND GELS—
APPLICATIONS—CLEANSING ACTION OF SOAP—DECOLORIZING
SUGAR—COLLOIDS IN TANNING HIDES—COLLOIDS IN AGRICUL-
TURE—COTTRELL PROCESS—COLLOIDAL FUEL—COLORS OF
GEMS—ORIGIN OF DELTAS, CLOUDS AND HALOS—COLLOIDS
AND THE HUMAN BODY—COLLOIDS IN MEDICINE—OTHER
APPLICATIONS.

WHO has not seen the myriads of glistening dust
motes dancing in some stray sunbeam that has gained
entrance to a darkened room? Forever vibrating,
never settling, these minute particles of matter in finely
divided state of diffusion seem to saturate the air.
Swarms of meteoric matter attended by dust clouds of
exceedingly minute particles forever move in stupendous
orbits about the sun. Immense aggregations of finely
suspended matter surrounding the sun seem to account
for the zodiacal light. As Lars Vegard has suggested, the blue color of the sky and the beautiful aurora
borealis may be due to tiny crystals of frozen nitrogen in
the upper strata of the atmosphere. Nebulæ are vast
whirlpools of matter in finest state of subdivision. An

automobile headlight shooting its rays through an atmosphere of fog or haze forms a conelike beam of light by reflection from countless numbers of water droplets or dust particles. So does the extremely tenuous matter in the comet's tail, the "stuff that dreams are made of," reflect the sunlight and make itself visible to mortals here on earth. In both, we have instances of what is called the Faraday-Tyndall light effect. These are examples from the field of astronomy of the *colloidal state* of matter. Here, as in innumerable other illustrations, we behold the twilight realm of matter.

Suppose I stir some fine dirt in a tumbler of water. On standing for a time, the particles of dirt settle and the water becomes clear. These particles are insoluble and at first remain suspended in the liquid. Now, let us stir a teaspoonful of ordinary table salt in a tumbler of water. As you know, this quickly dissolves and disappears from view as a solid, imparting a salty taste to the water. Upon evaporation, the salt may be obtained again in solid form. We believe that the crystal particles of salt assume the molecular state and, in accordance with the electrolytic theory of solutions, many of these molecules dissociate, or break up, into positively and negatively charged particles called ions. Sugar also dissolves readily, but the resulting solution will not conduct the electric current and therefore its molecules do not ionize. Nevertheless, both are true solutions. Each is a uniform mixture of a solid in a liquid. The solid will not settle. It is in such a finely divided state of division that its invisible particles will readily pass through the pores of filter paper. Here we have two extremes,—the coarse, heavy, visible particles of dirt which quickly settle and the exceedingly minute molecules which lose their visibility and remain in permanent suspension. Between the two we find a complete gradation of successive states. From the imperfect suspension to the true solution, lies a shadowy borderland replete with interesting phenomena.

In 1861, an English scientist named Graham discovered that some substances apparently dissolve but pass through membranes much more slowly than do the water solutions of ordinary inorganic salts, acids and bases. Some of these are gelatin, albumin in the white of egg, soap, cooked starch, glue, rubber and cement. Graham called these two states of matter, the one which diffuses readily through a membrane and the other which does not, crystalloids and colloids respectively. A little experimenting soon showed him that he could make use of this difference in properties to separate a mixture of two such substances. Into a container having a porous bottom such as fine parchment paper, he poured a mixture of two solutions such as sugar and starch and set this into a larger vessel of pure water. The sugar passed through the membrane into the water, while the starch remained behind. This apparatus is called a dialyzer and with it many separations are possible.

Clearly this difference in diffusibility is due to some difference in the states of matter of the two substances. It seemed perfectly correct to assume that the particles of a colloid are too large to pass through the pores of the membrane. Although the colloid appears to be a true solution and its particles are too small to be visible, these particles are nevertheless large aggregations of molecules too big to squeeze through the minute openings of the membrane. Later experiments have shown that there is no very sharp line between the two states of matter, the same substance behaving both as a crystalloid and a colloid under different conditions. The colloidal state refers to matter of any kind when it is sufficiently finely divided. The chemistry of such matter is colloid chemistry, and its applications are numerous and important.

In ordinary light a colloidal solution does not disclose its true nature. To all appearances, it is like any other solution. Suppose, however, that we place such a solution in a glass jar in a darkened room and pass through it an intense beam of light. The scattering effect of these colloidal particles on the light now reveals their presence. The visible effect is very similar to that of dust particles on a beam of light admitted to a darkened room. Here again, we have the Tyndall-Faraday phenomenon.

About a quarter of a century ago, Zsigmondy and his associate Siedentopf invented the ultramicroscope, which makes visible particles having a diameter as small as one one-hundred-thousandth of a millimeter in diameter, and it takes 25.4 millimeters to make an inch. His purpose was to study the color effect produced by mixing metallic gold with glass. He passed a concentrated beam of light horizontally through the substance under examination and viewed it from above with an ordinary microscope. In this way he discovered that the minute particles of gold dissolved in glass could be easily distinguished. And a beautiful picture it was that this converging pencil of light revealed. The particles of gold stood forth, glistening points of light, like stars in the mellow haze

of the Milky Way. Although red when viewed by transmitted light, these colloidal particles, for such they were,
appeared to be green and they danced to and fro in
zigzag paths with a very rapid motion. But their true
nature was not disclosed. They seemed to be structure-
less disks of light like blazing suns rather than planets
shining by reflected light, as are the objects of ordinary
microscopic vision.

The next step was to turn the search-light of this new
instrument upon true colloidal solutions. The first revelation was the reason for the permanent suspension of
colloidal particles, that is, why they do not settle. The
ultramicroscope at once made plainly visible a vibratory
motion, known as the *Brownian movement.* This is the
most characteristic property of colloids. It is due to the
constant motion of the molecules of the liquid in which
the particles are suspended. But all the molecules of a
liquid do not move with equal velocities. Consequently,
the colloidal particles may be unequally bombarded on
opposite sides. These unequal blows set a particle in
motion, and their continuation keeps it in motion. Thus
it does not settle. When the particles are too large, this
rain of molecular missiles is unable to produce the
Brownian movement. In that direction, we move toward
temporary suspensions which settle. In the opposite
direction, we approach true solutions in which the particles are of molecular dimensions. Colloids occupy the
twilight zone between.

Colloidal particles are large enough to reflect rays of
light, and upon the size of the particles will depend the
color of the reflection. Thus, gold may give such colors
as green, red, blue and violet. These particles, too, bear

electric charges, both positive and negative, although when water is the suspending liquid most colloids are negative.

To distinguish colloidal solutions from true solutions, they are called *sols*. Some substances, such as glue, gelatin and cooked starch, are always colloidal in solution. This is because their molecules are undoubtedly very large. But in some instances special means must be used to obtain aggregations of molecules large enough to prevent passage through a porous membrane and yet small enough to exhibit the Brownian movement. An electric arc struck between two metallic electrodes beneath water will produce colloidal particles of the metal in question.

When a colloidal solution, or sol, sets, it forms a gel. A gelatin dessert and a boiled egg are examples. This is due to an agglomeration, or union, of the colloidal particles. In the cellular spaces of the microscopic, sponge-like structure are large quantities of water. Even a small quantity of gelatin can give a large quantity of water a semi-solid appearance. The jellying of fruit juices depends upon a substance present in ripe fruits, known as pectin. If the fruit juice is heated too much, the pectin is destroyed. Then the "jelly will not jell." The remedy is to use artificial pectin, which is everywhere upon the market. The curdling of milk by the action of a little acid is an example of gel formation. The acid causes the particles to collect into large aggregations. Although milk itself is a colloid, if another colloid like gelatin is added to it, curdling will not easily take place.

APPLICATIONS

If I shake a few drops of olive oil with a test tube full of water, a mixture of the two liquids results. But, upon standing for a few moments, the oil rises to the surface. The suspension is not permanent. If now I add a little soap solution and shake again, I obtain a permanent suspension. Such a colloidal solution is called an emulsion. It is of great practical value in the cleansing action of soap. Soap emulsifies grease and in so doing removes it. It also breaks up the particles of ordinary dirt and wrapping itself about them washes them away. Soap often makes of the dirt itself a colloidal suspension.

Again, olive oil and vinegar will not mix. But, if we introduce the yolk of an egg, we obtain a suspension known as Mayonnaise dressing. Artificial preparations of cod-liver oil are examples of emulsions. Protective colloids added to milk tend to stabilize it and to emulsify the fat, thus modifying cow's milk for infants so as to resemble more nearly mother's milk. Colloids such as eggs or gelatin used in the preparation of ice-cream prevent the cream from becoming gritty or sandy upon standing. Gelatin so used is not a "filler" but contributes the smooth, velvety texture so desirable in this universal product. Such colloids as gum arabic, glucose and soluble starch are used in "gum drops" to prevent the crystallization of the sugar.

One of the most marked properties exhibited by colloidal substances is that of adsorption. This means the ability of a substance to cause another to adhere to it. We see this in paste, glue and asphalt. Many dyes are colloids which adhere to fibers in this way. Animal charcoal or bone black thus decolorizes sugar through the colloidal adsorption of the coloring matter. Silica gel, a colloid, is employed to adsorb impurities from crude petroleum and gasoline. The efficiency of various kinds of charcoal in adsorbing poisonous gases found application in the gas masks during the war. Sand filters and particularly those having interspersed colloidal substances, such as aluminum hydroxide, afford excellent mediums for the removal of bacteria from water.

The colloidal nature of animal skins plays a big part in the tanning of leather. In the preliminary operation of soaking, the skins adsorb water and form gels. The tannin used is also colloidal. But the colloidal particles of the hides are positively charged while those of the tannin are negatively charged. Thus the two sets of substances attract each other in the tanning process. Coagulation followed by chemical action completes the change from hide to leather.

In agriculture, the colloidal state is of great importance. Let it be understood that this state refers to any finely dispersed mass of particles held in suspension. We may have solids in gases, as in smoke or dust clouds; liquid droplets in gases, as in fogs; liquids in liquids, as in emulsions; and solids in solids, as in gold or copper dissolved in glass.

The western fruit grower wards off the frost of late spring or early summer by the use of smudge pots in which he burns crude petroleum to form dense clouds of smoke. The innumerable colloidal particles of smoke afford nuclei upon which moisture condenses. These droplets of moisture together with the carbon dioxide gas generated so prevent radiation of heat from the earth that the temperature in the orchard is kept above freezing and the fruit is saved.

The colloidal condition of finely divided soil together with the colloidal products of decaying vegetation are essential to the life processes of plants. Because clay soils, devoid of vegetable matter, lack these substances they are unproductive. Many of the properties of soils are dependent not so much on the chemical composition as on the state of physical division of soil particles. The finer a fertilizer, like phosphate rock, can be ground, the more available does it become as a plant food.

A most practical application of colloidal chemistry is the electrical precipitation of finely dispersed substances from air smoke and flue gases. It is known as the Cottrell process and was devised by F. G. Cottrell, now Director of the Fixed Nitrogen Research Laboratory at Washington. Suspended in the center of the flue or chimney is a high tension electric wire carrying a charged point by which the smoke or furnace gases are made to pass. As they do so, these colloidal particles become charged and are attracted to the walls of the chimney, which are oppositely charged. Valuable by-products, formerly allowed to go to waste, are now recovered. Cement kilns yield potash, and from smelters selenium, arsenic and other metallic substances are salvaged. Sulfuric acid may thus be separated from waste gases. This process also removes colloidally dispersed water from petroleum.

Powdered coal in colloidal form is beginning to assume importance as a possible substitute for petroleum. Solidified alcohol, widely used as a fuel, is a colloidal gel obtained from a mixture of alcohol, calcium acetate and stearic acid. The oil of oil shales is so finely dispersed, so highly colloidal, that it can not be removed by gas pressure, and mining followed by distillation must be employed. "Fire-Foam," a fire fighting froth of carbon dioxide bubbles, is kept in the colloidal state by the addition of a colloid such as glue or dextrin.

The beautiful colors of many precious gems are due to the presence of colloidal impurities. Iron contributes the colors to ruby and topaz; chromium to emerald; and manganese to the amethyst. The colors of diamonds have a similar origin. Opals are colloidal gels. It is well known that X-rays or radium will change the colors of gems. This is probably due to a change in the sizes of the colloidal particles. Mother-of-pearl, colloidal in character, has already been synthesized.

Large rivers like the Mississippi carry down immense quantities of fine clay consisting of negatively charged colloidal particles. When these particles reach salt water, the positively charged ions of the salts in solution neutralize the negative charges on the particles of clay, which are then precipitated. The geological evidence shows that such deposits have added about a thousand miles to the length of the Mississippi. The varying colors of bodies of water, such as the blue of the Mediterranean, are due chiefly to the scattering of light by finely dispersed particles of matter.

A cloud is simply an immense aggregation of colloidal droplets of water, each droplet bearing an electric charge. This charge is entirely upon the surface, and, as the droplets coalesce to form larger ones, these charges increase enormously in voltage until the lightning flashes. Colloidal ice particles at high altitudes give rise to halos, sun-dogs and moon-dogs. The sunset colors are caused by the scattering of light by colloidal dust clouds. The brilliant sunsets seen throughout the world following the eruption of Krakatoa were due to finely suspended dust and ashes carried to high altitudes.

The essential element in thyroxin, the secretion of the thyroid gland, is iodine. As is told elsewhere, improper functioning of this gland results in cretinism and goiter. It has been a matter of much observation that these conditions are more prevalent in regions far removed from the sea. The source of iodine in the soil for plant availability is the ocean. Colloidal sea-salt dust, originating in the ocean's spray, is carried inland to be washed down by the rain for plant use. And it is in mountainous regions, such as Wyoming, Idaho and Switzerland, to which the least of this salt-dust penetrates, that cretinism and goiter are most pronounced.

But it is in the human body that we find the most important illustrations of colloidal substances. We are simply bundles of colloidal systems. Disturbance of them leads to ill-health and often death. In the healing of a wound there is an exudation of a colloidal solution, which sets to a gel, thus cementing the parts together and forming the scar tissue. Colloids and colloidal catalyzers called enzymes play a big part in the digestion of foods. Colloids are controlling factors in the growth of tissues and organic structures. The mystery of life processes is wrapped up in the colloidal nature of protoplasm and the living cell.

The action of antiseptics in destroying bacteria is controlled by colloidal factors. Bichloride of mercury poisoning is due to the coagulation of the cell colloids of the kidneys. Colloidal silver is an excellent germicide. Injections of the colloid gum-arabic in salt solution has saved many lives in cases of bleeding and surgical shock.

The latex of the rubber tree is a colloidal substance which yields a gel upon coagulation. In vulcanization the sulfur is first adsorbed by the rubber, but upon heating is thought to enter into a true chemical combination. Fillers in colloidal dispersion increase the strength and durability of rubber. Thus we might continue. The colloidal state of matter has a multitude of phases which we can not even glimpse. It is a factor in sewage disposal and in the manufacture of paper. The sensitive preparation on a photographic plate is a colloidal solution of silver bromide in gelatin. Many insecticides, such as lime-sulfur and Bordeaux mixture, are colloidal suspensions. Soaps are colloidal products, and we have seen that their cleansing action is such. Colloids enter into the production of paints, pigments and varnishes. Blasting gelatin is a colloidal gel of nitrocellulose and nitroglycerin. Another application is found in the flotation process of separating ores from the rock or gangue and in the ceramic industry. The delicate odors of perfumes are borne on the wings of colloidal dispersions.

Here in this twilight realm of matter, in the borderland between chemistry and physics, lie profound secrets as yet untouched. Wide fields of research beckon to the investigator. Deeper insights, broader knowledge, are bound to yield discoveries of the utmost usefulness. Colloid chemistry is still an infant. It has but just been recognized as a separate division by the American Chemical Society. But its phenomena are legion and its possibilities immeasurable.

CHAPTER X

The Age of Metals

ORE SHIPS AND BLAST FURNACES—ORIGIN OF BLAST FURNACE—
CATALAN FORGE—PUDDLING FURNACE, ROLLING MILL AND
BESSEMER CONVERTER—STEEL AND ITS MULTITUDINOUS
USES—CHEMISTRY AND STEEL—DEPOSITS OF IRON ORE—
UTILIZATION OF LOW-GRADE ORES—COMBATING CORROSION—
STEEL ALLOYS—RUSTLESS IRON—METAL RESERVES—METAL
WASTES—AGE OF ALUMINUM AND MAGNESIUM—ACHIEVE-
MENT OF HALL—USES OF ALUMINUM—RISE OF MAGNESIUM—
OTHER METALS—CATALYSTS—CATALYSIS IN INDUSTRY—
TWITCHELL PROCESS FOR SOAP—ELECTROMETALLURGY—BAR-
IUM IN PURE FORM—X-RAY IN METALLURGY—ULTRAMICRO-
SCOPE AND ITS REVELATIONS.

THE present is a many-sided age, but for a few minutes let us think of it as The Age of Metals. Not long
ago, I stood beside one of the Great Lakes ore ships and
watched the huge clam-shell shovels as, dipping through
the hatchways and into the hold of the ship, each removed at a single bite as much as seventeen tons of ore,
transferring it with all the ease of a mighty giant to the
immense stock piles along the water-front. Then, I
turned to the blast furnace, towering ninety feet into the
air and swallowing up each twenty-four hours 800 tons
of ore, 400 tons of coke and 100 tons of limestone, besides
consuming 1,200 tons of air, and in this same time turn-

ing out 600 tons of molten pig iron, 500 tons of slag and 1,400 tons of gases. I reflected, too, that in 1923, the peak-year of recent production, the blast furnaces of this country alone were responsible for an output of more than forty million tons of this basic metal of industry and progress.

As I stood there, my thought traveled backward six thousand years and more. In imagination I saw two men, brawny sons of toil, squatting beside a roaring wood-fire, piled high with ore and partly covered with clay to keep in the heat, while with a goatskin bellows they vigorously fanned the flames. By dint of much labor, these men obtained a dozen pounds of pasty metal in a day. Although very impure, I saw the ancient smith forge from this product of the primitive blast furnace crude axes, knives and spear-heads, vastly superior to those fashioned from chipped stone or bronze.

Quickly passing down the centuries, I found myself in the lower Rhine Valley at about the middle of the fourteenth century. I stood beside the "Belgian Blow Oven," in which the first molten pig iron in history was produced. Sixteen feet high and operated like one of the Titans of the modern steel plant, this furnace burned charcoal for fuel and a bellows run by water-power supplied the blast. At intervals, molten iron was tapped from the well-hole at the bottom and ran into a large puddle with a number of little ones, thus resembling an old pig and her brood and giving rise to the name "pig iron."

Sometime along the pathway, I saw originate at Catalonia, Spain, the old Catalan forge, which for centuries was the most important means of smelting iron ore.

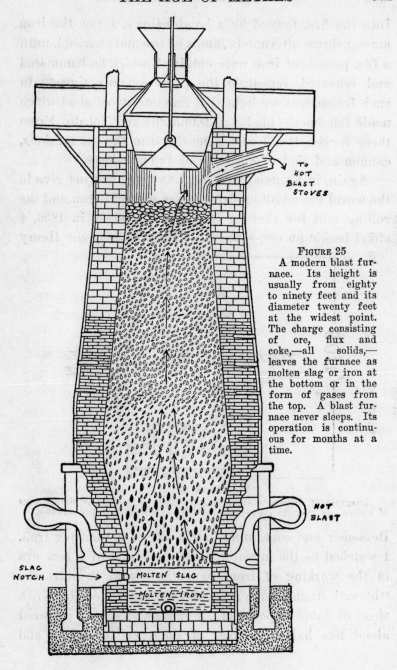

TO
HOT
BLAST
STOVES

FIGURE 25
A modern blast furnace. Its height is usually from eighty to ninety feet and its diameter twenty feet at the widest point. The charge consisting of ore, flux and coke,—all solids,— leaves the furnace as molten slag or iron at the bottom or in the form of gases from the top. A blast furnace never sleeps. Its operation is continuous for months at a time.

HOT
BLAST

SLAG
NOTCH

MOLTEN SLAG

MOLTEN IRON

Into the fire, fanned by a hand-bellows, I saw the iron master throw alternately lumps of ore and charcoal, until a few pounds of iron were obtained, which he hammered and reheated, repeating the process many times. In such forges was wrought that fine quality of steel which made famous the blades of Damascus and Toledo. From these forges, too, I saw come the iron for the muskets, cannon and shot of our War of Independence.

Again, in England, in 1784, I saw Henry Cort give to the world the puddling furnace for wrought iron and the rolling mill for shaping its product. Then, in 1856, I stood beside an egg-shaped crucible, built by Sir Henry

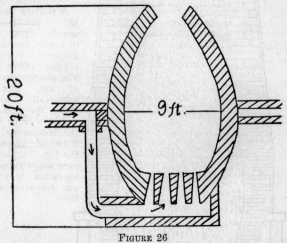

FIGURE 26

Diagram of Bessemer converter, in which approximately fifteen tons of molten pig iron are converted into steel in almost as many minutes.

Bessemer and containing half a ton of molten pig iron. I watched as the inventor, with the vision of a new era in the working of iron, gave the signal to start the "blow." Immediately, a deafening roar filled the air, a sheet of flame leaped forth, a shower of sparks pattered about like hail, the cover of the crucible melted and

Sir Henry Bessemer

Running molten iron into molds for forming ingots, called ''pigs''

Removing samples of steel from an open-hearth furnace for testing purposes
By this testing, the composition of the steel is kept under chemical control

mixed with the contents of the fiery caldron, while the supporting chains became red and threatened to pull asunder. Then, all became quiet, the flame disappeared, and workmen poured from the crucible an excellent quality of steel. Bessemer had bridged the gap between the Age of Iron and the Age of Steel. In due time came the open-hearth furnace and the immense plants which in prodigious quantities supply the metal that has become the symbol of modern power.

Of course, iron was not the first metal used by primitive men. Long before its coming, the working of gold and silver, copper and tin, had become highly perfected arts. But with the passing of the centuries iron, because of its greater abundance and its multiplicity of uses, gradually assumed the leading rôle. To-day, through its alloy steel, it dominates the industrial life of nations and upon its control hinges the military and political sway of empire.

In a multitude of ways steel is indispensable to agriculture. A steel plow, drawn by a steel tractor, turns under the sod in the spring. Steel harrows and disks fit the ground. A steel drill sows the seed. Tractor-drawn reapers of steel cut the ripened grain. Threshing-machines of steel separate the wheat, barley, rye and oats. Elevators of steel hold the grain in storage. Steel trains and ships carry it to distant markets. The gasoline motor and a score of machines of high-grade steel have become the willing burden bearers of the farm. Directly or indirectly, steel is essential to every other industry. The automobile and motor-truck reflect in high measure the iron master's art. Fingers of steel spin and weave the fabrics of the world. Sewing-machines

of steel stitch them into garments. Drills and tools of
the most durable steel remove the ores from the mines.
Furnaces of steel smelt them. Steel is rolled into acres
of sheet metal and drawn into thousands of miles of
wire. The railroads that span the continents, the locomotives that bid defiance to time and space, the floating
palaces that bridge the seas, the big guns and armor

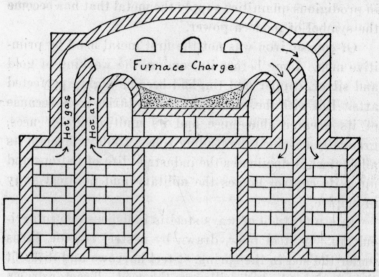

FIGURE 27

Open-hearth furnace, which has now largely displaced the Bessemer
converter for the production of steel.

plate of the world's proudest navies, the huge sky-
scrapers of our cities, the mighty turbines, dynamos and
motors of our power plants and factories, the multitudes
of machines that fill the workshops of the world, and the
millions of nails, bolts, nuts and screws that hold things
together,—all these and much more are largely wrought
of steel. Fashioned into delicate hairsprings or balance
wheels for watches, steel is worth more than its weight

in gold. In the Great War, steel was supreme. More than any other material necessity, it was the stupendous mass production of America's thousands of furnaces that turned the tide of battle. And in time of peace, steel occupies a no less strategic position. Power-driven machinery in the United States performs work equivalent to four billion human slaves. In other words, machines of steel place at the service of every man, woman and child the equivalent of thirty-five hard-working servants. Yes, steel wears the crown and wields the scepter of supreme power in the present epoch of the Age of Metals.

But what has this story of steel to do with chemistry? Everything. From the days of the primitive iron master to the present moment, metallurgy has been a strictly chemical art. True, for centuries it was an art directed by rule-of-thumb knowledge and practise. Nevertheless, albeit unwittingly, the operation of the iron furnace and the quality of its product have depended upon fundamental chemical reactions. Just in proportion as the metallurgist has gained a mastery of the chemistry of his processes, progress has been sure and certain. To-day, the industry fairly bristles with chemical problems at every point. Let us see what some of them are.

CHEMICAL PROBLEMS

Sir Robert Hadfield estimates that twenty-nine million tons of steel at a cost of $1,400,000,000 are rusted away annually and therefore irrevocably lost to industry. Can this old earth continue indefinitely to yield up iron ore in sufficient quantity to make good such prodigious loss? Already the petroleum industry has been compelled to add a rust charge of one cent a gallon to the price of gasoline. Spurred by this economic loss, the leaders of the industry are planning a nation-wide study of the problem of correction. Such loss is not an inescapable necessity. Two years of cooperative research have reduced corrosion losses in the refrigerating industry by eighty per cent. At the Institute of Chemistry, held at Pennsylvania State College, in the summer of 1927, it was asserted that each industry must and will develop its own corrosion-resisting alloy.

A little more than a decade ago, a Norwegian scientist estimated that in something less than a century and a half the world's deposits of iron would be gone. What can be done to prolong their life? Of course, estimates are always tentative. Vast new deposits may be found. At greater depths than we now go, more than likely large supplies remain untouched. Still, the cost of tapping them may be staggering. What can be done to insure a more economic use of the present known resources?

Each year in the United States, we mine seventy-five million tons of iron ore, yielding fifty per cent. or more of iron. In fact, present methods of smelting seem to make it impossible to use ore containing a smaller percentage of metal. When we consider that copper ore having one per cent. and less of metal is successfully worked, the loss involved in sacrificing all deposits of iron of less than fifty per cent. seems appalling. The utilization of low-grade ores is becoming imperative. The chemist must solve the problem. Already, one method is offering a partial solution. Billions of tons of this low-grade ore are magnetic, that is, the ore will be

attracted by an electromagnet. Accordingly, the ore
is crushed and the iron-bearing particles are picked out
by electromagnetic methods, after which they are
smelted in the usual way. When the chemist shall have
made possible the utilization of iron ores yielding as low
as five or ten per cent. of metal, worry about their ultimate exhaustion may be deferred for several centuries
to come.

Many problems in the combating of corrosion still
confront the chemist. But recently Dr. A. V. Blom, a
Swiss chemist, announced a new method of protecting
iron. Through melted lead, he blows air and certain
other gases. The result is a yellow oxide of lead in
which are mixed finely divided particles of the unchanged
metal. When the product is mixed with a specially prepared linseed oil and applied to an iron surface, the
particles of lead gradually penetrate the iron, thereby
conferring an immunity to rust which seems to be permanent. The cloud on the horizon, however, appears to be
the growing scarcity of lead, which is rapidly qualifying
for membership in the class of precious metals. Alloys
of iron with chromium, nickel and silicon, or special
steels, also confer rust-proof and acid-resisting properties. Every industry brings to the laboratory of the
chemist for solution its own peculiar corrosion problems.
It is estimated that the annual loss from corrosion,
directly and indirectly, is close to three billion
dollars. Here is a field for research which chemistry is
only beginning to work. In place of the steel that rusts
must be put the steel that will not rust.

Already the chemist has solved a multitude of problems. From the wholly empirical methods of the ancient

metallurgist, the making of steel has emerged into the scientifically controlled industry which we know to-day. Chemically guarded at every point, nothing is left to chance. In particular, chemists have discovered that small quantities of certain metals alloyed with steel produce amazing effects. Early in the present century, two brothers, J. J. and J. M. Flannery, learning of the wonderful influence of vanadium, then a chemical curiosity, upon the cutting qualities of steel, ransacked the earth for a source of this metal and at length located the world's richest ore supply in the Peruvian Andes, at an altitude of more than sixteen thousand feet above sea level. As a result, the shock-absorbing properties, elasticity, and high resiliency of the steel which goes into your automobile has lightened it by a thousand pounds as well as strengthened it to a degree undreamed of in the earlier years of motoring. This steel, too, is important in airplane and railroad construction. It contributes to comfort and safety and in particular to that chief consideration of the age in which we live, namely, speed. Sir Robert Hadfield in England and Winfield Scott Potter in America solved the problem of manganese steel, whose astonishing strength, toughness, ductility, and non-magnetic properties marked a new departure in the manufacture and use of steel. The elements tungsten, chromium, and manganese are responsible for "high-speed" tool steels, which hold their temper, or hardness, when working at red-heat. This discovery has multiplied many times the output of our machine shops. Powerful machines, to-day, cut metal so rapidly that it is difficult to carry the chips away as fast as they are cut. During the war, when Germany was cut off from a supply of tungsten, her chemists discovered that molybdenum, another metal, could be substituted. In silicon steel, the electrical industry finds the almost perfect magnetic iron for the cores of transformers. A silicon-chromium steel has made possible the seamless boiler tube with its higher efficiency and greater resistance to corrosion. And now, according to a *New York Times* dispatch, from Germany comes transparent steel, as clear in thin sheets as the finest glass. The day is already at hand when the consumer will specify precisely the kind of steel he wants for a particular purpose and the chemists of the steel plant will produce it to order. Still, research has only begun. Vast possibilities, at present hardly suspected, are surely waiting for the great moments of discovery.

In 1820, the production of pig iron in this country was five pounds per capita. A century later, it had risen to five hundred and ninety-seven pounds and in three years more to eight hundred and nine pounds. The time is coming when the annual need for iron will be one ton for each individual in the land. And this use of iron is a fair measure of the industrial progress of a people. Upon the chemist rests the responsibility of providing it in ever-increasing quantity. The work of the world waits on him. He must not slack.

THE GIFT OF CHROMIUM

Stainless steels and rustless iron are meeting a host of needs in our homes, farms and workshops. The element which confers this property is chromium. When present in percentages between twelve and fourteen, together with from a quarter to four-tenths per cent. of carbon, the product is stainless steel, so widely used in cutlery. But to obtain this property of stainlessness special heat-treatment is essential. Heating to a bright red followed by rapid quenching produces an alloy of iron and chromium which retains in solution carbides of these two metals, thereby preventing an otherwise corrosive action. Chromium also imparts great strength and resistance to abrasion. Rustless iron differs from stainless steel in having much less carbon, usually less that a tenth per cent. It requires no heat-treatment, for few carbides are present, and it is softer than stainless steel, being easily rolled, forged and cold-worked. The softness of rustless iron limits the field of usefulness. For instance, it can not be employed in the making of tools and cutlery. Still its applications are numerous, and rustless iron is a decided chemical triumph. Used in proportions of twenty per cent. and more, chromium increases to a much higher degree the resistance to the action of corroding substances. Such iron-chromium alloys will resist oxidation up to temperatures of 1100 degrees Centigrade.

The increased use of these chromium alloys in industry has excited some alarm regarding the supply of the metal. Chromium-plate, that is iron or steel protected with a thin layer of chromium, is augmenting the demand. The domestic consumption of the mineral chromite, the source of the metal, has increased eighty-two per cent. since 1921. Our own mines do not meet our needs. However, deposits in Rhodesia and elsewhere promise an adequate supply for many years to come.

Before me lies a news column of *The New York Times*. The headline reads "Tin Consumption Tops Production." In the first paragraph, I note: "Heavy consumption of tin, which outruns production, has placed the product in a stronger position than at any time in the post-war period. . . . It is pointed out that annual world requirements of tin have been regularly exceeding yearly output for several years past." Dr. Charles L. Parsons, Secretary of the American Chemical Society, speaking at the Williamstown Conference in the summer of 1926, estimated the world's annual consumption of metals at seventy-five million tons and asserted that the reserves of copper, lead, tin, zinc and antimony will probably be exhausted in thirty years more. Already, in this country, metal reclaimed from the junk pile supplies one-half of our copper, one-third of our lead, one-eighth of our zinc, two-thirds of our tin, and three-fifths of our antimony. And the consumption of all metals steadily grows from decade to decade.

Some metals, in particular uses, are irretrievably lost. Zinc for galvanizing iron never comes back to the melting pot. Neither does the zinc used in the manufacture of pigments. Of the ninety thousand tons of virgin tin used in this country annually, thirty-six thousand tons go for the manufacture of tin-plate, practically none of which is recovered as metallic tin for reuse. And all of our tin is imported. Here is a problem for the chemist. He must discover a practical method of removing the thin film of tin on the surface of sheet iron and restoring it to the food-preserving industry to be used again. The alloys of tin, like those of other metals, come back to the metallurgist in large measure, but the cost of separating the metals is still great. One-third of the lead mined in this country, the world's largest producer, is used in paint pigments and therefore wholly lost. Existing sources are rapidly nearing exhaustion. This is one of the most disquieting aspects of the metal situation. Much as the chemist may accomplish in providing substitutes, he can not yet synthesize atoms and replenish the supplies of an exhausted element. The twenty-nine million tons of iron rusted every year are a complete loss. And yet much is recovered. In a recent year, thirty-five per cent. of the burden charged into the open-hearth furnaces of this country was scrap steel.

Gold, silver and platinum suffer little waste. Supplies of these metals are actually accumulating. Their recovery from other ores, even when present only in minute quantity, is a matter of considerable economic importance. One bitterly cold day in January, I nearly froze in walking across the wind-swept meadows of New Jersey to the plant of a large smelting and refining company, but when I arrived I was accorded the privilege of warming myself over caldrons of molten gold, silver and platinum. And I was permitted to enter the "strong room" of the plant and handle gold bricks, silver bars and platinum dust. This wealth represented the recovery of these precious metals in very small quantities from the refining of lead bullion.

In 1924, the Alaska-Juneau mine, producing ore containing but eighty-seven cents' worth of gold to the ton, added two million dollars to the world's output and paid an operating profit besides. It is this fact, that the yellow metal slowly accumulates, coupled with its freedom from corrosion and deterioration, which makes for stability of value as the monetary basis of world currencies.

The probable periods of exhaustion of tin, nickel, lead, copper and zinc, as given by Frederic W. Willard, of the Western Electric Company, in speaking before the Williamstown Conference, range from eleven years for copper to twenty years for zinc. Since 1900, the world has used more of its mineral resources than in all preceding history. The per capita consumption of copper (virgin metal) in this country rose from 7.96 pounds in 1910 to 12.42 pounds in 1925. And it is not only in America but throughout the world that the use of metals shows a steady increase. Backward peoples are learning that the comforts and luxuries of civilization spring from an abundant utilization of metals. The desire to possess tools, implements, and machines of all kinds permeates the world. Even in the heart of Africa, the Kaffir wants a sheet metal trunk in which to store his goods, free from molestation by invading insects. The native women proudly display sewing-machines. European countries are showing an increase in the use of telephones, motor-cars and domestic plumbing.

From the *Mineral Resources of Future Populations,* I take the following summary: "In the hundred years from the close of the Napoleonic wars to the outbreak of the World War, the white population of the world increased three-fold, but the output of tin increased twenty-six-fold, of copper sixty-three-fold, of the mineral fuels seventy-five-fold, and of pig iron over one hundred-fold. Lead and zinc showed a corresponding increase. In

1815, aluminum and the ferro alloys (nickel, vanadium, tungsten, manganese, and chromium) were known, if at all, as curiosities.'' And the war with its wide-spread unsettling effects, its intermingling of populations and dissemination of ideas gave the most tremendous impetus to the use of metals which the world has ever seen. The potential demand for metals grows ominous. How will it be met?

AN AGE OF ALUMINUM AND MAGNESIUM

There is no need of growing pessimistic. If certain metals disappear from the markets of the world, others must take their places. In the very clay beneath your feet and scattered most plentifully throughout the rocks in the upper ten miles of the earth is to be found a metal which may give its name to a new age. Eight per cent. of the solid crust is aluminum, a metal which, alone and in its alloys, can meet the world's need in a multitude of ways for centuries to come. Just let some chemist discover a process for obtaining cheap and abundant aluminum from ordinary clay, and iron may be toppled from its lofty throne and made to assume a rôle of secondary importance.

The Danish scientist, Oersted, first made aluminum in 1825. Three years later Wöhler obtained it in the laboratory by reduction from its oxide. In 1854, Louis Napoleon subsidized Henri St. Claire Deville in the development of a practical process of manufacture, and by 1888 the French chemist was turning out a maximum annual production of five thousand pounds. When he began, the price was ninety dollars a pound, but at the later date it had fallen to five dollars. Still, the white metal was only a curiosity and was used almost entirely for souvenir and ornamental purposes. With less than three tons per annum, not much else was possible.

The next man to try his hand at liberating aluminum from its ores was Hamilton Y. Castner, of Brooklyn. He devised an electrolytic method of producing cheap sodium metal and used this for the reduction of aluminum from its oxide. He succeeded in obtaining five hundred pounds of aluminum a day and sold it for four dollars a pound. The goal was alluring, for, when hammered and rolled, the metal became nearly as hard as iron; it was lighter than glass and did not tarnish or rust.

The man who did solve the problem of producing relatively cheap and abundant aluminum was Charles Martin Hall, a classical student in Oberlin College, who following his graduation in 1885 obtained permission to experiment in the college laboratory during the summer vacation. He had read of the wondrous metal, and his imagination was fired with the idea of separating it from the ore by means of the electric current. A man better versed in science probably would not have been bold enough to tackle the problem. But Hall's very ignorance was an asset. Summer and autumn passed without success and the weeks ran into midwinter. He was seeking some means of liquefying the ore, for in the raw state it would not conduct the current. Finally, in February, 1886, he made the notable discovery that melted cryolite, itself an aluminum mineral, will dissolve aluminum oxide as sugar dissolves in water. Delighted, he attempted to pass a current through the solution, but no metal resulted. Guessing that his difficulty lay in the clay crucible containing his melt, he substituted a carbon crucible, a conductor of electricity, making this the negative pole of his cell, and quickly obtained globules of the long-sought metal.

Still, Hall was a long way from a commercial process. Difficulties beset him on every hand. Without chemical training or technical knowledge, men with capital were reluctant to finance his operations. The carbon electrodes which he thrust into his solution of ore for the positive poles of his cell quickly burned up, and platinum, though satisfactory, was too expensive. He experimented a year with copper but was forced to abandon it. For a time, it seemed as though his process must be consigned to that long list of inventions designated as theoretically sound but practically unworkable. For three years, he struggled alone. During this time, a patent was granted him and later others, but unscrupulous men infringed upon them, and he was compelled to defend his rights in the courts. Judge William H. Taft, now Chief Justice, upheld his claims. At length, manufacturing interests, first in Boston and later in Lockport, New York, assisted him, but success eluded his grasp. Then, he went to Pittsburgh, where he secured the financial aid he needed. A small plant was built near by at Kensington, and by November, 1888, he was producing fifty pounds of metal a day at two dollars a pound, the lowest price it had ever touched. Deville and Castner now retired from the field. Hall's process prospered; technical difficulties were overcome; he enlarged his plant; uses for aluminum were rapidly discovered; a second plant was built at Niagara Falls, the first to use power from the great cataract; and, when in 1911 he received the Perkin Medal for his discoveries, his three plants were using 140,000 horse-power and producing 40,000,000 pounds of aluminum a year at twenty-two cents a pound.

We must not forget to state in passing that a brilliant French chemist, Paul T. L. Héroult, simultaneously with Hall and independently of him, invented the same process. At the awarding of the Perkin Medal to Hall, Héroult was present and told of his work of discovery.

Still aluminum at twenty-two cents a pound could not compete with pig iron at fifteen dollars a ton or with open-hearth steel at twenty-eight dollars a ton. And that is the difficulty to-day. Cheap and abundant aluminum, giving as it does alloys approximating, if not exceeding, iron and steel in strength with not more than one-third their weight, would inaugurate a new era in transportation and construction. Practically all the aluminum to-day is obtained from bauxite, an ore which does not exist in sufficient quantity to make possible the aluminum age. But clay, an essential constituent of which is this very metal, is everywhere. Here is the supreme chemical problem in the field of metallurgy. It can and must be solved. The world needs aluminum. To-morrow, it will be a necessity. Chemistry must find a way of quickly and cheaply breaking the tenacious bonds which hold aluminum in union with the other elements of common clay and thus liberate it to perform its part in the world's work. That the solution will be forthcoming, there can be no doubt. It is only a matter of time.

Weight for weight, aluminum has twice the electrical conductivity of copper. Already, more than one hundred and fifty thousand miles of aluminum conductor are in service, and the mileage is rapidly increasing. Owing to the larger size of the conductor, transmission losses are less with aluminum than with copper. With the discovery by Alfred Wilm, twenty years ago, of the heat treatment of aluminum, alloys having the ductility and strength of mild steel became possible. Sheet metal, castings, forgings, structural shapes, stampings, bars, rods and tubing, of high quality and in a variety of grades are now on the market. The dream of structural aluminum, not only for automobiles and airplanes, but for construction and railroad transportation, may be realized to-morrow. Aluminum would reduce the dead weight of a railroad passenger car by eight or ten tons. What this would mean in the saving of motive power and in reduced wear and tear both on train and road-bed as well as the possibility of quicker starting and stopping may easily be visualized. With the reduction of the impact load on the rails, aluminum will make possible more powerful locomotives. In the internal combustion motor, aluminum connecting rods and bearings will give increased speeds. Aluminum in the reciprocating parts of machinery will effect economies and increase efficiency. Duraluminum, an alloy consisting chiefly of aluminum with small quantities of copper, zinc and tin, afforded the material for the construction of German airplanes during the latter part of the war. Magnalium, an alloy of magnesium and the white metal, is as light as aluminum and nearly as strong as steel. The use of aluminum in alloys has only just begun. In a thousand ways aluminum can serve the needs of men. It is the metal of to-morrow, as bronze was the metal of an earlier age and steel is the metal of to-day. Light, strong, durable, ductile and non-corrosive, it combines in large measure the qualities of the ideal metal.

After aluminum and iron, magnesium is one of the most plentiful metals in the earth's crust. Its commercial development has only just begun, but, light and strong, it is already entering into competition with aluminum. A particular make of airplane engine has seventeen different parts made of magnesium castings. Magnesium propellers are replacing those of aluminum. Alloyed with very small quantities of certain other metals, its properties are greatly improved. A host of uses seem but to await the production of the metal in larger quantity. Supplementing aluminum and alloying with it, it may well be that magnesium will attach its name to the new age of metals which some day will come. When metals upon which the arts and industries have relied for centuries have performed their utmost of service and have passed from the stage, those still remaining in abundance must assume the leading rôles. The supremacy of aluminum and magnesium is but a matter of time.

OTHER METALS

Every metal doubtless has its uses. It is a part of the business of chemistry to find them. Even in minute quantity, a metal often exerts a marvelous influence. One per cent. of cerium oxide in a gas mantle multiplies the light-giving qualities manyfold. Two-tenths of a per cent. of vanadium increases the elasticity and tensile strength of mild steel by fifty per cent. One per cent. of chromium and two per cent. of nickel have an amazing effect upon the hardness and toughness of steel, making possible big guns, armor plate and armor-piercing projectiles. As we have seen small quantities of tungsten, chromium, manganese and molybdenum have made possible high-speed cutting tools. A certain combination of nickel and iron have produced "permalloy," the most easily magnetized and demagnetized of any metal known. Small quantities of titanium have a wonderful effect in deoxidizing the steel of the open-hearth furnace or Bessemer converter.

Sixteen hundred alloys are said to have been made, and still chemists have hardly begun to explore the possibilities latent in the multitudinous combinations to which metals may be subjected. An alloy for any particular purpose may almost be made to order. Platinite, having forty-six per cent. nickel and the remainder iron, possesses the same co-efficient of expansion as glass and may be substituted for platinum as the lead-in wires for the filament of an electric lamp. An alloy of nickel, chromium and iron is ideal for the resistance element of electric heating apparatus. Such alloys as monel metal, stellite and platinum-indium afford non-corrosive materials for the chemical industry. Invar, an iron-nickel alloy, neither expands nor contracts with change of temperature, making it invaluable as a material for clock pendulums, balance wheels, and measuring tapes. And so one might continue.

Often metals, long thought to have no use, assume a vast importance. Tungsten, as the ideal filament for the electric lamp, is a case in point. Tantalum, tried as a lamp filament and discarded, is now employed in the radio industry. Selenium, for years regarded only as a troublesome impurity in copper, now imparts a beautiful red color to glass and is the strategic element in the photoelectric cell, which makes possible the transmission of photographs by wire and wireless and talking movies. But there are still many metals which have not yet found their niches of usefulness. No important uses have been found for calcium, and yet it is one of the most plentiful metals. For barium and strontium, there are no cheap methods of extraction. Boron is a metal of mystery. So, too, is beryllium. Better and cheaper methods of producing titanium, zirconium, uranium and molybdenum are imperative. And the rare earth metals, of which illinium, recently discovered here in America, is an example, must find their places in the eternal scheme of things. Here on the frontiers of metallurgy vast fields for investigation invite the research chemist.

CATALYSTS

We are all familiar with the vivacious, energetic individual who with his presence and good cheer can in almost the twinkling of an eye convert the atmosphere of some stiff and formal social gathering from that of gloom to animated gaiety. Such an individual is a catalyst. He enlivens and accelerates the social activities of the group, and when the affair is over he is good for many more performances. So it is with many of the metals. Often in minute quantities, they speed up by their mere presence chemical reactions which would otherwise proceed with the utmost slowness. And the remarkable part of it is this,—the catalyst is not affected by the change. It can be used over and over, almost indefinitely. The "magic" gas lighter, containing a few threads of fine platinum wire, is an example. In some way, which no chemist understands, the platinum is able to convert the oxygen of the air from the molecular to the atomic state. Chemists call this the nascent state. In the form of atoms, the oxygen is much more active chemically, bringing about oxidation so rapidly that the kindling temperature of the gas is soon reached and it spontaneously bursts into flame. At first only a scientific curiosity, this phenomenon has long since been put to work. It is the basis of many commercial processes of vast importance.

Sulfuric acid is one of the three basic raw materials of chemical manufacture. You can not name anything from a pin to a locomotive which does not use directly or indirectly in its manufacture this "oil of vitriol," said to have been first obtained by the old alchemist, Basil Valentine, in the distillation of a green shale from Bohemia. To-day, the fundamental feature of one of the two commercial processes for the manufacture of the vast quantities of this acid demanded by modern industry is the catalytic action of platinum dust in bringing about the oxidation of sulfur dioxide gas. When you consider that statesmen have even contemplated measuring the degree of civilization of a nation in terms of the amount of sulfuric acid it uses, you will gain some idea of the immense significance of this catalytic process.

Known for nearly a century, it fell to two French chemists of our own day, Sabatier and Senderens, and the German chemist Normann to usher catalysis into industry. It so happens that two of the three chief constituents of cottonseed oil differ from edible lard only in having fewer atoms of hydrogen in their molecules. If one of these, oleate, could be induced to take on two more atoms of hydrogen in each molecule, it would be converted into stearate, a substitute for lard in cooking, and its value thereby multiplied many times. Mixing the gas with the oil, with or without heat and pressure, accomplished nothing. Then one day, by some happy turn of the wheel of fortune, these French chemists brought the vapor of oleic acid into contact with hydrogen gas in the presence of finely divided metallic nickel. A seemingly magic transformation was wrought. Each molecule of the acid united with two atoms of hydrogen, and stearate, a hard fat, resulted. Nickel dust had catalyzed the essential chemical reaction. Then, Normann soon showed that it was unnecessary to vaporize the oleic acid. You know the result. A former waste assumed large commercial value and became the source of an important foodstuff. Further, the discovery here made pointed the way to the conversion of the most nauseating fish oils into soaps of the rarest quality. Even whaling, which had languished for half a century and more, has been revived as in the halcyon days of yore, so that whale oil may be had for catalytic conversion into the raw material of soap manufacture.

The Twitchell process of making soap calls catalysis into play. Our grandmothers made soap by boiling together in an iron kettle fat scraps and lye. Lye is the strong caustic solution of potassium hydroxide obtained by leaching water through wood ashes. The chemical change taking place during this process of boiling lye and fats is known as saponification. It is also effected by using sodium hydroxide in place of lye. The sodium soap is hard while that of potassium is soft. A by-product of the process, one entirely neglected in the early days of the industry, is glycerin, now needed in enormous quantities for the manufacture of nitroglycerin and dynamite. In huge copper kettles often holding a million pounds of soap stock, the process is carried out for the production of these two products. But the separation of the glycerin from the spent lye is a difficult undertaking. Ernst Twitchell, an American chemist, developed a catalytic process of soap manufacture which requires no lye. He saponifies the fats by boiling them with water containing a small amount of sulfuric acid and a fraction of one per cent. of a catalyst. The result is a chemical action between the fat and water which yields glycerin free from any contamination with lye. The other product is an organic acid, called a fatty acid, which is neutralized with sodium hydroxide to form soap. The fatty acids form a layer upon the surface of the mixture in the kettle with the glycerin dissolved in the water below. The separation and purification of the glycerin is easily accomplished by processes of neutralization, filtration, evaporation and distillation.

Catalytic action in industry has already found a wide application. Not long ago in a German dye plant, some chemists were endeavoring to convert naphthalene, the substance in ordinary moth balls, into phthalic acid, but all their efforts proved unavailing. Then occurred one of those lucky accidents which occasionally punctuate the course of scientific investigations. An awkward laboratory assistant in taking the temperature of the reaction tank broke the thermometer and spilled a trifling quantity of mercury. Forthwith, something happened.

The contents of the tank seethed with activity. The long-sought transformation was an accomplished fact. Mercury had catalyzed the reduction of naphthalene to phthalic acid. Again, reduction in the viscosity of solutions under the influence of catalytic agents has made possible the new lacquers for finishing automobiles and furniture. Catalysis is responsible for speeding up the vulcanization of rubber. A catalytic process for manufacturing nitric acid from the nitrogen of the air made Germany independent of Chile saltpeter during the war and by providing her in abundance with this indispensable raw material for the production of explosives saved the Central Powers from early defeat. The catalytic preparation of methanol, or wood alcohol, by French and German chemists has wrought a near-revolution among the distillers of wood in this country. Catalysis is an important factor in Doctor Bergius' method for the liquefaction of coal. It is the basis, too, for the synthesis in France and Germany of alcohols and petroleum substitutes from mixtures of hydrogen and carbon monoxide. And in all of these processes metals are the catalyzers, although, as in the case of the enzymes which cause fermentation and decay and bring about other chemical reactions, there are also non-metallic catalytic agents.

An important property of some of these catalyzers is the ease with which they become "poisoned," that is, rendered unfit for performing their respective rôles. Why dust, sulfur and other impurities will incapacitate a catalyzer, we do not know. Fortunately, however, as in the case of platinum, the substance may be regenerated. Sometimes a catalyzer is deliberately poisoned to a certain extent, to slow down its action, just as the physician administers a sedative to a patient in a state of nervous excitation.

As yet, chemists have scarcely entered upon the numerous paths blazed by these pioneers in the field of catalytic action. Beyond doubt vast possibilities await the research chemist. To-morrow, catalysis may reveal the secret spring which will release the illimitable quantities of subatomic energy and with it usher in a new era in the evolution of the race.

While catalysts have already accomplished much, their scientific introduction into industry has only just begun. The method so far employed in their selection and in discovering varieties of application has been that of "cut and try." Here is one of the big opportunities for pure research. Chemists do not yet understand the scientific explanation of catalysis. When they do, its possibilities will be immeasurably enlarged. But a beginning in this field has been made. Hugh S. Taylor, of Princeton University, is leading the attack upon this problem. Doctor Taylor says:

"Anyone who wishes to scan the pages of romance should linger over the records of catalysis in the past two decades, for the science and the art of the catalytic chemist have transformed industrial and commercial life. Gone are the indigo plantations of India; they fell a victim to the discovery of synthetic indigo. This synthesis required for its fulfilment the contact sulfuric acid process, since the organic chemist required 'oleum' where formerly concentrated acid was adequate for the inorganic field. Indigo required also the oxidation of naphthalene to phthalic acid, and this has twice been revolutionized catalytically. Firstly, there was oxidation with sulfuric acid and mercury sulfate; latterly we have learned of the air oxidation of naphthalene vapor over oxide of molybdenum as a catalyst. An enormously expanded whaling industry in Arctic and Antarctic seas, new tracts of cocoanut plantations in tropical Africa and America, an expanding market in cottonseed oil—all these are reflexes of the discoveries of Sabatier and Normann that hydrogen molecules could readily be added to unsaturated hydrocarbon chains, liquid or gaseous, when in contact with finely divided nickel as a catalyst. Two decades ago the ships of all the nations hurried their cargoes of saltpeter from Chile to home ports. To-day all the great nations are drawing supplies of fixed nitrogen from the air, whether as ammonia, cyanide, or nitride. The hurrying pace of motor transport facilities creates a need for solvents and enamels, the catalytic chemist produces alcohols and acids and esters in response to the demand. Has he not threatened thereby a whole American industry with extinction? Did not the advent of a shipload of synthetic methanol in the port of New York threaten the whole wood alcohol industry of this country, spread consternation throughout its ranks? Is it not abundantly plain that no tariff wall, however high, can hold back the flood tide of—progress?

"There can be no room for complacency in any chemical industry of which the development department has not its finger on the pulse of chemical research. For the catalyst which accelerates chemical reactions also accelerates the decay of established industries. Who could have forecast the transformation of the paint and varnish industry now in progress? . . . Tradition constitutes no bulwark against the cold facts of thermodynamic calculation and chemical affinity. The catalyst is the key that liberates the latent forces within the molecules and yields them their fullest opportunities."

ELECTROMETALLURGY

From the early years of the last century, when Sir Humphry Davy by means of the electric current broke the chemical affinities which held in bondage six new elements, electrometallurgy has assumed a constantly increasing importance in the separation and purification of the metals. During the Great War, it was my privilege to visit a great copper refining plant of the East. There over a large area, like lumber in a mill yard, were piled ingots of copper, weighing five or six hundred pounds each, brought thither by boat and rail from distant ports and from the copper smelters of our West. Gathered in those piles was a king's ransom—and many of them. Could that vast store of precious metal, so needful to the Central Powers, have fallen into the hands of the Kaiser, it would have meant more than a substantial victory on the battle front. At one point, I saw a specially constructed melting pot and forms for casting the metal into rectangular slabs, called anodes, preparatory to the electrolytic refining process. Then, I entered a huge room with a floor space of possibly an acre, covered as closely as it could well stand with refining baths, in which the silent flow of electric current, ceaselessly, day and night, was busy transferring ions of metallic copper from the positive anodes to the negative cathodes, thin slabs of pure copper which served as the basis upon which to deposit the refined metal. And the purity obtained was 99.98 per cent., better than the far-famed purity of a well-known brand of soap. In the mud, removed from time to time from the bottoms of the tanks, was found gold, silver and platinum, also refined in part by aid of the electric current.

Plating with many metals is carried out electrolytically. Even the deposition of brass and other alloys, in which mixtures of metals occur, may be done with the

Source of the world's supply of vanadium

At Mina Ragra, 15,500 feet above sea level, in the Andes of Peru; the highest
mining operation in the world

A white-hot steel ingot being hammered into shape under the terrific blows
of a steam hammer

Pouring molten steel from a two-ton Héroult electric furnace

The electric furnace is rapidly coming to the fore in the manufacture of high-grade steel

Slabs of electrolytically refined copper, lifted from the refining bath

Copper is one of the purest of commercial metals

electric current. Zinc as well as copper is refined electrolytically. The process by which the publisher makes the
plates from which this book is printed is an electrolytic
one. Metals such as sodium, potassium and aluminum
are obtained by electrolysis. Electric furnaces are be-

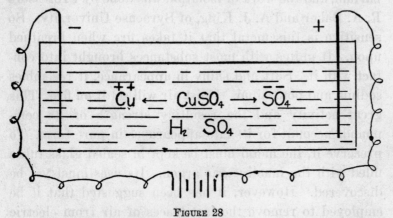

FIGURE 28

Bath for the electrolytic refining of copper. A thick slab of impure
copper is placed at the anode, or positive pole, and a thin slab of pure
copper forms the cathode, or negative pole. A solution of copper sulfate
serves as the electrolyte. As the current flows, the positively charged copper
ions are drawn to the cathode, where they give up their charges and attach
themselves, gradually building this up into a thick plate of the purest copper. At the same time the negative sulfate ions pass to the anode, where
they draw into solution more copper ions, leaving the impurities behind.
As fast as copper ions are deposited upon the cathode an equal number are
drawn into solution from the anode.

coming important in the manufacture of steel. Electrolytic iron of great purity is now being produced at
Niagara Falls. Magnesium, a chief metal of the coming
age, is an electrolytic product. Ferrosilicon, essential as
a deoxidizer in the manufacture of steel, is made in the
electric furnace. In a score of other ways, electricity is
a factor in metallurgy, and it promises to become of
constantly increasing importance with the passing of the
years.

A METALLIC NOVELTY

At a recent meeting of the American Chemical Society, a metal long known in its compounds was exhibited in pure form for the first time. The metal is barium, and the work of isolation was done by Professors R. A. Baker and A. J. King, of Syracuse University. So sensitive is this metal that it takes fire when breathed upon. It unites with most substances brought into contact with it. Soft and shiny in appearance, it resembles sodium and potassium. Moist air will set it on fire. This great activity and the resulting strength of its compounds account for its late appearance in pure form. To preserve it, the metal must be kept in sealed glass tubes filled with the inactive gas argon. Its uses must yet be discovered. However, it has been suggested that it be employed to remove the last traces of air from electric lamp and radio bulbs. Barium occurs in the same group in the Periodic Table with radium, but it is considerably lighter and exhibits no radioactivity. Let it be emphasized that the work of obtaining this metal in pure state promised no commercial rewards. It was undertaken solely for the love of science. This spirit of discovery is at once the foundation of past progress and the hope of the future.

THE X-RAY, A TOOL OF THE METALLURGIST

Although known for a generation, the X-ray has but recently given to the metallurgist a new means of testing metals. We have already seen that the work of the Swiss physicist, Laue, made possible X-ray spectra and the determination of crystal structure. Even the atomic composition of the molecules in a crystal becomes almost visible. The spacings of the atoms and their relative positions may be known with the utmost accuracy. These atomic X-ray patterns show that metals crystallize in the cubic form, and each metal has its own characteristic spacings of the atoms. If, as in an alloy, more than one metal is present, the X-ray pattern will disclose it. Furthermore, the particular elements present may be known. If the metals have actually entered into combination, this, too, will be shown. The great value of the X-ray to the metallurgist lies in its revelation of strains and imperfections in castings and other metal products, defects utterly beyond the power of the microscope to detect. For instance, the X-ray examination of the alloys entering into air-ship construction may in the future make impossible disasters such as befell the ill-fated *Shenandoah*. The X-ray literally makes known the underlying cause of the remarkable properties of certain alloys. Thus, if a large atom is introduced into the "lattice" spacing of a smaller one, the property of rigidity results. However, if a smaller atom is thrust into the lattice of a larger one, ductility emerges from the combination. And now it is asserted that through the X-ray analysis of metals the chemist will be able to determine in advance whether or not a newborn alloy will resist the corroding action of moist air. No longer will it be necessary to wait through long months of testing to obtain this important information. The properties of a new alloy will be specified in advance as precisely as an engineer specifies the requirements of girders in a bridge.

A recent demonstration with the ultra-microscope by F. F. Lucas, of the Bell research laboratories, showed by means of pictures thrown on a screen the details of the various constituents of alloys and the causes of strength or weakness. A crack just starting in a piece of pure iron was seen to follow the line of slight amounts of non-metallic material in the sample. The instrument employed makes visible a particle only one five-millionth of an inch across. The use of the shorter waves of ultraviolet light makes visible still smaller particles. It is estimated that these particles, so made visible, contain about five hundred atoms, a closer approach to this chemical unit than was ever before believed possible.

There is something almost uncanny about such revelations. This seeing atoms is like seeing ghosts. No scientist of a generation ago would have believed it possible. But more than ever this scientific control of metals and a mastery of their production, properties, and uses mean power and more abundant material well-being.

And now with this altogether inadequate survey of a field of chemical investigation which stretches from before the dawn of history to the latest instant of recorded time and projects itself forward into the remotest future of human progress, we must turn to another chapter.

CHAPTER XI

In the Realm of Synthetics

GERMANY'S DEBACLE AND HER RECUPERATION—FACTORS IN
RECUPERATION—PART PLAYED BY SYNTHETIC CHEMISTRY—A
SYNTHETIC AGE—ACTUAL ACHIEVEMENTS—IMPOSSIBLE TO
SYNTHESIZE METALS—ARTIFICIAL FOOD INDUSTRY IMPROB-
ABLE—SYNTHETIC MEDICINALS—COMING OF RAYON—CHAR-
DONNET'S PROCESS—VISCOSE PROCESS—RAYON INVADES MANY
FIELDS—BAKELITE—PERFUMES AND FLAVORINGS—SYNTHESIS
A MASTER KEY.

THE year 1923 marked the lowest ebb of German
fortunes. A great people seemed to reel between two
worlds. On the one hand were the pomp of former
military glory, the might of industrial supremacy, the
control of world markets, merchant ships everywhere
upon the "seven seas," the "Made in Germany" trade-
mark almost as familiar a sight as that of a postage
stamp, German universities the Meccas of foreign students, her discoveries dominating the scientific thought
of the world, a monetary system apparently as rugged
as the surrounding hills, and the bright dreams of world
conquest silhouetted against the foreground of German
hopes and ambitions. On the other hand was the black
night of military defeat, political revolution, and economic chaos. Swept away by the cruel fate of war were
10 per cent. of Germany's population, 13 per cent.

of her Continental territory, her colonial possessions entirely, 74 per cent. of her iron ore, 26 per cent. of her coal, 68 per cent. of her zinc, 30 per cent. of her potash monopoly, 85 per cent. of her merchant tonnage, and her exports of sugar to the last ton. Her currency, touching the absolute zero of exchange value, had become an international joke. Her bitterest foe held the Ruhr with its rich mines of coal. The secession of Bavaria seemed imminent. Civil war threatened in Prussia and Saxony. German troops were disaffected. The Cuno Government faced collapse and the Empire tottered on the brink of dissolution. Never before had the debacle of a great world power seemed so complete.

To-day, Germany's recovery has become the outstanding miracle of the contemporary world. In every field of business and industry, she has staged an extraordinary come-back. Her currency has been stabilized. Her export trade is but ten per cent. below the pre-war level. Her coal production actually exceeds the figures of 1913. Shipping tonnage is sixty per cent. of normal. In commercial aviation, Germany leads the world. German pig iron can be delivered in Philadelphia at four or five dollars a ton cheaper than it can be had from western Pennsylvania. Her synthetic ammonia for refrigeration purposes is cutting into the trade of other nations. Standards of living are improving. Building is on the increase. Railroads are operated with matchless German efficiency. Her industrial plants are marvels of equipment and administration. In short, the industrial and commercial supremacy of the old-time Germany is once more becoming a dominant factor in world affairs.

And, when we seek the answer, three outstanding

instrumentalities seem to be responsible for this remarkable transformation. They are an abundance of raw materials, particularly coal, creative chemistry and the German genius for organization. When we say chemistry, we mean to a large extent synthetic chemistry, and thereby hangs the reason for the foregoing introduction.

What is synthetic chemistry and how has it operated so marvelously to Germany's material advantage? Analysis is taking apart. Synthesis is putting together. The burning of hydrogen and oxygen to form water is a simple example of chemical synthesis. We take the two constituent elements and put them together to form a compound. The synthesis of common table salt may be effected by the burning of metallic sodium in an atmosphere of poisonous chlorine gas. Hydrochloric acid, of vast industrial importance, is sometimes synthesized by the direct union of hydrogen and chlorine. Many examples have been given in the foregoing pages of commercial synthesis. The direct hydrogenation of vegetable oils to form edible fats is a notable one. We shall refer to others as we proceed. The ideal chemical synthesis means the exact duplication of some natural product through building up from raw materials. A classic illustration is the production of indigo from coal-tar. The production of artificial silk, known in America as rayon and to be discussed soon, is often referred to as chemical synthesis. But it is so only by analogy. Rayon is not a duplication of natural silk. It is an artificial substitute. But when we speak of synthetics, we shall include both the real and the pseudo.

And now what of Germany and synthetic chemistry? Even when her people were staggering in the darkness of apparent economic ruin, her splendid laboratories and industrial plants with their superb equipment were all intact. The knowledge of applied chemistry obtained through many years of patient research had not been obliterated. The German genius for organization had been only temporarily eclipsed. At length came the turn of the tide. New leaders gained the ascendency in the business world. Industrial prosperity became the supreme object of a definite, scientific program. German initiative asserted itself. The people went back to work. The chemists returned to their laboratories. Production began, scientifically controlled production as of old, and in the bright morning of a new day Germany began to climb back to her place in the economic sun.

You know the story of synthetic dyes. Born in England, but early transplanted to German soil, this laboratory controlled industry had grown to large proportions before the war, and in that struggle it became a veritable arsenal of war-making products. In the renaissance of German industry, the hundreds of synthetic dyes and related organic compounds have again become sources of wealth as in former years. Just as synthetic indigo, a generation ago, laid waste to the natural cultivation of indigo in British India and German synthetic camphor more recently broke the Japanese monopoly, so does the new synthetic plasmochin of German laboratories threaten the Dutch East Indies monopoly of quinine. We have seen, too, how the synthetic nitrogen of German plants, now approaching an annual production of a half-million tons, has broken the Chilean nitrate monopoly throughout the world and become a constantly increasing source of revenue. Our distillers of wood have been brought face to face with German synthetic methanol, and only the protection of a high tariff has saved the industry from ruin. Already the hydrogenation of coal and its liquefaction to form synthetic petroleum as well as the direct synthesis of this key resource of the modern world promise to emancipate Germany from dependence upon a foreign supply. Even the synthesis of sugar from wood looms on the German horizon as a commercial possibility. The products of coal-tar and the host of synthetic drugs and medicinals obtained therefrom are sturdy contributors to Germany's economic recuperation, even as they were to her pre-war dominance in the chemical field.

Yes, synthetic chemical products together with the chemically controlled production of iron and steel, and of potash, glass, textiles, ceramics and a multitude of other commodities are tremendous factors in weaving the economic rainbow which promises the rehabilitation of the German nation. In Germany, we see synthetic chemistry at its highest points of achievement. As we have learned, without synthetic nitrogen, the war would have ended almost before it began. The synthesis of organic compounds, which began with Wöhler in a German laboratory in 1828 and is now approaching its first centennial, has grown to an industry of large extent and immense significance. And the possibilities in this fertile field of chemical research, both for Germany and other nations alike, are yet legion. Chemical synthesis is becoming a master key to world progress. In the stress of war, synthetic rubber helped to mitigate a real crisis of the German people, and it may yet spell economic freedom for them and other peoples.

A SYNTHETIC AGE

We hear much these days of a synthetic age. It is even intimated that in the near future three portions of laboratory-designed pills at stated intervals may become satisfactory substitutes for three square meals a day. A prominent automobile manufacturer has suggested that in time the cow as a factor in economic life may become as obsolete as the extinct animals of former geologic ages. Synthetic milk of uniform composition and superior nutritious qualities will replace the liquid food of the bovine species. The proteins and carbohydrates essential to human food will some time be factory made instead of being raised on the farm. The soils may be released for the production of other raw materials, such as the starches for conversion into artificial rubber, alcohols, and motor fuels. Houses of steel and artificial stone must ultimately replace those of lumber. House furnishings will be fashioned from synthetic substances. Wall coverings, decorations, and tapestries will be derived from substitutes. Furniture from synthetic resins, floors of composition materials, rugs of artificial leather, and draperies of rayon will become the order of the day. The exhaustion of minerals and metals will be made good by synthetic substitutes. Dr. John E. Teeple, speaking at the Williamstown Conference in the summer of 1926, said: "I can't get excited because of any impending shortage of cellulose, or manganese, tin or copper, and of the other materials that are not actually essential to life or can not be easily reproduced. This does not mean, however, that we should ignore the subject of waste or shortage."

The foregoing picture is both fanciful and real. Artificial leather is already here. Millions of yards of cotton fabric treated with cellulose and colored with synthetic dyes are to be found on furniture, in automobile upholstery, and in a variety of other common uses. Last year the automobile industry used more than twice as much artificial leather as natural. And thanks to chemical research, the leather is not the cheap imitation of former years, but almost as good as that from real hides. Recently, the chemist has devised a way of vulcanizing rubber directly upon metals and at the same time giving to it the appearance of real leather. An electrotype is made of some handsome piece of leather, just as an electrotype for a page of this book is made. It is then etched with acid, impressed upon soft rubber and the rubber vulcanized in place. After suitable lacquering, a product superior for its purpose and beautiful to behold greets the eye. Linoleums, made from large mesh fabric impregnated with fillers of ground cork and wood flour held together with binders such as linseed oil, afford satisfactory floor coverings. Synthetic lacquers offer a substitute for tin as suitable linings for food containers. These nitrocellulose lacquers, too, are revolutionizing the paint industry. The discovery of synthetic paint constitutes the first important change in the manufacture of paint from natural substances in a thousand years. Bakelite, a synthetic plastic, the familiar story of which, recounted later in this chapter, is a romance in itself, has met a host of needs and has released expensive raw materials for other purposes. The chemically treated casein of milk is rendering the pencil manufacturer independent of natural cedar as a casing for his lead. Asbestos and cement are already willing soldiers in the great army of substitutes. From Italy, comes the news that the synthesis of artificial wool may some day displace the animal fibers from the sheep's back. Wood pulp or cotton linters are metamorphosed after the fashion of rayon manufacture. However, the product is vegetable and not animal. Chemists have recently been learning that synthetic alcohols, rubber, plastics and many other products may be produced from petroleum. Synthetic food is not altogether a fantastic dream. Report comes from England that a Liverpool chemist has synthesized from water and carbon dioxide, a sugar similar to dextrose. As we know, edible fats from vegetable oils have been articles of commerce for years, and it is not inconceivable that the chemist may evolve proteids from ammonia and nitrous acid in union with water and carbon dioxide. The triple combination of heat, pressure and a catalyst may do the trick. Synthetic drugs, dyes and perfumes we have without end. And, as in the case of synthetic nitrogen compounds, and the prospective synthesis of petroleum, these fabrications of the laboratory and the chemical plant are entering the stage of large-scale production. It would be rash to set any limits to future possibilities.

Still, the chemist can not accomplish the impossible. It would be exceedingly unwise for the world to allow these rosy dreams, born of what seem to be the magic accomplishments of synthetic chemistry, to lull it into a false sense of security. The chemist can not synthesize the elements, and metals are elements. He can offer no hope of synthetic substitutes for the great bulk of our vanishing ore supplies. As Dr. H. Foster Bain says,

"There is no more a royal road to metal reserves than to learning." And, in speaking of foods, Sir James C. Irvine, of the University of St. Andrews, Scotland, said at the Williamstown Conference: "But when it comes to the question of foodstuffs I must reluctantly confess that I can not regard the chemist as a serious competitor with Nature. I would be the last to disparage the triumphs of the scientist in synthesizing—that is to say, building up by artificial processes all manner of natural compounds. Frequently, he has in a measure beaten Nature, having produced substances artificially that no living thing, plant or animal, could possibly produce. Yet when we consider the two essential constituents of foods, namely carbohydrates (sugars, starches, etc.), and the proteins (albuminoids), the chemist has to admit what is practically defeat. True, he has produced his butter substitutes, materials that I hold in high esteem and the production of which I regard as one of the triumphs of chemistry; but otherwise I can see no prospect of the development of what may be termed an artificial food industry." It would seem difficult for the chemist to master the secret of putting into foods those elusive substances known as vitamins and so vital to human health.

Synthetic chemistry is big with portent. Of course, it has its limitations, but the achievements of to-morrow may dwarf into insignificance the accomplishments of to-day. Still, that the world will ever see a synthetic age, in which truly synthetic products will chiefly supply the needs of men, may well be doubted And yet, no man in these days dares to say that anything in the realm of science is impossible.

SYNTHETIC MEDICINALS

A half-century ago, synthetic medicinals were almost unknown to the medical world. To-day, large numbers of such organic compounds, built in the chemical laboratory, have proved of distinct value in the treatment and cure of disease. With some of them, we are already familiar from the chapter on Chemistry and Disease. Others have been gradually taking their places on the druggist's shelves and in the arsenal of valuable remedies available to the practising physician.

Among the antiseptics, we have the dyes, already discussed and all of them synthetic products. Methylene blue, first suggested about 1890, is an important urinary antiseptic. Scarlet red gives relief to sufferers from burns and ulcers, while mercurochrome, gentian violet, acriflavine, brilliant green, and others proved to be of untold value in the treatment of wounds in the World War. The famous Carrel-Dakin solution gained great vogue in wound dressing during the war, and since, Doctor Dakin has devised chlorinated organic substances for the same purpose. Carbolic acid, a coal-tar product, has been in use for more than fifty years, but synthetic derivatives of it, of which we have a considerable number, began appearing in the eighties of the last century. In 1884, beta-naphthol came into use as a skin, mouth and intestinal antiseptic. To rescue it from falling into disuse on account of its disagreeable taste, the chemist has produced a number of artificial substitutes. For iodoform, a powerful antiseptic but of disagreeable odor, the chemist has given the physician a number of odorless derivatives, the first of which, iodol, appeared in

1884. From creosote has been extracted the active
principle, guaiacol, a valued antiseptic in pulmonary and
intestinal troubles. To rid it of its characteristic odor
and irritating effect upon the stomach, chemists have
succeeded in preparing synthetic creosote products in
solid and tasteless form.

A committee of the American Chemical Society a few
years ago placed the nation's drug bill at approximately
a half-billion dollars annually, a large portion of which
goes for synthetic products. Within thirty years, the
number of drug items on the market has grown from
about three thousand to nearly fifty thousand. In 1874,
the German chemist Kolbe prepared from carbolic acid
salicylic acid, long used as a preservative and remedy for
rheumatism. When treated with strong acetic acid, this
drug gives "aspirin." We may gain some idea of the
prevalence of headache in this country from the fact
that in 1925, 1,476,000 pounds of this compound, worth at
wholesale $1,025,000, were sold to the American public.
In this same year, the arsphenamines, the arsenic derivatives for the treatment of syphilis, represented a value
of a million and a half dollars and were dispensed in
about two million doses. So small is the dose, however,
that five thousand pounds probably covered the quantity. If synthetic chemistry had done nothing more than
to score this brilliant triumph of "606" and its derivatives, its niche in the hall of medical fame would
forever be secure. As we have seen "Bayer 205"
another synthetic product, is proving its value in helping
to rid half a continent of sleeping sickness.

Some of our most valued remedies may be traced to
primitive peoples who discovered that chewing the bark

or leaves of certain trees or shrubs gave relief from particular ills. From such sources have come quinine, morphine and cocaine. Within the last half-century, chemists have succeeded in isolating in the pure state the active principles of these and other drugs of similar origin. From a knowledge of the compositions and molecular structures, attempts at synthesis followed. Quinine and cocaine have been thus obtained, but their commercial production, save for plasmochin, the synthetic rival of quinine, is still in the future. But synthetic substitutes for cocaine, such as procaine, better known as novocaine, have been forthcoming from the laboratory. Because procaine does not render insensitive the mucous membrane, the chemist has synthesized butyn, which does. These drugs, too, are free from the toxic effects of cocaine itself.

For the allaying of fever, the chemist has provided such antipyretics as antipyrin, antifebrin, acetanilide and phenacetin. With the discovery of the beneficent properties of one of these, is associated an interesting story. Back in 1883, Doctor Knorr, of Germany, discovered that antipyrin is better for the treatment of fever than quinine. In a short time large quantities of the drug were being made and enormous profits reaped. Two physicians, who had a friend in the employ of the chemical works where the antipyrin was manufactured, were in the habit of sending there for their supply. One day they determined to try the effect of naphthalene on a patient suffering from some skin disease. The boy sent to put up the chemical carelessly filled the bottle with acetanilide. Upon receiving the drug, the doctors immediately proceeded to administer it. But the effect was altogether different from what they had expected. The substance promptly reduced the fever from which their patient was suffering. When it was gone, they sent for more. This time the chemist of the plant filled the order, and they got naphthalene, what they supposed they had received before. But this had no effect on the fever at all. Investigation explained the mystery, and ever since acetanilide has been an active competitor of antipyrin and is manufactured in large quantities.

Research in the field of sedatives for inducing sleep have resulted in providing such synthetic hypnotics as veronal, luminal, adalin, bromural, iodival, nirvanol and ural. These, too, are free from the dangers of chloral and the habit-forming trionals and sulphonals of an earlier day.

The amount paid in this country in a recent year for cinchophen, a synthetic alkaloid for the treatment of gout, reached nearly a half-million dollars, and that at wholesale prices. Ten years ago, the manufacture of synthetic medicinals in the United States was comparatively small. To-day, they constitute a large proportion of the total drugs sold, and there are few such synthetics not made here. And research is everywhere in evidence. No large drug-manufacturing house is without its chemical research staff.

Already, we have discussed in these pages the isolation and present developments in the synthetic preparation of the important secretions of the ductless glands. In every field of synthetic medicinals much has been accomplished, but large areas yet remain to be explored, and nowhere more so than in the work upon these vital principles, a knowledge of which means so much to the well-being of the race.

Two years ago the word *rayon* would have meant nothing to the wisest person. To-day this magic name, associated with which is so much of the romance of modern business and science, is a subject of absorbing interest in directors' meetings, to boards of trade, in chemical laboratories, to plant managers in charge of vast establishments with millions of dollars invested in equipment, to discriminating housewives, shop girls, and connoisseurs of taste and fashion, and to every one directly or indirectly interested in the subject of textiles. Rayon, a word coined in America to designate the first and only man-made fabric, is now synonomous with artificial silk. And fitting it was that America should give the name, for in the manufacture of this new competitor of other textile fabrics she leads the world. While in 1913 the output of American factories was but a million and a half pounds, in 1926 it had risen to sixty-one million. Fortunes have already been made in the rapid rise of this infant industry. It is said that the five hundred dollar investment of an English parson in Courtauld's Limited, of England, has grown since 1913 to a present value of $1,550,000. So valuable has rayon stock in the various producing companies become that little of it is available to the public. The meteoric rise of rayon is an astounding phenomenon of the contemporary scientific and industrial world.

The story of silk is a romance of wondrous charm. With it is associated splendor and beauty, royalty and

Courtesy, Eastman Kodak Company

Fractional distillation in the preparation of synthetic organic chemicals

Actual ''spinning'' of rayon thread by the viscose process

Courtesy, The Industrial Fibre Company, Inc.

The twisted yarn is being reeled into skeins

wealth, art and science. Rising out of the immemorial past, we see in imagination the unknown discoverer in distant China, the early horticulturist, the skilful craftsmen and the gifted artists who worked out the first idea. Then follows the long procession of adventurers and traders who bore westward over the old caravan routes the message of beauty, that kings and queens, conquerors and ambassadors, brave knights and fair ladies, arrayed in silks and satins, might grace the glittering pageants that adorn the pages of history. With the coming of automatic machinery, this matchless beauty of the East, transplanted to European soil, becomes the common possession of those in humbler walks of life. Discoverer, explorer, soldier, merchant, inventor, craftsman, artist, designer and tailor,—all have contributed to brighten the lives of people everywhere with this fabric which for centuries has been the mark of distinction.

Certain it was that sometime human ingenuity should seek to imitate with man-made creations this textile of the ancient East. Within the present generation that time has arrived. For centuries, cotton, wool, silk and flax formed the "big four" of the textile industry, providing the fabrics with which the world was clothed. To-day, this new gift of chemistry has forged ahead of natural silk and occupies fourth place among the basic fibers of spinning and weaving. The triumph is as brilliant an achievement as that of the motor-car, the motion picture, or the radio, and the swiftness with which it has arrived has been just as amazing.

Shortly after the middle of the last century Andemars, a Swiss chemist, patented a process for transforming an ether-alcohol solution of nitrocellulose into artificial fibers. But not until 1884 did the French nobleman, Hilaire de Chardonnet, conceive the idea of producing a practicable commercial substitute for natural silk. The problem was to imitate with chemical and mechanical processes the silk-worm, which, feeding upon mulberry leaves, transforms this raw material into a fiber of wonderful delicacy and fineness of texture. In spinning its cocoon, the silk-worm forces through two exceedingly fine openings in its mouth, known as spinnerets, a semi-liquid substance, which hardens immediately upon contact with the air. As a result, a single cocoon produces on an average five hundred yards of raw silk filament. The idea was simple enough, and the problem seemed clear-cut and definite. Chardonnet determined to solve it.

He began with precisely the same raw material that the silk-worm uses, the cellulose of wood pulp or cotton fibers. However, neither he nor any chemist since has been able to transform this into an animal product. Vegetable it is in the beginning and vegetable it remains throughout. Therein, the composition of natural silk and imitation silk differs. To the carbon, hydrogen and oxygen of the cellulose with which it starts, the silk-worm adds in chemical combination nitrogen, producing a truly animal compound. This the chemist can not do. But, for his purpose, Chardonnet did not need to do this. He acted upon the cellulose of cotton linters with concentrated nitric and sulfuric acids, thereby producing nitrocellulose, just as in the manufacture of smokeless powder. This, he dissolved in alcohol and ether, forming a viscous solution, which he forced through fine glass tubes similar to the spinnerets of the silk-worm. Upon

striking the air, the alcohol and ether evaporate, leaving
a delicate filament which can be twisted into threads and
wound into skeins. But, left in this condition, the
product is exceedingly inflammable. This is due to the
nitro groups from the nitric acid, which have been combined with the cellulose. They were removed by a
process of denitration, consisting of treatment with a
warm solution of sodium hydrosulfide, after which the
skeins were washed free of chemicals, bleached, dried,
and made ready for shipment. The nitrocellulose process
devised by Chardonnet is one of the four commercial
processes in use to-day, and the French inventor lived to
see the revolution in the textile industry which his
ingenuity initiated, for he did not die until 1924. Little
did he realize, however, when he started upon this scientific adventure, whither the trail would lead.

Although it was in 1889 that Chardonnet gave to the
world his first successful process, commercial production
did not begin until 1891. This was at Besançon, France.
In 1890, another French chemist, Despaissis, made the
discovery which seven years later was developed by
Pauly in Germany into the present cuprammonium
process. In the meantime, three English chemists, Cross,
Bevan and Beadle, did the chemical research which became the basis of the viscose process, the process by
which more than three-fourths of the world's rayon is
fabricated to-day. Let us review it briefly.

The viscose process starts with a raw material consisting of bleached spruce pulp or cotton linters, or sometimes a mixture of the two. The basic chemical compound
in both is cellulose, the food of the silk-worm. The
material is allowed to soak in a solution of caustic soda,

which causes the fibers to swell and changes the substance into a new compound known as soda-cellulose. After hydraulic pressing to remove the caustic soda solution, the resulting sheets are shredded to fine crumbs and placed in constant-temperature containers for a period of aging. In a few hours, the material is transferred to revolving "churns" and sprayed with a liquid compound known as carbon bisulfide. The chemical change resulting was the fundamental discovery of the English chemists. This treatment gives a yellow-orange product called cellulose xanthate. Here, too, is a critical point in the process, for the chemical reaction is a delicate one and must be under perfect control. The insoluble cellulose has now been transformed into a water-soluble compound. The solution is then put through another aging process at a low uniform temperature, after which it is filtered and pumped to the spinning machines. The stuff has now been reduced to the consistency of honey, being thick and viscous, thus giving the name "viscose" to the process.

Placed on the spinning machines are mechanical regulators, each regulator permitting a constant quantity of viscose to be continuously pumped to the perforated platinum nozzle. From the exceedingly minute openings in the nozzle, fine streams of viscose issue into an acid bath which immediately coagulates, or hardens, the viscose into long slender filaments, at the same time converting the compound back to pure cellulose. A revolving spool brings the filaments together and winds them into thread.

At every point, the process is under chemical control. Even the slightest deviations from the prescribed chemical process may result in ruin to the product. The skeins of rayon are treated with sodium sulfide solution to remove small quantities of sulfur compounds and then bleached with chlorine, after which another solution, called an antichlor, must be used to destroy any traces of chlorine. Thorough washing and drying by centrifuge complete the process.

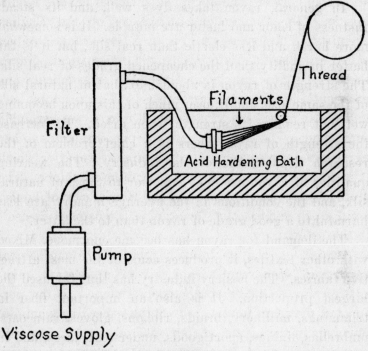

FIGURE 29
Diagram to illustrate the viscose method of making rayon.

A fourth process produces cellulose-acetate silk, claimed by its manufacturers to be a distinct textile fiber, differing entirely from ordinary rayon. The product is frequently called "Lustron," and its luster is said to resemble more closely that of natural silk. It possesses one characteristic which presents both difficulties and advantages. Cellulose-acetate silks are difficult to dye, and they do not take the same dyes as those commonly used for other silks, wool and cotton. This, however, permits a great variety of colors in a given pattern, which may consist of a combination of fibers, each taking a different dye.

In general, rayon takes dyes well, and its steadfastness of color and luster are notable. It is somewhat more harsh and less elastic than real silk, but it is far better in quality than the cheapened grades of real silk. The strength of rayon is about half that of natural silk of the same size, and it loses much of this upon becoming wet, but regains its strength when dried. To increase the strength of rayon fibers is a chief problem of the research departments of the industry. The wearing qualities of rayon are even superior to those of natural silk, and the conditions in the average laundry are less harmful to a good grade of rayon than to the latter.

The demand for rayon has become enormous. Mixed with other textiles, it produces some of the most attractive fabrics. The hosiery industry has thus far used the largest proportion. It is also an important fiber in trimmings, millinery, braids, ribbons, gloves, raincoats, umbrellas, linings, sport goods, underwear, laces, and in many other fabrics. Unlike natural silk, rayon will absorb perspiration from the body and permit of its evaporation, and at the same time it does not rot or turn yellow. Rayon is never weighted as is real silk. Any degree of softness may be given to rayon through the art of spinning, and the filaments may be spun as fine as cocoon fibers.

In every manufacturing country, the rayon industry is becoming strongly intrenched. England has carried its production to Canada, where wood is abundant. Germany has turned old munition plants over to rayon manufacture. In France, the land of its birth, although boycotted at first, rayon is now forging to the front. Italy is becoming a chief producer, and Belgium and Switzerland are contributing to the grand total. South America is a big consumer of rayon, and it is even making its way to the Far East. China, Japan and India afford growing markets. As already stated, the United States is the largest producer, as it is also the largest consumer.

Rayon is having a tremendous influence on the cotton industry. It is seriously curtailing the use of cotton in the finer fabrics. The makers of cotton yarns for stockings have been badly hit. Yarn mills in New England have been compelled to install weaving departments for cotton-and-rayon goods. On the other hand, rayon has been of benefit to the cotton industry. It has made possible the substitution of brighter designs and more artistic patterns for the plain, standard goods prevailing in earlier years, and, when the readjustment has been made, the coming of rayon will undoubtedly be found to have been a decided gain to the cotton industry.

Thirty years of research and the perfection of chemical and mechanical processes were required before rayon came into its own. Not until 1920 did its spectacular rise begin. It is still the infant of the textile world, but it is a lusty one, and its growth has been startlingly vigorous and rapid. That it will proceed to even larger proportions, there can be no doubt. Many problems remain to be solved, particularly that of increasing the strength of rayon fibers. With this assured, rayon would become the dominant member of the textile family. It is a striking commentary upon the money value of research that it has been able to convert wood pulp at a price of five cents a pound into a finished product worth approximately two dollars a pound. Although not a strictly synthetic product, rayon affords one of the most notable examples of a satisfactory chemically produced substitute for a natural product.

OTHER SYNTHETICS

Not only does the chemist seek to imitate Nature, but he often succeeds in surpassing her handiwork. Nowhere is this more notably true than in the synthetic production of resins, chief of which is that marketed under the trade name of "bakelite." Although little more than a dozen years old, this newcomer to the world of arts and industry is familiar to every one. Its uses are numbered by the score. It forms the ideal material from which to fashion most anything from collar buttons, pipe-stems, and billiard balls to electric insulators, radio cabinets, and artificial gems, rivaling the beauty of precious stones.

A resin is a non-crystalline substance, of which rosin, shellac, asphaltum, and various waxes of animal, mineral and vegetable origin are examples found in Nature.

The deliberate attempt to duplicate these products was made by Dr. L. H. Baekeland, a Belgian chemist, who came to America in 1889 and ever since has been a foremost member of the chemical profession of this

country. Nine years after his arrival, Doctor Baekeland
had, through the invention of Velox paper for photography, won for himself financial independence, and
was looking about for a new problem to tackle. Familiar
with the unsuccessful work of Bayer, Kleeberg and Story
to perfect synthetic resins through the combination of
carbolic acid, better known to the chemist as phenol, and
the well-known fumigant formaldehyde, he decided to
make the accomplishment of this undertaking his immediate goal. In his laboratory adjoining his home at
Yonkers, New York, Doctor Baekeland began the research. For four years he worked, meeting time and again
with apparent defeat, but through it all enjoying what he
now asserts was the "happiest time of his life." At length
he succeeded in obtaining from his steam-jacketed
reaction kettle a clear substance, resembling amber in
appearance, but brittle like rosin, easily melted and
soluble in alcohol and similar solvents. But, and this
was the great achievement, when this substance was
heated again under pressure, it became transformed into
a hard, inelastic resin of remarkable strength, which will
not melt and which is insoluble in all ordinary solvents.
These unique properties, rendering it different from all
natural resins, conferred upon this synthetic product its
multitude of uses.

Put into solution in its initial state, before the great
transformation has occurred, bakelite gives a most durable protective coating for metals and substances which
are affected by exposure to the air. It is bakelite which
cements to its metal base the glass bulb of an electric
lamp. It is an ideal electric insulator, promptly setting
after application from its initial state into a strong, rigid

covering which will not melt or change with heat. As a plastic molding material, it possesses superior qualities, copying every detail of a mold, even including its polish. Every make of automobile to-day has some portion of its equipment fashioned from bakelite. Its resistance to heat makes it an excellent binder in the manufacture of grinding wheels. Noiseless bakelite gears and pinions are used everywhere on all sorts of machines. But the uses of this rare product of the synthetic laboratory are so numerous that it will be impossible to enumerate more than a fraction of them here. The only obstacle to a very much larger use is the cost of the ingredients. Comparatively cheap as drugs, phenol and formaldehyde are not abundant enough to permit of immense quantity production. Seldom has a new product won so easily and quickly a universal and enduring application. It will remain one of the distinct triumphs of American chemistry in the synthetic field.

PERFUMES AND FLAVORINGS

We can not leave the realm of synthetics without mentioning perfumes and flavorings. Between 1914 and 1924, the value of the perfumes produced in this country alone rose from sixteen million dollars to eighty-five million, and many of them are the artificial duplications of natural scents. This application of chemistry to a new branch of industry began back in 1872, when Tiemann and Wallach obtained synthetic vanillin, the active principle of the vanilla bean. Vanilla beans sufficient to yield a pound of this chemical substance would cost about three hundred dollars, whereas the artificial flavoring is marketed for less than ten dollars. Three years later, Sir William Perkin prepared coumarin, a constituent of tonka beans with the scent of new mown hay. Heliotropin, with the odor of heliotrope, was obtained by Eykman and Poleck in 1885, and shortly after French chemists prepared from turpentine a substance having the odor of lilac. Artificial musk soon followed. Despite the prejudice against the use of laboratory-made scents and flavorings, the chemical invasion of this field became sure and certain.

Many of these synthetic perfumes and flavors belong to the class of organic compounds called esters. Thus amyl acetate, the ester, or salt, of amyl alcohol and acetic acid, gives the flavor of pears. Ethyl butyrate, the ester of ordinary grain alcohol and butyric acid, yields the flavor of pineapple, while the acid itself is responsible for the odor of Limburger cheese and is found in butter. An alcohol known as geraniol is the chief constituent of otto of roses, and its oxidation product, an aldehyde known as citral, is present in citrus fruits. Derivatives of the benzene ring yield aromatic perfumes, such as the essential oils of tuberose, heliotrope, musk, orange blossoms, jasmine, and others. More delicate perfumes are obtained from a ring of six carbon atoms lacking the double bonds of the benzene ring. From coal-tar as a source, all the aromatic compounds may be synthesized.

Oil of wintergreen is made from salicylic acid, a light fluffy powder useful in the treatment of rheumatism and as a preservative, and methyl alcohol, now known as methanol. The flavor and odor are identical with those of the natural substance. Many flowers, such as magnolia, honeysuckle, mayflower, lilac, sweet pea, arbutus, and lily of the valley, yield no extracts, or essential oils, for perfume purposes. But in most cases acceptable substitutes can be synthesized in the laboratory. Artificial neroli, a substitute for the natural product of orange flowers, has improved the quality of the famous Eau de Cologne. The chemist synthesizes the terpenes, a group of compounds occurring in turpentine, and thereby duplicates the scents and flavors of such forest products as eucalyptus, lavender, pine needles, sage, and caraway. The end of this chemical pathway is not yet in sight.

Tiemann's investigation of irone, the perfume producing compound of orris root, is interesting. By combining citral, a substance found in lemon and orange oils, with acetone, he obtained a product having the same number each of atoms of carbon, hydrogen and oxygen as irone. But, to his astonishment, it had no odor. Here were two substances of seemingly identical compositions, the one having a delightful odor and the other none at all. Then, he began to change the molecular architecture of the new substance, and presently he had a compound with a distinct violet odor. He named it "ionone," and the firm to which he licensed the right to manufacture and sell it became famous. When it was introduced into the United States, this synthetic perfume sold in ten per cent. solution at one hundred and twenty-eight dollars a pound, or ten times that amount for the compound in full strength. To-day, a better product sells for less than ten dollars a pound.

Synthetic menthol, an anti-neuralgic and chief constituent of peppermint oil, now threatens the Japanese monopoly of this product. An artificial musk, better than the original at upward of two hundred and fifty dollars a pound, sells as low as four dollars. New acetylene products not only imitate the odor of violet but improve upon the flower itself, and the quantity required is exceedingly small. To produce a pound of Bulgarian rose oil requires from 250,000 to 750,000 roses according to the character of the crop. The synthetic chemist prepares in his laboratory an imitation at a much lower cost. Still, the genuine natural product contains in small quantities possibly a score of elusive substances difficult for the chemist to compass in his blended mixture. This usurper of ancient processes, through waging an unequal contest, has not yet banished the old-time distiller of natural perfumes.

The chemist began with the isolation and analysis of the natural compounds responsible for the desirable properties of perfumes and flavors. His next step was to synthesize them in the laboratory. Then the chemist made a great discovery. He found that compounds not at all related to the natural products possess similar odors. Furthermore, they are much more powerful and lasting. This discovery opened a whole new field. Up to that time, the true odors of many flowers had been unobtainable, for the extracts of these flowers gave poor results, and often none. One of the more recent triumphs is the extraction from citronella oil of a lilac substance which finds wide application in the compounding of many perfumes. Many duplications of natural scents and flavors remain to be made. Here is a large field for the synthetic chemist, and a most inviting one.

As we have seen, synthetic products are a big part of past chemical achievements. More and more, synthesis seems to be a master key to future progress. If a certain desirable or essential substance is not to be had cheaply and abundantly, its artificial duplication or the production of a satisfactory substitute from other materials must be forthcoming. The possibilities in this field will never be exhausted. Horizons constantly grow bigger. Pathways multiply. The prizes become more alluring. In many fields the harvest only awaits the coming of the reapers. But the army of workers must constantly be recruited. Men and women of rare ability coupled with faith, hope and vision must be summoned to the colors. Here is opportunity for genius.

CHAPTER XII

AMERICAN PROGRESS IN CHEMISTRY

PRESENT POSITION OF UNITED STATES IN MANUFACTURE OF
CHEMICALS—RECORD OF PROGRESS FROM COLONIAL TIMES TO
BEGINNING OF MODERN ERA—CHEMICAL EDUCATION IN AMER-
ICA—COOKE, ELIOT, CHANDLER, AND REMSEN—AMERICAN
CHEMICAL SOCIETY—FOUNDING OF DU PONT POWDER WORKS—
ALL-AMERICAN PROCESS FOR SYNTHETIC METHANOL—DR.
WILLIAM H. NICHOLS—AMERICAN ACCOMPLISHMENTS IN
METALLURGY—ELECTROCHEMISTRY—DYESTUFFS IN AMER-
ICA—AMERICAN GLASS—FUSED QUARTZ—MECHANICAL INVEN-
TIONS—PRODUCTION OF FINE CHEMICALS—AMERICAN CHEM-
ICAL TRADE—AMERICAN SULFUR—INDUSTRIAL ALCOHOL—
ACETONE AND BUTANOL—RISE OF LACQUER INDUSTRY—CHEM-
ICAL PRODUCT FROM WASTE OAT HULLS—FUTURE NEEDS.

"WITHOUT boasting, the United States now can lay
claim to a greater chemical industry than that possessed
by any other country. The infant industry of a few short
years ago has outgrown its German and British competitors."

The foregoing statement was made by the Washington correspondent of *Chemical and Metallurgical Engineering* in June, 1926. Subsequent developments have
abundantly substantiated its truth. Were our export
trade commensurate with our domestic consumption, the
United States would dominate the chemical industries of
the world. To capture for American producers a larger

391

share of the foreign trade is the present goal of Secretary Hoover in cooperation with the executives of chemical manufacturing concerns in this country. But seven per cent. of our total production is exported to world markets. To make our export trade comparable to that of the principal other chemical manufacturing countries, this figure must be quadrupled. The inferiority complex developed through so many years of defensive tactics in this field must be overcome. The lusty growth of the industry gives assurance that that day of accomplishment is near at hand. The degree of excellence of American products, and indeed the superiority of many, are winning customers in every quarter of the globe. More than all else, our country is achieving a chemical independence indispensable to national integrity.

A short time ago, I noticed in a publication of the American Chemical Society a chronological record of the development of chemical industry in America from colonial times to the World War. Beginning with a new process for the extraction of silver, invented in Mexico in 1557, there are few years in the long stretch of more than three and a half centuries which do not chronicle some new departure, some fresh application of chemical science or some discovery. No one can peruse the record without a profound realization of the large part which chemistry has had in the industrial development of the country. Even though many of the processes were not recognized as chemical and the procedure was wholly by rule-of-thumb, chemistry was performing its service and preparing the way for the time when its intelligent application should unlock the natural wealth of the nation. In a thousand ways, chemistry touched the lives of the struggling colonists. Thus, I read that, in 1608, the "manufacture of tar, potash, and glass were attempted in Virginia." Four years later began the manufacture of fire bricks, and, in 1620, leather, salt and iron were produced on a small scale. In 1633, "John Winthrop, Jr., of Massachusetts, imports laboratory chemicals and apparatus." That was nearly a century and a half before Priestley discovered oxygen and while Europe was still under the magic spell of the alchemist. In 1650, this colonial chemist plans a chemical stock company to manufacture saltpeter. There is much chemical significance in this, for saltpeter was the essential oxidizing ingredient of old-fashioned gunpowder, and gunpowder was as indispensable to the early settler as seed for the planting or flax for the spinning-wheel. In the following year, a monopoly was granted by Connecticut for the working of "lead, copper, tin, antimony, vitriol, alum, etc." In 1697, paper manufacture began at Germantown, Pennsylvania. Lead mining in Missouri began as early as 1720, and ten years later the first large sugar refinery was erected by Nicholas Bayard on the present site of Wall Street, New York City. Just before the War of Independence the provincial congress gave encouragement to the "domestic manufacture of iron, steel, lead, glass, salt, saltpeter, gunpowder, sulfur, paper, linseed oil, leather, dyestuffs, and other chemical products." And well that the congress did, for, largely cut off from trade with the outside world, the colonists could not have prosecuted the war without many of these basic materials.

With the birth of the nation, these infant chemical manufactures began to gain a firmer foothold. In 1791,

Alexander Hamilton made an appraisal of the national industries, including in his report iron, steel, copper, lead, coal, glass, powder, paper and sugar. Two years later, the manufacture of sulfuric acid was begun at Philadelphia. In 1798, a dyestuff plant started operations in New York. The first year of the new century saw the invention by Robert Hare of the oxyhydrogen blowpipe, long the source of the highest temperature known to science. This same year, too, witnessed the discovery in Mexico of vanadium, a metal which has only just been obtained in the free state. In 1802, E. I. du Pont de Nemours founded at Wilmington, Delaware, the powder works which have grown into one of the largest chemical plants in the world, a story of progress of which we shall have more to say later. In 1805, the Havemeyer sugar refinery opened its doors in New York. Potash, important then as now, mounted in price from one hundred dollars to three hundred dollars a ton as a result of the embargo of 1808, temporarily stimulating the development of a domestic potash industry in New York and Vermont. The first platinum still for the concentration of sulfuric acid was introduced by John Harrison, of Philadelphia, in 1814. So great were the importations of foreign chemicals in 1815 that domestic producers petitioned Congress for protection, and in the following year a tariff bill gave relief. By 1818, chemical manufacture had established itself as far west as Steubenville, Ohio. Three years later, at Fredonia, New York, natural gas was first used for lighting, and in 1823 the New York Gas Light Company, the first American company of its kind, was incorporated. In this same year, Rosengarten and Sons, forebears of Dr. George D. Rosengarten, now president of the American Chemical Society, began the manufacture of quinine sulfate, sulfuric ether, spirits of niter, ammonia water and acetic ether. In 1825, Isaac Babbitt, of Taunoon, Massachusetts, invented Babbitt metal, an alloy which has been of much importance from that day to this. The famous Joseph Dixon lead pencils came upon the market in 1830. On October twelfth of the following year, chloroform was discovered by Samuel Guthrie. The first American beet sugar made its appearance at Northampton, Massachusetts, in 1837. In 1839 came three events of world-wide importance. William Lyman, at Pottsville, Pennsylvania, substituted anthracite for charcoal in the smelting of iron ore; John W. Draper took the first photograph from life; and Charles Goodyear discovered the process of vulcanization of rubber. At Jersey City, Thomas Kingsford, in 1842, began the production of starch from corn, a process which, in its manifold developments, has since grown into an industry of vast extent.

In the forties began the period of the extension of chemical industry. Before the middle of the century, William Kelly, co-discoverer with Bessemer of the process for removing the carbon from pig iron with a blast of air, was carrying out his experiments. In 1851, five years before the success of his British rival, Kelly's first converter for changing pig iron into steel was in action. Gail Borden manufactured the first condensed milk at Walcottville, Connecticut, in 1856. The year 1858 will forever be memorable for the discovery of gold at Pike's Peak and the year following for the drilling at Titusville, Pennsylvania, of the first successful oil well, the latter marking the beginning of one of the largest chemical industries in America. In 1865 began the rolling of steel rails from steel ingots. Two years later, B. C. Tilghman invented the sulfite process for converting wood pulp into paper. In the following year, the first open-hearth furnace in this country for the manufacture of steel was established at Trenton, New Jersey. In 1869, the Hyatt brothers began, at Albany, New York, the manufacture of celluloid, the first of the synthetic plastics, and in 1872 D. O. Saylor introduced the manufacture of Portland cement.

The foregoing review is but a meager outline. Only a few of the more important events in the development of chemical industry down to the beginning of the modern period have been sketched. However, they serve to illustrate the intimate relation between the growth of national industries and the applications of chemical knowledge, a relation which grows more pronounced with each succeeding year. Let us turn to that period of progress beginning with 1876 which has transformed this nation from a provincial dabbler in chemical processes into the world's foremost producer of chemical commodities.

CHEMICAL EDUCATION

Before 1876, there was no systematic instruction in chemistry as a profession in the colleges and universities of this country. Going back to 1853, we find only four laboratories in America in which the advanced study of chemistry might be pursued. They were the laboratory of the Lawrence Scientific School at Harvard, the chemistry laboratory at Yale, the Amherst College Laboratory and a private laboratory in Philadelphia. To obtain special training in chemistry, American students were compelled to go abroad, and the majority of such students went to Germany. Of thirty research students working in Wöhler's laboratory, at Göttingen, in 1855, thirteen were Americans.

And yet, America at that time was not without some great teachers of chemistry. The pioneer of the modern era in this field was Josiah P. Cooke, first professor of chemistry in the college department of Harvard University. Under Professor Cooke, the late President Charles W. Eliot received the training which was to prepare him to assume leadership in the chemical instruction given in this country from 1853 to 1869, when he was elected to the presidency of the university. Although Doctor Eliot became one of the world's foremost educators, his work as a teacher was done in the field of chemistry, during the last four years of which he was a member of the first formal faculty of the Massachusetts Institute of Technology with the title of professor of analytical chemistry and metallurgy. The state of chemical instruction in this country at that time may be inferred from the fact that this work was begun in a "small, poorly equipped room in the second story of a building which also housed a mercantile library and a commercial school." In collaboration with his associate, Dr. Frank H. Storer, Doctor Eliot wrote two text-books in chemistry, which had a wide field of usefulness, and throughout his long career as an educator he never failed to emphasize with voice and pen the benefits to be derived from chemical education and the strategic place it occupies in the national development.

I shall never forget two most delightful evenings

spent with the late Professor Charles F. Chandler, in which he lectured upon the history of photography before the Chemistry Teachers' Club of New York City and showed rare exhibits from the Chandler Chemical Museum of Columbia University. Long the dean of the profession of chemistry teaching in this country and a pioneer, often working without remuneration both as instructor and as a public servant in the solution of important chemical problems, Professor Chandler, with that rare gift for friendship which was always a source of joy and inspiration to all he met, endeared himself to his fellows as few others have ever done. To the last of his nearly eighty-nine years, his was the spirit of perennial youth. At the age of fourteen, before chemical instruction had gained a foothold in this country, he had decided to become a chemist. After a preliminary course in the Lawrence Scientific School, Professor Chandler went abroad, studying under Wöhler at Göttingen and later at Berlin with Heinrich Rose, the father of analytical chemistry. His instruction also included courses in geology and minerology, and he formed a pleasant acquaintance with the great geologist Alexander von Humboldt. In possession of his Ph. D. from Göttingen, Professor Chandler returned to America. As an indication of the caliber of the man, he accepted a position as janitor at Union College at four hundred dollars a year, with the opportunity of assisting Professor Joy in the chemistry department. In 1864, he was elected to the chair of chemistry in the newly opened Columbia School of Mines, accepting in lieu of salary the fees he could obtain from students. From that time until his death in 1925, Professor Chandler was a foremost leader in all things chemical.

It would be difficult to appraise at their true value his services to the cause of chemistry in this country, and especially during the formative years. As Ellwood Hendrick has so well said, "He was a gentleman to his finger tips, who never forgot his own obligations. His friendship was a benediction."

And we must not forget Dr. Ira Remsen, one of America's great chemists in the field of education, whose passing was so recent that he still seems to be among us. My own introduction to chemistry as a freshman in college was obtained through his text-book, long the standard for instruction everywhere. Graduating from the College of the City of New York in 1865 and from the College of Physicians and Surgeons two years later, Doctor Remsen went abroad to study chemistry at the universities of Tübingen and Göttingen. Returning to America, he became professor of chemistry at Williams College, remaining there until 1876, when he joined the teaching staff of the Johns Hopkins University, where as professor of chemistry, director of the chemical laboratory, secretary of the Academic Council, and president of the university, he served until 1912. In 1879, he established the *Journal of the American Chemical Society,* continuing to edit it until 1914. Doctor Remsen specialized in the field of organic chemistry and his interest was that of a pure scientist. His most notable discovery was that of the synthetic compound saccharin, which as a substitute for sugar has proved a boon to diabetes sufferers. The recipient of medals for distinguished services and revered by his associates, he died in 1927, full of years and honors.

I shall not venture into the realm of the living further

than to mention such eminent contributors to chemical education as Doctors Edgar F. Smith, Arthur A. Noyes, Theodore W. Richards, and Francis P. Venable. And there are others equally worthy of mention. But I do wish to emphasize that it is no longer necessary to go abroad to obtain instruction in chemistry. America has more universities than any other country in the world, and in addition there are many technical schools and a host of colleges, all offering advanced instruction in the various branches of chemistry. The opportunities for research are just as good in American universities as they are in foreign laboratories. A degree from a recognized American university counts for as much to-day as one from a foreign institution. Happily, our years of apprenticeship to foreign masters have passed. And yet, we can never forget the debt we owe to those great leaders of chemical thought in European seats of learning who laid the foundations of that science which has become so tremendous a bulwark of American industry and independence. It must become the constantly increasing purpose of the profession in America to add its full quota of newly discovered knowledge in this basic field of scientific investigation.

THE AMERICAN CHEMICAL SOCIETY

The modern period of chemistry in this country began with the organization of the American Chemical Society in 1876, the semi-centennial of which was recently commemorated. The idea of forming such a society originated at the Priestley Centennial, in August, 1874. A group of chemists and scientists had gathered at Northumberland, Pennsylvania, to do honor to the memory

Henry E. Niese

One of the two surviving charter members
of the American Chemical Society, present
at the meeting, April 6, 1876, in which
the Society was organized

Prof. Theodore W. Richards

of Harvard University; the world's foremost investigator in the field of atomic
weight determinations

Dr. George D. Rosengarten

President of the American Chemical
Society (1927)

Late Prof. Charles F. Chandler

of Columbia University; long the dean
of American chemists

A glimpse at the product of the beehive coke oven

Before the war, approximately eighty per cent. of American coke was produced by this wasteful process

Courtesy, H. Koppers Company

A by-product coke plant

To-day, eighty per cent. of the coke in this country is produced in this type of modern plant

of the discoverer of oxygen, who passed the declining years of his life in this country and whose grave overlooks the Susquehanna River. At evening-time, after the events of the day, the company gathered at Priestley's grave. There, Dr. H. Coppée, President of Lehigh University, delivered an address, from which I quote his closing words:

"This is an unusual celebration, and this particularly is the strangest scene of this singular drama. This peaceful field, an acre of God, at this most charming evening hour, happily suggested by a lady chemist; these surrounding hills, this gleaming river, which lend breadth and beauty to the landscape; this distinguished assemblage standing reverently, but not mournfully, around a grave: these do not tell of death, but of life; breathing, varied, sunny life; not of decay, but of resurrection; not of oblivion, but of immortality. They tell us that in the inexorable past there is but a semblance of imprisonment; that the good and the true, the magnanimous and the noble, break the flimsy bonds, and come back to gladden the hearts of men, and to flourish in perennial beauty. Such are the pleasant thoughts, fancies, and yet living facts which cluster around the grave of Joseph Priestley."

Fitting it was that on the occasion of this centennial celebration Dr. Persifor Frazer, Jr., of the University of Pennsylvania, should suggest that the chemists of the country be brought together in an "American Chemical Society." Chief among those who sponsored the idea was Professor Chandler, and it was largely due to his efforts that in April, 1876, a meeting of chemists was held in New York to carry out the suggestion.

The meeting was held on April sixth, in the lecture room of the College of Pharmacy of New York University. Thirty-five were in attendance and of that historic number only two, Dr. William H. Nichols and Mr. H. E. Niese, are now living. Many of those who gathered at that first meeting rose to distinction in the profession. Little, however, did those men realize that the society which they there organized was in a half-century to become the largest and strongest of its kind in the world. Nowhere else is to be found a more striking example of the relation of the Society to the public welfare than in its war record. At the close of the war, 4,003 chemists were in uniform service in a chemical capacity. An equal number were serving in civilian laboratories under government control. Practically all who remained were at work in the country's chemical and munition plants providing the sinews of war. In speaking of this service, the Secretary of War in a public address said: "The American Chemical Society presented a striking instance of preparedness. It certainly had the largest body of its kind in the world and comprised in its ranks 14,500 of the 17,000 chemists of the country, and when the country's call went out for chemists the coöperation of this society was a splendid substitute for any preparation the Government had to make. Almost instantly the Government was able to put its hand on the man who was needed for the particular job, to call him to Washington or service wherever he might be needed. Your society was by its very existence anticipatory of the calling into being of the forces to collect these data, and the Government owes to this society, therefore, a debt of gratitude for this closeness of association and intimate knowledge of the profession, which it was able to place at the Government's disposal and thereby to render the chemical knowledge of the country speedily available. The chemists did their share. They did it superbly.''

In 1891, the organization of local sections in various cities of the country was initiated, the first being formed at Providence, Rhode Island. There are now sixty-nine such sections. The science has become so specialized, too, that the society embraces sixteen subdivisions, each having its own officers and being of particular interest to a special group. The publications of the society are among the most important and authoritative of their kind in the world. Dr. Charles L. Parsons, the secretary of the society, says, ''The society has within its membership all of the leading chemists of America. They constitute a body of scientists which is growing in numbers, in prestige, and in knowledge. There are no educational institutions in the world better equipped to turn out qualified chemists than those of America.''

A PIONEER OF CHEMICAL INDUSTRY

Mention has already been made of the founding of a powder works by E. I. du Pont de Nemours back in 1802. The man who gave his name to this enterprise was a member of a distinguished French family and, as a youth of sixteen, had studied chemistry in the laboratory of the renowned Lavoisier. Because the leaders of the Revolution had ''no need for chemists,'' Lavoisier lost his head by the guillotine, and the du Ponts, broken in fortune and victims of the unsettled state of political affairs, came to America. The story is told that, running out of powder on a hunting trip, young du Pont was compelled to buy some from a local dealer. The quality proved to be so bad and the price so high, there was born in his brain the idea of establishing a powder works in this country, after the fashion of those operated by the French Government. A trip to France resulted in raising by subscription thirty-six thousand dollars for the undertaking and in obtaining through the French Government the necessary machinery and materials. Within six years the company had produced six hundred thousand pounds of powder. In the early years, too, it placed upon the market such chemical products as saltpeter, charcoal and pyroligneous acid, obtained from the distillation of wood, and creosote.

For more than a century, the company confined itself chiefly to the manufacture of explosives, at all times keeping thoroughly abreast of the research in this field. In due course the production of nitroglycerin, dynamite, smokeless powder, and other forms of explosives became large features of the business. In 1912, the du Ponts embarked upon a much more extensive chemical business, becoming manufacturers of artificial leather, rayon, nitrocellulose lacquers and synthetic nitrogen compounds. The business has grown to vast proportions. In particular, has it had a large part in the very recent revolutionizing development of the new types of lacquers, an activity in which the du Pont knowledge of cellulose and its derivatives and the facilities for producing them on a big scale played a large part. The famous "Duco" automobile finish is a du Pont product.

Announcement, however, has just come of a still more important achievement. Research chemists and engineers in the employ of the du Pont company have worked out an all-American process for the production in this country of synthetic methanol. It is really a by-product of their synthetic ammonia process. The synthesis of methanol is accomplished by the catalytic union of hydrogen and carbon monoxide, while synthetic ammonia is the catalytic product of hydrogen and nitrogen. Now carbon monoxide has been an unavoidable waste gas in the usual method of obtaining the gas mixture of hydrogen and nitrogen for the synthesis of ammonia. In order not to poison the catalyst, it has been necessary to remove this carbon monoxide from the reaction mixture along with a number of other impurities by a very rigorous process of purification. The new process scores its triumph by passing the impure mixture on its way to the ammonia reaction chambers over a catalyst which causes the carbon monoxide and a part of the hydrogen to combine to form methanol, which is removed by condensation and at the same time all but traces of the other impurities are removed too. Thus the purification of the nitrogen and hydrogen for the synthesis of ammonia, the first step in the production of nitrogen compounds for fertilizers and explosives, is made to produce methanol. No longer will Germany and France be able to monopolize the processes for the artificial synthesis of this immensely important raw material of chemical manufacture.

Already, the du Ponts announce that "plans have been drawn to allow for plant expansion sufficient to meet the entire American demand for methanol." This announcement, however, may sound the death knell of the wood distillation industry in this country, for that has hitherto been the chief source of methanol. Even within recent months, to prevent disastrous competition from German methanol, President Coolidge has been compelled to raise the import duty to eighteen cents a gallon.

It is interesting to know that this colossal enterprise is still under the direct control of men bearing the name of the founder and in the direct line of descent. This company has been a large factor in that tremendous expansion of chemical industry which is rapidly winning world leadership for the United States. Its products are known and used the world over.

ANOTHER PIONEER

If I were to single out any one individual whose activities in the field of chemical industry have been co-extensive with the modern era and who has himself had a large part in this vast expansion, it would be Dr. William H. Nichols, one of the two surviving men who were present at the organization of the American Chemical Society, in 1876. Probably no other man has contributed more to the industrial development of America in the last half-century than has Doctor Nichols.

Even as a lad in Brooklyn, in the sixties of the last century, when the facilities for the study of chemistry in this country were exceedingly meager, Doctor Nichols determined to make this field of investigation his life-work. At the age of thirteen, he became a student in the Polytechnic Institute in Brooklyn. Upon graduation three years later, he entered New York University, from which in 1870 he received the degree of B. S. and in

1873 the degree of M. S. I shall not attempt to name here the foreign rulers, learned societies and universities of this and other lands who have honored themselves by conferring distinctions upon him.

In 1870, when only eighteen, Doctor Nichols began his career as a manufacturing chemist. He formed a company under the name of Walter and Nichols for the manufacture of acids, and since he was not of age his father became the financial sponsor of the undertaking. Within a short time the senior member of the partnership was killed in an accident, thus throwing the entire burden of the business upon young Nichols. As may be imagined, those were strenuous days. They were too strenuous. The multitude of duties incident to the supervision of chemical manufacture, office management and sales could not be performed by one individual, however willing the spirit. A factory manager was found in the person of J. B. Herreshoff, whose original contributions in the field of chemical industry have been of immense importance.

An incident in the early career of Doctor Nichols gives a noteworthy index to the large success with which he has met. His competitors in the manufacture of sulfuric acid secretly entered into an agreement as to prices which robbed the young firm of its orders. Financial ruin seemed inevitable. But let me give the outcome in Doctor Nichols' own words. He says, "When I began making this acid, I found that, although all the sulfuric acid on the market was labeled as sixty-six degrees, much of it was under strength, usually only sixty-five degrees. I made mine sixty-six degrees and marked it accordingly. Before long I was waited on by a body of my competitors, who declared to me: 'You are making a fool of yourself. You are only a young man and new at the business and perhaps that's why you don't seem to know that you are incurring unnecessary expense to yourself by making your acid sixty-six degrees when sixty-five degrees is just as good.' I told them that if I made sixty-five-degree acid I must put 'sixty-five degrees' on the package and that if I put 'sixty-six degrees' on the package I must make sixty-six-degree acid. They went off very much dissatisfied and disgruntled.

"About this time the process of refining oil was discovered and orders for sulfuric poured in to us faster than we could fill them. But though we were swamped with demands for our product, our competitors were not. Of course they set about finding out the reason why, and they discovered, as the oil refiners had already discovered, that sixty-five degree acid was not strong enough for refining oil, whereas sixty-six-degree acid met every requirement."

And all the while Doctor Nichols was applying his knowledge of chemistry to the practical business of manufacturing. He found that iron pyrites could be used as the source of sulfur in the making of acid, and Herreshoff developed a burner for the purpose.

At this time, a man brought to them a sample of ore from a mine he owned in Canada. Doctor Nichols at once recognized it as a combination of iron and copper pyrites. The mine was bought and methods were developed for the extraction of the copper in conjunction with the use of the sulfur in the pyrites in the manufacture of acid. The product was what is called "copper matte," an impure form of copper which must be subjected to refining. This the firm sold to the refiners. But there came a day when the refiners refused to buy any more of this matte. Again competitors had combined against him. But Doctor Nichols was equal to the emergency. He immediately embarked in the refining business himself, and for the first time introduced the electrolytic refining of the metal. As a by-product, he obtained gold and silver. In a short time, he had revolutionized the industry and become the world's largest refiner of copper. One of the most interesting excursions I ever enjoyed was a visit to Doctor Nichols' copper plant in Brooklyn, where I saw immense quantities of the crude metal brought thither from far distant points for the refining process.

As president and director of vast enterprises, Doctor Nichols for more than half a century has exerted a tremendous influence in shaping the chemical progress of this country. Under his direction new discoveries were utilized as they appeared. The contact process for manufacturing sulfuric acid was introduced. The manufacture of organic chemical products was undertaken. And when the country's need demanded it, the development of a synthetic ammonia process was begun. He has made the whole field of industrial chemistry his domain. And through it all he has exhibited that rare genius for organization essential to the development of colossal enterprises. That wealth came was only incidental to his main purpose. It was never the goal. But wealth has made it possible for him to dispense gifts to education and charity with princely generosity. And he has given not only of his wealth, but of his personal services. As chairman of the board of trustees of the Brooklyn

Polytechnic Institute for many years, he exerted an influence upon the development of technical education in this country which can never be measured. A man of sympathetic interest in his fellows, of warm friendships, of unbounded optimism, and of vast ability, Doctor Nichols is America's outstanding captain of industry in the field of chemistry.

IN THE FIELD OF METALS

To keep the record straight, we shall review briefly some contributions of America in the field of metallurgy. As we have seen, simultaneously with Sir Henry Bessemer, William Kelly gave to the world the converter and thereby built the highway from the age of iron to the age of steel. While it is true that the open-hearth and electric furnaces for the production of steel were invented abroad, the big-scale development of the industry has come in America. It is here that the making of steel has been placed entirely upon a machine basis. The highway from mine to finished product fairly bristles with machinery at every point. Electric- and steam-shovels, cranes, shears, rollers, stamping-machines, power-scrapers, immense unloaders for ore, furnace-charging machinery, and many other labor-saving devices have reduced in America the man-power of the industry to a minimum. Nowhere in the thousand-mile journey of ore from the Lake Superior mines to the steel plant or in the later processes of smelting and manufacture are the various materials and products touched with human hands.

We have already discussed the alloys of steel, in the production of which American chemists have had a large part. In particular vanadium steel is largely an American product. It is interesting to know that J. W. Marden and M. N. Rich, two research chemists in the Westinghouse laboratories, have just now succeeded in isolating for the first time metallic vanadium in pure form. It has hitherto been known only in its alloys. Its finders state that the "beads of vanadium are very bright, have a steel-white color and are quite malleable, soft and ductile." As yet, no use for the pure metal is known, but then it is only an infant in the metal world. Its uses have doubtless only to be discovered.

Again, it is in its vast output of steel that America excels. The birth and expansion of the modern chemical era and the rise of steel have been oustanding features of that romantic and picturesque period of empire-building which has seen this country grow from a provincial people to a mighty nation. The products of the iron- and steel-mills have provided in inexhaustible quantities a fundamental raw material for this unparalleled development. And America, through its rich mines of coal and iron, will for many years remain the leading producer of steel and therefore the dominant industrial power of the world. Great as has been the accomplishment of the chemist in placing this industry upon the sure foundation of scientific control, we must not forget the contributions of such giant leaders as Andrew Carnegie. Of remarkable vision and boundless enthusiasm, bold, restless as one of his own fiery furnaces, a creator of big ideas, it would be difficult to picture the industrial progress of the last half-century without the achievements of this first of the steel kings.

The large development of the copper industry has

come about in America. We are the largest producers and consumers of copper in the world. American mechanics have invented the compressed-air drills for lessening the drudgery of mining methods, and American chemists and engineers have developed the processes of smelting and refining. The flotation process for the separation of copper and other ores, whereby sixty million tons of ore a year are treated in this country, has largely been the outgrowth of American invention and initiative. It was a woman, Mrs. Carrie J. Everson, of Denver, Colorado, who discovered the affinity of oils for mineral particles. Although a long series of unfortunate circumstances denied to her the fruits of her discovery, the process based upon it has made millions for its exploiters. From the waste piles of former processes metals of great value have been recovered. Finely crushed ore is churned with water and oil until a froth is produced. Then, difficult as it may seem to understand, the particles of metal and their compounds cling to the bubbles of oil, while the particles of rock sink to the bottom. What scientists call "surface tension" causes a selective flotation, and the particles of ore are marvelously removed. In 1925, 1,481,000,000 pounds of copper were separated by the flotation method in this country. Although first employed abroad, this process was rediscovered and developed in America.

We are already familiar with the story of Hall and his electrolytic method for the separation of aluminum. The fact that this process was worked out simultaneously by Héroult in France detracts in no way from the credit due to each.

Ductile tungsten, one of the marvels of modern chemical invention, is an American achievement. Dr. W. D. Coolidge in the Research Laboratory of the General Electric Company, after many years of failure, developed the process for producing wrought tungsten and thereby made possible the tungsten filament lamp. The tensile strength of this theretofore brittle and incorrigible metal is amazing, being "about 600,000 pounds per square inch for wire one-thousandth of an inch in diameter."

Much of the world's supply of radium comes from this country through methods of extraction developed by American chemists. To obtain the gram of radium given by the women of America to Madame Curie upon her visit to this country in 1921 required the working of six hundred tons of ore and the labor of five hundred men for six months. In the process of extraction, there were consumed ten thousand tons of distilled water, one thousand tons of coal and five hundred tons of chemicals.

The foregoing is but a bare outline of the contributions of America in the field of metallurgy. Particularly have American chemists had a large part in the production of new alloys. In the super X-ray tube invented by Doctor Coolidge, the metallurgist has found an instrument of the utmost usefulness for detecting the hidden defects of metals and alloys. In X-ray photographs, he reads the deep-seated changes which rolling, tempering and aging produce. Because of such inspection, the lives of aviators, motor drivers, and the traveling public are immeasurably safer.

Of one thing the producer of metals is no longer in doubt. He needs the chemist in his business. Applied chemistry has become the very foundation of metallurgy.

ELECTROCHEMISTRY

Dr. Arthur D. Little, one of America's most notable chemists, some time ago said, "To no chapter in the history of industrial research can Americans turn with greater pride than to the one which contains the epic of the electrochemical development at Niagara Falls." The electrochemical industry is the largest user of electric power in this country to-day. In support of Doctor Little's statement, I can do no better than to quote from a paper by Dr. F. J. Tone, war-time president of the American Electrochemical Society. He said:

"America has long enjoyed a supremacy in electrochemistry, but in spite of the strong position of the industry before the war no one would have dared to predict the expansion which the war would demand of us. It has called for chlorine, cyanamide, air nitrates, and phosphorus in vast quantities. It has required the ferroalloy industry, the electrode industry, and the abrasive industry to quadruple their outputs.

"As a single example, consider briefly the contribution of electrochemistry and electrometallurgy to the aircraft program. The airplane motor has a crank case and pistons of aluminum. Its crank shaft and engine parts subject to the greatest strains are all composed of chrome alloy steel. All of these parts are brought to mechanical perfection and made interchangeable by being finished to a fraction of a thousandth of an inch by means of the modern grinding wheel made from electric furnace abrasives. Calcium carbide, and its derivative, acetylene, are making possible an ample supply of cellulose acetate for airplane dope. When the aviator trains his machine gun on an enemy plane, his firing is made effective by tracer bullets of magnesium or phosphorus. When bombing planes begin to carry the war into Germany, it will be with bombs perhaps of ammonium nitrate or picric acid or other high explosives, all depending largely in their manufacture on electrochemical reagents. Without the pioneer work of Hall, Acheson, Willson, Bradley, and others (all Americans), the present aircraft program would be impossible of achievement.

"Then there is gas warfare, the very basis of which is chlorine. . . . It is interesting to note that chlorine, the product of the electrolytic cell, is the basis of mustard gas, chloropicrin, phosgene, and almost all of the important war gases. Thus does electrochemistry enter fundamentally into the modern military machine."

A distinct contribution in this field is found in the artificial abrasives, of which carborundum invented by Acheson and alundum produced by the Norton Company are most important. And along with these, other electrolytic products are also made. The expansion of the electrochemical industry is bound to be great in the years to come. The possibilities have as yet only been tapped.

DYESTUFFS IN AMERICA

Dyestuffs,—that is the chemical product about which every one knows something. The experiences at the beginning of the World War and in the years immediately following are too vivid in the minds of all now living to be soon forgotten. Those hectic days when the commonest dyes with startling abruptness shot up to fabulous prices and most dyes could not be had at any price told us that even a war in far-off Europe could touch the lives of American citizens. At that time the United States produced less than three per cent. of the world's output of synthetic dyes, and yet we consumed a larger proportion than any other nation. Still, we were without knowledge of the chemistry of their production.

Most of our chemists and engineers had had no experience in the manufacture of synthetic organic compounds. Foreign competition had successfully prevented the organic chemical industry from becoming established on American soil. Utterly oblivious to the consequences inevitable to the interruption of foreign trade, we were living in a fool's paradise. Then came the great day of disillusionment.

For two years we managed to get along with existing stocks or went without. In 1916, there were only seven dye factories in the country. By the end of 1917, they had increased to eighty-one, and the output of dyes was about forty-six million pounds,—equal to the pre-war importation. Besides, we were actually exporting dyes to other countries. And, too, the infant industry met the demand for war chemicals and the raw materials for synthetic resins.

We are to-day meeting about ninety-five per cent. of domestic consumption, and our exports exceed imports. In 1926, 88,000,000 pounds of coal-tar dyes were produced here, the largest quantity in any year with the exception of 1923, when the figures were 93,667,524. The quantity of coal-tar dyes exported in 1926 reached 25,811,941 pounds, and the imports were 4,658,464 pounds. These figures tell a wonderful story of chemical independence achieved in the face of dire necessity.

In the production of what are called "vat colors," the American industry has scored a brilliant victory. For the manufacture of a certain series of vat colors, an organic compound known as anthraquinone is required. In 1917, Gibbs, an American chemist in the Color Laboratory in Washington, succeeded in obtaining phthalic anhydride by passing naphthalene vapor over a catalyst, and from phthalic anhydride anthraquinone can be synthesized. The entire requirements for this compound are now met by this synthetic process, and more economically than by the older process. This discovery has proved to be a great stimulus to the production of vat colors in this country, and the colors themselves are said to be superior in every respect to those produced anywhere else in the world. In several instances the American manufacturers of these dyes have produced entirely new colors, not previously known to the trade. And for phthalic anhydride new uses outside of the dye business have been developed, as in the production of nitrocellulose lacquers. Further, the price of this compound has been reduced through the agency of this synthetic process from fourteen dollars a pound in 1916 to eighteen cents a pound to-day.

As to the prices of dyes, we may cite indigo. In 1914, it sold for about 15.5 cents a pound. Three years later the American-made dye brought $1.42 a pound. To-day it may be bought for 14 cents, which at the pre-war value of money would be about $8\frac{1}{4}$ cents. Other dyes tell a similar story.

We are also interested in the quality of American dyes. Are they equal in all respects to those from abroad? On this point, Mr. M. L. Crossley, of the Calco Chemical Company, has this to say: "Old processes have been improved and in certain cases entirely new processes for these products (dyes) have been developed. Economy in production and quality of finished product have been the dominating ideas in the industry.

The quality of the organic products made in this country is equal to that of the pre-war products, and in certain cases better. . . . Among the other achievements of the decade are the development of economic processes for the manufacture of the most important of the vat dyes, the production of new dyes for printing, the discovery of a new class of spirit-soluble dyes which are capable of producing every desirable hue and which are of excellent fastness to light. . . .'' And again, Mr. O. M. Bishop and Mr. J. H. Sachs, of E. I. du Pont de Nemours and Company, say: "It therefore comes about that the chemist, the chemical engineer, and the design engineer have combined their skill in solving the most perplexing problems that have been encountered in the building up of this industry. Their work has resulted in the production to-day of a complete line of vat colors in America, the quality of which is fully equal and in many cases superior to that of German manufactured colors. . . . These figures (omitted) illustrate not only the progress made in America in the manufacture of these colors, but also the remarkable increase in the quantity consumed in this country. This increase has been brought about by two outstanding developments in the application of these colors to textile fibers and fabrics—namely, (1) their application to silk, and (2) their application on piece goods by the 'pad and jig' method. Both developments are of American origin. To-day large quantities of silk and an enormous yardage of cotton piece goods are being dyed with these, the fastest of all dyes.''

Similar statements might be multiplied. Of course, in the early days of the industry, some dyes were unsatisfactory. It seems difficult for people to forget this. However, that condition was only incidental to the work of building a new industry and placing it on a sure foundation of chemical fact and practise. Our chemists and engineers had to learn the technique of the business. But we have now at great cost won independence in the dyestuff and organic chemical industry. We can retain it only through the eternal vigilance arising from the work of pure and applied science.

One of the most brilliant accomplishments in this field has come in the dyeing of furs. To give you a picture of it, I can do no better than to quote from a paper by Mr. William E. Austin, of the Stein Fur Dyeing Company, Inc. Mr. Austin says, "About ninety per cent. of the dyed furs worn here before 1915 bore the stamps of foreign dyers, chiefly German, in spite of the fact that most of these furs came originally from North America. Purchasers of dyed furs were accustomed to ask for the Leipzig dye, this being considered universally the standard of quality. . . . With characteristic American energy and initiative, the fur dyers took advantage of the opportunity (created by the war), and within a few years were enabled adequately and satisfactorily to take care of the domestic requirements for dyed furs. By 1922 the expression 'Leipzig dye' had become practically an historical phrase in this country, and American-dyed furs were in universal demand, in spite of sporadic attempts by propagandists to disparage and discredit the domestic products. Not only did the American artisans succeed in superseding the German dyers, but they advanced beyond the traditional methods and formulas and developed fur-dyeing along new lines. . . . To-day there are about ninety fur-dyeing plants in America, most of them in New York and vicinity. About forty million skins are dyed annually, and more than ninety-five per cent. of the domestic consumption of dyed furs is of furs dyed here; furthermore, American-dyed furs are being exported to all parts of the world, including Germany. It is impossible to estimate the number of shades and color effects which are being produced now, but about four hundred thousand pounds of oxidation colors are used every year, exclusive of aniline salts, of which several million pounds are used, and representing in all an expenditure for dye materials of between one and two million dollars.

"The application of the results of science, especially chemistry, to the fur-dyeing art, has evolved in this country a highly progressive, scientific and efficient industry which to-day is envied by fur-dyeing organizations throughout the world. Only last year a German commission, sent here to study American methods in the fur trade, marveled at the remarkably efficient management and organization obtaining throughout the fur-dyeing branch of the industry."

And Mr. Austin states that the dyes used are manufactured in this country. Let me quote him again: "At first the new dyes were imported from Germany, but they were soon reproduced here. To-day there are available for the dyers' use thirty-five to forty individual, distinct dyes, as well as numerous mixtures, all of the oxidation type, representing shades from the palest cream or ivory through yellow, orange, red, brown, gray, blue and black. Occasionally, also, when exceptionally brilliant colors are desired, certain of the textile dyes are used."

Surely, this is a record of which every citizen may well be proud.

In the development of rubber, too, the dyestuff industry in America has made a contribution of immense importance. As we have seen, organic accelerators developed by chemists in the dye plants hasten the speed at which rubber is vulcanized from three- to five-fold. In addition, these compounds, used to the extent of about one per cent., increase the wearing qualities of rubber goods and prolong their life. It is estimated that this factor alone "annually saves the motorist and the rubber industry $100,000,000." The value of these accelerators used by the rubber industry in a year is about $5,000,000. Therefore, the dividends are twenty per cent.

The antioxidants, also used to prolong the life of rubber goods, are products of the dye chemist. In speaking of the research work along this line, Mr. Donald H. Powers, of E. I. du Pont de Nemours and Company, says, "Hundreds of organic compounds were prepared and tested by the dyestuff industry to study their effect on the rate of the deterioration of the rubber and also to gain further insight into the exact mechanism of this deterioration. As a result of these studies, products were found which retarded the rate of aging in certain stocks as much as sixfold. It meant converting a stock, which would be markedly deteriorated before it was half worn out, into a stock that would show little signs of aging during its entire life."

And further, these chemists have found that the large quantities of inorganic pigments formerly used in the coloring of rubber can be replaced with very small percentages of organic dyes. In some instances, less than one per cent. of an organic dye will produce a brighter hue than was formerly obtained with ten per cent. of an inorganic pigment.

Let me give you another view of the gain to the motorist from the use of organic accelerators in the vulcanizing of rubber. It has been estimated by one of the large rubber companies that "the increased mileage of tires made with accelerators over the mileage which would have been obtained without such ingredients has in the last ten years aggregated 240 billion tire miles, or equivalent to sending 2,500,000 automobiles around the world at its equator."

The building of the dyestuff industry in America is possibly the most brilliant achievement of applied chemistry in recent times. And in another direction this industry has made for a vast degree of progress. At the opening of the World War but little more than twenty per cent. of our coke was produced in by-product ovens. Millions of dollars' worth of irreplaceable substances, including the raw materials for the manufacture of dyestuffs and organic chemicals, went up in smoke each year. To-day the figures are reversed. Less than twenty per cent. of the coke is made in the old wasteful beehive ovens. The coal-tar, ammonia and gas are saved. With the coming of the low-temperature carbonization of all bituminous coal not coked for the steel industry, the quantity of basic materials for the production of organic chemicals will be increased many times.

This country has traveled a long way since 1914, and along no other route has greater progress been made than that which led to synthetic dyes and allied products.

AMERICAN GLASS

Long before the dawn of history glass-making was a highly perfected art. That and the art of pottery are probably the world's oldest examples of applied chemistry. We find glass in the Egyptian tombs. The Phœnicians exported it. It is mentioned in the Bible. The Romans were proficient in its manufacture. The beautiful products of the Venetian artisans have become the wonder of succeeding centuries. Germany and later Bohemia became the centers of glass manufacture. France and Belgium practised the art. At the beginning of the Great War, all the chemical and optical glass used in America came from Europe, chiefly from Germany.

Yes, then came the Great War, so revolutionary to a host of time-honored practises. Imported glass for the time being was a thing of the past. American ingenuity was compelled to assert itself. But our scientists and technicians were equal to the occasion. A record has been written of which no citizen need be ashamed.

Let us begin with chemical glassware. Shortly after the war, I visited the chemical laboratories and store-rooms of one of our large technical institutions. The glassware, of which large quantities were everywhere in evidence, bore the mark of *Pyrex*. In former years the trade-mark *Jena* had stood for the highest degree of perfection in this kind of ware. It no longer does. Pyrex is now the standard the world over. Its development at the Corning Glass Works by a staff of chemists under the direction of Dr. E. C. Sullivan marks one of the great triumphs of industrial chemistry in America.

The thick glass for a trainman's lantern must be able

to stand sudden changes of heat and cold in all sorts of weather. Upon the signals which he gives may depend the lives of thousands. If the glass breaks at a critical moment, catastrophe is likely to follow. It is sudden expansion with change of temperature which breaks such glass. Pyrex glass expands only one-third as much as ordinary glass when heated. It is the ideal glass for railroad purposes, and its introduction has lessened in no small degree the hazards of travel and transportation.

Originally intended as a glass for baking-dishes in the home, its composition and unsuspected resistance to chemical reagents have made Pyrex superior to all its predecessors for laboratory purposes. Pyrex glass used by Army medical authorities during the war proved to be better than any ware ever obtained from abroad. Kolle flasks of Pyrex for growing the organisms for the typhoid vaccine were ahead of similar flasks fashioned from the famous Jena glass. Pyrex, too, was found to be an ideal substitute for the narrow-mouthed porcelain jars used in grinding the bacteria for lipovaccines.

Pyrex has found a host of uses in industrial chemistry. Pipes of Pyrex are used in acid-pumping lines in nitric and hydrochloric acid plants. It does duty in still columns and gas mains. Evaporators and condensers are built of this general service glass. It is molded into solid glass rollers for use in artificial silk manufacture and textile dye-machines. It is an excellent electric insulator, and one-piece bearings for machinery are being shaped from it. Pyrex glass was a factor in the success of Commander Byrd's flight to the pole. His radio set was insulated with it throughout.

Never again will German-blown glass dominate the

chemical trade of the world. American chemists have produced something better.

More than a million electric light bulbs are blown in this country every day in the year. Before the war potash glass was considered essential for this purpose, but potash was cut off. Chemists immediately began the development of non-potash glasses, and in many respects these have proved better than the former. But the first of this glass contained a considerable percentage of lead, an expensive material and one which made necessary the melting of the batch materials in pots. By 1916, a glass which could be melted in tanks and which contained neither potash nor lead had been developed. In this connection, let it be noted, too, that, whereas twenty-five years ago electric light bulbs were blown by hand, machines of American invention now perform this task. A single machine will produce more than sixty thousand household bulbs in a day.

Possibly, in the field of optical glass, American chemists scored their greatest triumph. Optical glass was imperative to successful warfare. Without range-finders, gunsights, binoculars, camera lenses and periscopes, military forces would have been compelled to fight in the dark. At any cost optical glass must be had. Immediately, commercial manufacturers, the United States Bureau of Standards, the Geophysical Laboratory of the Carnegie Institution, and the Council of National Defense began investigations. Analyses were made of one hundred and ten different types of German glass. As a result of this combined attack, within a month methods were developed by which the qualities of the glass from a certain batch of materials could be computed in advance with wonderful accuracy. It at once became possible to control the product with great exactness. Improvements in many mechanical details were made. Melting-pots, previously made in Germany, were fashioned from American clays, and the hand methods of stirring prevailing abroad were displaced by machines. The time of furnace operation was shortened from two and a half days to twenty-four hours. The period of annealing, that is, bringing the temperature of the glass from that of the furnace down to 370 degrees Centigrade, was reduced from four weeks, according to German practise, to three days. The rolling of optical glass into sheets was introduced. The proportion of acceptable glass from a given melt was increased by three to eight per cent.

And let us remember that optical glass requires the highest degree of skill of the glass-maker's art. His product must be physically perfect,—free from "stones," bubbles, lines and strains. In addition, it must have definite optical properties. It must be free from color and highly transparent, tough, hard and unaffected by weather conditions. The actual achievement of our chemists and allied scientists was brilliantly successful. During the war, nearly three-quarters of a million pounds of optical glass were manufactured in this country. It is to be regretted that a triumph so great should have failed to meet with the country's support and that the industry has now become a thing of the past. However, the knowledge and industrial technique gained will remain, ready again for service in time of national emergency. As a demonstration of what may be accomplished when a great need arises, this war-time production of optical glass will stand supreme.

Selenium ruby glass for danger signals on railroads is an American product. So superior is it to copper ruby glass that samples of the latter are difficult to obtain. It should be understood that the colors given to glass are obtained by dissolving in the glass certain metallic substances. For instance, cobalt gives blue; iron gives yellow and green; chromium also gives green; gold was formerly used for the highest quality of ruby glass; copper also gives red. The superiority of selenium is due to its transmission of practically all the red rays, and nothing else except a little yellow. American chemists, too, have succeeded in producing a standard green signal glass, much superior to the large number of glasses of different hues which were on the market only a few years ago.

To protect the eyes of workmen in electric arc welding and in the use of thermit and the oxyacetylene torch, glass has been developed which will absorb both the ultraviolet rays and the infra-red, or heating, rays. At the same time, this glass eliminates the glare.

Most of you have heard of fused quartz, a remarkable product of the General Electric laboratories and the most completely transparent substance known to science. I have heated chemical ware of this quartz to redness and suddenly thrust it into water without damage. And this illustrates one of its most striking properties. It has the lowest rate of expansion with change of temperature of any known substance. For this reason, the mercury bulb of a thermometer made of this glass will not change in size with age. The fixed points, the boiling and freezing points, will not become displaced. But more remarkable than this, fused quartz will actually transmit light around corners, and there is little loss of light in the transmission. Bent rods of fused quartz permit the physician and surgeon to examine either by direct observation or by photograph hitherto inaccessible cavities of the body. Further, this substance will transmit the ultraviolet rays, coming to be so important in medical treatment. You will recall from the chapter on Chemistry and Disease that these rays are widely used in the treatment of rickets.

But fused quartz glass is expensive and somewhat difficult to produce. Recently, a chemist of the Corning Glass Works has developed a glass almost as transparent to ultraviolet light as quartz, and it can be made in quantity. There seems to be no limit to what the glass chemist is able to do. What he needs, he forthwith invents.

In the purely mechanical phases of the glass industry, American artisans have accomplished much. About a quarter of a century ago, Mr. Michael J. Owens invented the bottle machine for blowing bottles. Its use was soon extended to blowing tumblers and thermos bottles. Automatic feeding-machines, mechanical methods of producing window- and plate-glass, and machines for drawing sheet glass and tubing are products of American invention. A new type of lehr has cut the time of annealing in half.

Nowhere has the resourcefulness of American chemists and engineers been better demonstrated than in the glass industry. But preceding this success and essential to it lay a century and more of scientific research in this and other lands. Without that background of chemical knowledge and experience, these brilliant solutions of urgent problems would have been impossible.

Once more we go back to the Great War, that stupendous crisis from which this country took so many new departures. In 1914, our supply of synthetic organic chemicals, indispensable to research workers, came from Germany. The purification of the technical chemicals supplied by industrial plants into the fine products required in research work was not carried out in this country. In fact, we had no organic chemical industry of any account at that time. This, however, in due course came, but the production of fine chemicals of a high degree of purity lagged. There was no money to be made in their preparation. It had always been far easier and vastly cheaper to allow Germany to meet our needs. Chemical independence had not entered into the picture. At the University of Illinois, Professor C. G. Derick, in charge of organic chemistry, attempted to meet the need by setting students to work during summer vacations to prepare such compounds as his own laboratories required. His successor, Professor Roger Adams, extended the work, but the output was altogether inadequate to meet the situation. The need grew more acute with each succeeding month and year. Something had to be done, and in the summer of 1918 a solution of the problem began.

This philanthropic task was undertaken by Mr. George Eastman. Under the direction of Doctor C. E. K. Mees, head of the Eastman Research Laboratory, he organized a Synthetic Chemistry Department. The chief purpose of this laboratory is to supply the fine chemicals needed by research workers in this country. As the company itself puts it, "of primary importance is the synthesis of compounds which are not prepared technically but are required for laboratory purposes; secondly, the purification of technical materials obtained from the chemical manufacturers; and, thirdly, the distribution of such technical chemicals in the form in which they are purchased." Already more than twenty-one hundred such chemicals have been prepared and placed on the market, and the number is constantly growing.

As indispensable as the ignition system to an automobile motor, the production of fine chemicals is vital to our national independence. These products do not bulk large in the annual output, but research would be crippled without them. We may, of course, now obtain them from Germany, but to return to this source of supply would be to make our own establishment incomplete. In performing this patriotic service, Mr. Eastman has made, not only the chemical industry, but the whole nation his lasting debtors.

OUR CHEMICAL TRADE

The United States is to-day the world's largest producer of chemical commodities, but our foreign trade is disproportionately small. Our own domestic market consumes the major part of our production. In addition this country imports a great deal. This is not because American products are inferior to those from abroad. Indeed, in many instances they are superior. The reasons are to be found chiefly in the newness of the industry, the large capacity of the home market to absorb the domestic output, and the consequent lack of incentive to develop a foreign trade. Still, this condition can not long continue, for production in many lines is expanding more rapidly than domestic consumption. Either foreign markets must be developed or there will come an inevitable halting of the expansion of the industry. That America can compete in the chemical markets of the world has been amply demonstrated. Scores of our products are known everywhere.

Our imports of antitoxins, serums and vaccines for last year (1926) almost disappeared, being valued at only $3,400, while our exports of these substances reached a value of $1,439,000. The total value of the medicinals imported into this country in this year was $5,891,000, while our exports reached nearly twenty millions. The output of perfumery and toilet articles grew from about twenty-six million dollars in value in 1914 to more than a hundred and forty millions in 1925. In the latter year, our exports of these preparations reached a little more than eight million dollars, while our imports were about two million dollars less. Each nation seems to have a specialty in these lines. Germany supplies the cheaper synthetic perfumes and aromatic preparations, while France leads all countries in the manufacture of the more expensive toilet articles, particularly perfumes. The United States holds supremacy in the preparation of dentrifices. American dental equipment, tooth pastes and powders have long been regarded as superior to all others. The value of American dentrifices supplied to the world last year was $3,382,000. England is our best customer, taking a third of our total product. Her dependencies are good buyers. Latin America and the Far East demand our tooth pastes and soaps. American trade-marked brands are favorably known on the Continent. American shaving and toilet soaps are enjoying a constantly increasing trade. Last year the value of the exports in these reached $3,038,000. Our face powders, rouges and creams find a ready market in Latin America and Cuba. American paints and varnishes are favorably known in every civilized country. Our exports of these products are five times greater than our imports, reaching a value of nearly nineteen million dollars in 1926. While we import all kinds of fertilizers, we export ammonium sulfate and phosphate rock, being the world's largest producer of the latter. Although the United States imports from China more than three-quarters of a million dollars' worth of firecrackers, the exports of explosives, chiefly dynamite, are several times the imports in value. Owing to German synthetic methanol, imports of this commodity are considerably exceeding the exports of the distillers of wood in this country. But the new American process of production may soon change the picture. Things in the chemical world these days have a wonderful facility for changing with kaleidoscopic rapidity. While we are still heavy importers of coal-tar chemicals our exports are growing. In 1926, they registered a thirty per cent. increase over the volume of the preceding year.

Every branch of the foreign chemical trade for 1926 showed an excess of exports over imports with the exception of fertilizers. Here an unfavorable balance of about forty million dollars created a deficit of nearly ten millions for the industry as a whole. This was due to the large importations of Chile saltpeter and of synthetic nitrogen compounds and potash fertilizers from Europe. However, the prospective advances in the production of these fertilizers in America may be counted upon to make substantial reductions in this unfavorable balance in the not distant future.

On the whole this country has ample ground for self-congratulation. The value of our annual chemical exports has increased since 1914 from approximately fifty million dollars to nearly one hundred and twenty-five millions. This means an increase of one hundred and fifty per cent., while imports during this same period have grown by only fifty-three per cent. Furthermore, the United States now has the foundations of a chemical industry, which, in its present magnitude, diversity and capacity for rapid expansion in time of need, means that independence of foreign sources of supply so sadly lacking but little more than a decade ago. The future is, indeed, big with promise.

AMERICAN SULFUR

From time immemorial the element sulfur has bulked large in the development of all things chemical. Symbol of the fires eternal, it has figured in the literature as well as in the industries of men. It is mentioned in the Bible and in the writings of Homer. Paracelsus regarded sulfur together with salt and mercury as one of the three essential constituents of the human body, among which there must at all times be maintained a proper balance. Sulfurous gases issuing from volcanoes and dissolved in the water of natural springs are familiar phenomena the world over. But not until the coming of the modern age of chemistry did sulfur become a factor of vast importance in the industrial world.

Up until 1900, nearly all of the world's supply of sulfur came from Sicily. But in drilling for oil, during the latter part of the last century, vast deposits of exceptionally pure sulfur were discovered in Louisiana and Texas. Still, the successful removal of this sulfur was for long an unsolved problem, for it was buried at depths of several hundred feet beneath beds of clay, rock and loose quicksand. Such a treasure-house of potential wealth, carrying with it as it did the assurance of independence from a foreign supply, could not long remain untapped. The ingenuity of Herman Frasch provided the method which has since brought this yellow element to the surface in prodigious quantities. Sinking a hole into the deposit, he drove through it three concentric pipes. Through the outer pipe, water heated under pressure to a temperature considerably higher than its boiling point is pumped down to the sulfur. Through the innermost pipe hot compressed air is pumped. The hot water melts the sulfur and the pressure of the air forces the resulting liquid upward through the middle pipe and into large vats at the surface, where it solidifies. The purity of this sulfur is 99.5 per cent., the purest sulfur in the world. Millions of tons are thus obtained.

The most important use of sulfur is in the production of sulfuric acid, the largest single raw material of chemical manufacture. Basil Valentine, an old alchemist, is said to have discovered this acid through the distillation of a shale rock, found in Bohemia and known as "green vitriol." This rock was a compound of sulfuric acid and contained enough water chemically combined so that its distillation yielded the acid. The acid proved to be a heavy oily liquid, which because of its source, was called "oil of vitriol." It is even known to this day by that name, and its salts are frequently called vitriols. Thus copper sulfate is known as blue vitriol and zinc sulfate as white vitriol.

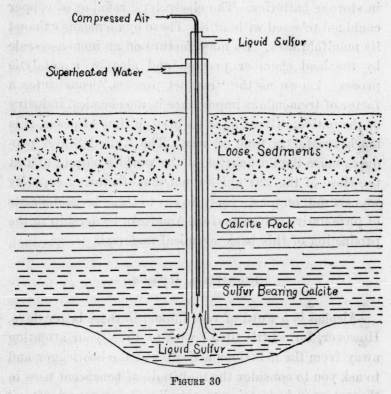

FIGURE 30

Diagram showing the method of obtaining sulfur from its deposits in Texas.

I used to tell the students in my classes that they could name nothing from a pin to a locomotive which did not directly or indirectly use sulfuric acid in its manufacture. Without it industry would be crippled, literally and figuratively. Sulfuric acid is essential to the production of fertilizers, the making of other acids, the refining of petroleum, the manufacture of dyes, leather, alums and the vitriols. It is important in metallurgy, in the manufacture of explosives, and in the transformation of starch into sugar. Every one is familiar with its use in storage batteries. The electrolytic refining of copper could not proceed without it. These by no means exhaust its manifold uses. Its manufacture on an immense scale by the lead chamber process and also by a catalytic process, known as the "contact process," constitutes a factor of tremendous importance in the chemical industry of the nation. Great as is its need in time of peace, it is much greater in time of war. The United States produces more than a quarter of the world's output, and at the close of the war our annual manufacturing capacity was six million tons. Easy access to these large deposits of pure native sulfur confers American leadership in the production of this basic chemical material.

INDUSTRIAL ALCOHOL

Alcohol is a word of vast import in these latter days. However, for a little time I wish to direct your attention away from the nefarious activities of the bootlegger and to ask you to consider the multitude of beneficent uses in the arts and industries of this liquid compound of evil repute.

The use of alcohol in this country has increased amazingly in the last two decades. The domestic production grew from 3,560,552 gallons in 1908 to 18,933,550 gallons in 1920, and to the prodigious quantity of 160,000,000 in 1925. As a solvent, alcohol is second only to water in importance. It is essential in at least a thousand chemical processes. There is scarcely an article of household use which does not involve at some stage of its manufacture the use of alcohol. In 1925, 35,000,000 gallons were required to prevent the freezing of water in the radiators of automobiles; 13,000,000 gallons were used in the preparation of perfumery and toilet articles; 500,000 gallons were necessary for shaving soaps; nearly a million gallons monthly went into the production of nitrocellulose, but this industry is growing so rapidly that any figures are out of date before they appear in print; about a million gallons are used annually in the preparation of pectin, used by housewives in the jellying of fruit juices; the tobacco industry uses more than a million and a quarter gallons; and alcohol is vital to the lacquer industry, the manufacture of rayon, varnishes, paints, straw hats, radio equipment, bakelite, food products, artificial leather, billiard balls, extracts, dyes, buttons, combs, explosives, moving-picture films, linoleum, mirrors, medicinals, vinegar, paint removers, cosmetics, hair tonics, mouth washes, deodorants, inks, glues, rubber goods, ether, electrical goods and a host of other products. The list is almost endless. Alcohol is the basis of the whole organic chemical industry.

Until twenty years ago, the United States Government, with a blind perversity frequently characteristic of those in authority, taxed the alcohol industry almost out of existence. Germany, recognizing the basic importance of alcohol to chemical industry, had long encouraged and subsidized its production. Here in America, a high internal revenue tax had worked in the opposite direction. Then came the war, that supreme detonator in modern times of latent possibilities. The exigencies of war could not be denied. And alcohol was a prime essential to the waging of war. In a host of ways it became imperative in the production of munitions. Already denatured alcohol, that is, alcohol rendered unfit for beverage purposes, had been made tax-exempt. The National Prohibition Act passed later still further provided for the needs of industry. But it was military necessity which gave the tremendous impetus to the expansion of alcoholic productions.

T. N. T., cordite, smokeless powder, and other explosives require alcohol in their manufacture. At the close of the war, more than half of the shells fired contained poisonous gas, in the production of which alcohol is essential. Mustard gas, for instance, is made by the action of sulfur chloride on ethylene, and ethylene is obtained from ordinary grain alcohol. The preparation of the fulminate compounds used in percussion caps, requires alcohol. The acetone absolutely indispensable to the manufacture of the type of powder used in British guns at that time had to travel the alcohol route. The "dope" used upon airplane cloth was an alcohol solution of nitrocellulose or cellulose acetate. The anesthetics, antiseptics and healing drugs used in the hospitals behind the lines required immense quantities of alcohol in their preparation. A host of other uses were equally important. Besides, all the peace-time demands remained in force. No wonder that the alcohol industry in this country expanded with startling rapidity. To-day, this country possesses at Baltimore, Maryland, the largest plant of its kind in the world.

The raw material for the commercial manufacture of alcohol in this country is chiefly molasses, brought thither in large tank ships from the sugar-mills of Cuba. Starch from corn, potatoes, or other products may also be changed to alcohol, first being converted into sugar. The time may come when immense quantities of crops rich in starch and sugar will be grown within the Tropics for this purpose. The molasses, mixed with water and a little acid, is subjected to fermentation with yeast. The resulting mash, containing from six to ten per cent. of alcohol, is distilled with steam. The product contains many impurities, which are removed by a further process of distillation, known as rectification. So highly developed is this process that alcohol is one of the purest chemical compounds known to the industry.

One of the most signal triumphs of chemical industry is the production in this country within the last two years of absolute, or anhydrous, alcohol in commercial quantities. Ordinary alcohol contains five per cent. water, which it is difficult to remove. Formerly, absolute alcohol, when sold at all, brought from ten to twenty dollars a gallon, and it was usually prepared by the experimenter in his own laboratory as needed. It is now obtainable in tank cars at less than a dollar a gallon. Anhydrous alcohol is quite different in its properties from ordinary alcohol. It has already found important uses, one of the most notable of which is as a solvent for nitrocellulose and resins in the new-born lacquer industry.

Another solvent of great importance in the preparation of lacquers is ethyl acetate, a product of ordinary alcohol known to the chemist as ethyl alcohol, and acetic acid, the acid of vinegar. The old methods of preparation required acetic acid of high concentration and a dehydrating agent to remove the water which was a product of the reaction, a chemical reaction known as esterification. Dr. Milton Whitaker, in charge of the research staff of America's largest alcohol company, put his whole force of chemists at work upon an intensive study of this problem of esterification. Although months were required to make the investigation, the result was a continuous process for converting dilute acetic acid and alcohol into ethyl acetate quickly and cheaply. The output of this plant is now one hundred and fifty thousand gallons of chemically pure anhydrous (without water) ethyl acetate a month. Here again is the concrete evidence that scientific research pays commercial dividends.

A WAR ROMANCE

The world long ago learned to associate war and romance. In the particular instance I am to relate, we have war and romance with an intermixture of chemistry and bacteriology.

It came about in this way. For the production of cordite, the explosive used in the British artillery and rifles during the war and without which these guns would have been ruined as far as accuracy was concerned, acetone in enormous quantities was required. Acetone is an organic compound obtained along with methanol in the distillation of wood. It may also be made by the transformation of ordinary grain alcohol, first into acetic acid, then to calcium acetate and eventually to acetone. But these sources of supply were inadequate. Still acetone must be had and that without delay.

Fortunately, a process born of the strenuous attempts

in the years preceding the war to produce artificial rubber offered a solution. The starting points in this rubber synthesis were two compounds known as butadiene and isoprene, neither of which could be easily produced. At this critical moment, the hand of destiny or possibly just good fortune brought upon the scene a micro-organism, possessed of the high sounding name *clostridium aceto-butylicum*. It was found that the particular diet of this microscopic creature was starch and that he was endowed with the remarkable capacity of transforming this sort of food into acetone and two other compounds known respectively as butanol and ethanol. From butanol both butadiene and isoprene could be obtained. Although considerably less than half the product was acetone, the British War Office seized upon this fermentation process, for that is what it is, the direct fermentation of starch, to eke out the indispensable supply of a prime necessity of war. Immediately, this hitherto insignificant microbe was put to work in England, India and Canada.

When the United States entered the war, an old whisky distillery in the corn belt of Indiana was also converted into a plant for the manufacture of acetone, to be used as a solvent in the production of smokeless powder and "dope" for the cloth of American airplanes. But what to do with the butanol, which constituted more than half the output, was a baffling problem. This compound, which is one of the higher alcohols, seemed to have no use whatever, and yet it was being produced at the rate of many tons a day. However, thinking that some use might be found and not wishing to throw the stuff away, huge vats were built to contain the "waste" liquid. To-day one of those vats serves admirably as a swimming pool.

Following the war, another discovery, an essential link in this tale of chemical achievement, was made. In the manufacture of explosives, chemists had acquired an intimate acquaintance with nitrocellulose, that is, cotton treated with nitric acid to give it explosive properties and solubility. In this work a method had been evolved for producing nitrocellulose of "low viscosity," when in solution. A viscous liquid is one which is thick like molasses. One of low viscosity is thin and will flow freely. Now this discovery led to the rise of the lacquer industry in America, one of the most spectacular and astounding phenomena of modern chemistry, an achievement which will be discussed presently.

Now for the connection with butanol. The salt, or ester as the chemist calls it, of butanol and acetic acid, known as butyl acetate, was found to be an excellent solvent for nitrocellulose in the production of lacquers, and, being capable of manufacture in large quantity and at low cost, it became doubly desirable. The waste material in the war-time vats was quickly utilized, and to-day two immense plants at Terre Haute, Indiana, and Peoria, Illinois, are turning out one hundred tons of solvents a day and even with twenty-four-hour days and seven-day weeks they are unable to keep pace with the demand. In 1926, the plant capacity was doubled and still further extensions are being planned. Of this one hundred tons, sixty are butanol, thirty acetone and the remainder ethanol. This output of acetone, which, while having a large number of important uses, is not so much in demand as during the war, has dealt a hard blow to the distillers of wood. Together with the synthetic production of methanol, this industry has been particularly unfortunate. However, it is but one of many inevitable episodes incidental to chemical progress.

Reduced to an absolute science under the rigid control of a staff of chemists and bacteriologists, the large scale production of butanol by the direct fermentation of starch is an outstanding triumph of the chemical industry in America. And the corn from which the starch is obtained is largely waste, unfit either for cattle feed or food. But this process of chemistry transforms it into an economic asset. The process is briefly this: low-grade corn is ground and screened; the separated bran is sold for feed, and the fine starch meal is carried to the mashing tuns, large, open steel kettles, each having a capacity of approximately ten thousand gallons; after being digested with warm water, the mash goes to pressure cookers, in which it is heated with live steam for two hours; thence it goes to the fermenting vats; after fermentation with the microbe *clostridium* for about two and a half days, the solution, containing something like 2.5 per cent. of the three essential products, passes to an underground reservoir, from which it is pumped to huge beer stills; this distillation increases the concentration of solvents to fifty per cent., after which the three are separated by fractional distillation. At every point, absolute cleanliness prevails, and the utmost care is exercised to prevent the intrusion of wild yeasts, which would cause undesirable fermentations. Sterilization of equipment must be repeatedly carried out. The growing of the microbe cultures, under the control of skilled bacteriologists, is a science in itself.

In the process of fermentation, hydrogen and carbon dioxide gases are produced. As yet but little use has been made of these. But they will not long be allowed to go to waste. By passage over hot carbon, a mixture of carbon monoxide and hydrogen may be obtained, and it has been suggested that a plant for their conversion into methanol could profitably be established as a by-product accessory.*

The uses of butanol have proved to be legion. While its chief use is in the manufacture of lacquers, it is also employed in the preparation of antiseptics, artificial leather, rayon, carbon removers, paints, varnishes and enamels, motion-picture films, drugs, synthetic resins, patent and enameled leathers and much more.

It will be recalled that acetone is a raw material for the synthesis of artificial rubber. Should that process be some day placed upon a commercial basis of mass production, acetone would no longer be in any sense a drug on the market. Starch in prodigious quantities would then be required for conversion into acetone, and it might well be that butanol would become the by-product manufactured in quantities in excess of the demand. The possibilities of the industry have scarcely yet been tapped. The demand for starchy crops which it is capable of creating may prove a boon to agriculture and put to work much waste land. Before this drama of war, science and agriculture is ended, I am sure you will agree there has been romance in it.

---

*Since the above paragraph was written, about six weeks ago, the synthesis of methanol from the waste gases mentioned has become a commercial success. An entirely American development, this process has already trebled the output of domestic methanol and promises additional independence of foreign sources, though it does deliver another severe blow to the wood distillation industry.

Courtesy, Corning Glass Works

Novel designs in radio articles of Pyrex glass, an American glass of the highest quality

Courtesy, Commercial Solvents Corporation

A huge still plant in the manufacture of butanol—a war-time waste converted by American chemists into an industrial necessity

Courtesy, E. I. du Pont de Nemours and Company

Bales of raw cotton linters in storage preparatory to being converted into nitrocellulose for use in the process of manufacturing automobile lacquers

Removing the nitrated cotton from the hydraulic press, in which it has been freed from water

RISE OF THE LACQUER INDUSTRY

Five years ago, the lacquer industry in America or anywhere else was practically non-existent. In 1926, our production of these new types of finishing materials was approximately twenty million gallons. The output had roughly doubled in each of the three preceding years, and it is quite likely to double in the present. One company manufacturing automobile bodies is reported to have said that, had not these new lacquers been available, it would have been compelled to spend ten million dollars more in two recent years for additional paint shops and drying equipment to take care of the increase in its business. This development of chemical research has been a factor in recent price reductions in American cars. The rapidity of the spray-gun method of applying these new lacquers has created a near-panic in painters' unions and has resulted in numerous walkouts. But no one can stem the tide of fate. The painter with his bristle brush may be compelled to travel the well-trodden route of many another old-time artisan. But more than a great division of labor is threatened. Manufacturers of paint and varnish, producers of linseed oil, flax growers, importers of gums, distillers of turpentine, operators of lead and zinc mines, and producers of other raw materials of the old-time paint and varnish industry are threatened with an upheaval of revolutionary proportions. And all because chemists have found a way of making a new type of finish for all sorts of materials from nitrocellulose left over from the war and new-born organic solvents, also products of the research chemical laboratory.

The modern lacquer is totally different from the oriental type, which has been in use for three thousand years. Its distinguishing ingredient is nitrocellulose, discovered about eighty years ago and long used in an alcohol and ether solution as collodion, familiar as "new-skin." The higher nitrates of cotton are the basis of smokeless powders. In addition to nitrocellulose, of which there are a number of varieties, a lacquer contains a resin, a pigment, solvents, diluents, and a plasticizer. The nitrocellulose is the film-forming constituent and produces a durable finish. Resins tend to give to the film the appearance of an oil varnish. They also give body, gloss, brilliance and hardness to the film, causing it to adhere to the surface and to be impervious to moisture. Resins permit of rubbing, thereby producing a polish. The pigment not only gives color but adds to the durability of the lacquer by shielding it from the effects of the ultraviolet rays of sunlight, the most potent cause of lacquer decomposition. A considerable number of solvents are available, chiefly various alcohols and their esters. Upon the proper selection of these depends much of the success of the product. The so-called "diluents" give bulk to the lacquer and serve as solvents for the resins as well as being blenders of the solutions of resins and nitrocellulose. The "plasticizer," also a blender of the solutions, makes the film smooth, glossy and plastic. A lacquered metal plate can be bent and twisted without destroying the film. This is the result of the plasticizer.

I do not need to tell you of the conquest which these new lacquers have made in the automobile world. They promise to repeat the performance in the railroad industry. Already they are enjoying a wide and favorable application to locomotives, freight cars, passenger and pullman coaches, being used both for exterior and interior finish. They adhere to steel, wood trim, plaster walls, wood floors and wall-paper. Magic-like, a lacquer will rehabilitate a shabby piece of furniture while you wait. Among the advantages of these newcomers in the fields of protective and decorative art are speed of drying, great durability of finish, ease of cleaning and of repairing scratches and dents, resistance to the destructive action of powerful cleaning agents and the permanence and beauty of the finish. Of course, these lacquers are not without disadvantages too, chief of which is the objectional odors of the solvents which pass off by evaporation in process of application. However, this is not serious and workmen are already becoming acclimated to this brand-new lot of scents.

The most unique advantage is rapidity of drying. Most lacquers will dry dust-free in fifteen minutes. In a half-hour floors are hard enough to be walked on. A hotel room may be lacquered in the morning and be ready for occupancy in the afternoon. Coat after coat may be put on within a few hours. Drying of lacquers is by evaporation and not by the slow chemical process of oxidation as in the case of ordinary paints and varnishes, continuing in the latter throughout the life of the paint or varnish and becoming a contributing factor in its deterioration. But this factor of speed of drying was found also to be a disadvantage. It seemed to limit the method of application to spraying. When spread with a brush, the lacquer put on at the beginning of the stroke had started to set before the end of the stroke was reached. This made it difficult to eliminate brush marks and produce a smooth finish. However, materials which delay the drying of the film have been added so as to permit of brush application. Still, the spray method is the method of the future, except on small pieces of work. Therein lies one of the distinct advantages of the new lacquers.

Thus, after centuries of comparative stagnation, the paint and varnish industry is being revolutionized by a whirlwind development of discoveries and inventions. And only a beginning has been made. Before this book is off the press, new conquests will have been accomplished. Both literally and figuratively, this triumph of nitrocellulose lacquers is the most picturesque achievement of applied chemistry since the advent of the coal-tar dyes. And it is an American achievement.

A CHEMICAL CURIOSITY

The accidental discovery in this country that the waste oat hulls obtained in the manufacture of rolled oats could be easily converted into a compound known as *furfural* has within the last half-dozen years converted a museum curiosity into a soldier of industrial chemistry. In casting about for some way to increase the digestibility of these hulls as cattle feed, it was found that what is called the pentosan content of the hull could by acid treatment be changed into this compound furfural. The Department of Agriculture had previously experimented upon a method of using corn cobs for this same purpose, but oat hulls at once supplied a much more accessible source of raw material.

At this time, however, no uses for the substance were

known. Up to 1922, furfural brought from six dollars and fifty cents to thirty dollars a pound and was hardly obtainable at that. In January of that year the price dropped to a dollar and by September it had reached twenty-five cents. In 1926, it dropped to fifteen cents, and it may become still cheaper. What is more it can now be had in tank car lots of fifty to sixty thousand pounds each. Still more important, a multitude of uses have been found for the chemical newcomer. It is used in large quantities in the preparation of synthetic resins such as bakelite. So deeply does it penetrate wood that it can not be kept in wooden containers. But this characteristic together with its germicidal and fungicidal properties make it valuable as a preservative for wood, such as railroad ties, telegraph poles and shingles. It improves the flavor of tobacco. It is displacing other solvents in the preparation of shoe dyes and leather dressings. It is an excellent solvent for nitrocellulose, and, were it not for its tendency to darken with age, it would be important in the lacquer industry. Its many derivatives, too, promise a new field for chemical exploitation. At every turn in these days, chemists stumble on to something.

And now we shall leave the subject of American progress in chemistry, not because we have by any means exhausted it, but because further illustration is unnecessary. Let it be emphasized, however, that American triumphs are largely those of applied chemistry. It is in commercial applications that we excel. For instance, the rayon industry was developed abroad, but America is the largest producer. The United States stands in the front rank as a manufacturer of chemical products. But the need for fundamental research is great. The future of these vast industries depends upon it. American chemists have accomplished much. They are eager to perform this public service. What they need is Government support, endowment funds and adequate facilities. The inducements in this field must be made attractive enough to draw men and women of the highest ability. Here lie great opportunities for our men of wealth, loyal citizens and public servants.

CHAPTER XIII

CHEMISTRY IN THE DAY'S WORK

DEBT TO CHEMISTRY BEGINS WITH SUNRISE—CHEMISTRY
CONTRIBUTES TO MORNING TOILET—PAPER A CHEMICAL PROD-
UCT—CHEMICAL ASPECTS OF BREAKFAST—CHEMISTRY OF
GARAGE AND CAR—CHEMICAL REMINDERS ON TRIP TO OFFICE—
CHEMISTRY IN THE OFFICE—HOMEWARD BOUND—CHEMISTRY
ASSISTS IN DOMESTIC ACTIVITIES—CHEMISTRY IN RADIO,
PHONOGRAPH AND MOVIES—CHEMISTRY AND SLEEP—CHEM-
ISTRY EVERYWHERE.

THE other morning I awoke as the approach of sunrise began to light the landscape and chase the shadows
from my room. The glass in the windows which admitted
the light was the product of a chemical art almost as
ancient as that which fashioned the porcelain flower vase
on the near-by table. I pulled a watch from beneath my
pillow and noted the time. As I did so, I never gave a
thought to the chemical process by which the dial had
been made from an oxide of the rare element zirconium,
I did not follow in imagination the gold of the case as it
had been separated as an "impurity" in the metallurgy
of copper or lead, or mayhap had been recovered by the
cyanide process of extraction from ore containing but
eighty-seven cents of the precious metal per ton; no
vision of fiery furnaces, special heat treatment, and more
than human machinery revealed the fashioning of the

451

matchless steel of the springs; nor, too, of the marvelous alloys which render the running of the movement immune to heat or cold; I did not see the chemist in his laboratory mix the ingredients responsible for a crystal of wonderful clearness and thinness; not even the luminosity of the dial carried me back to Madame Curie and her discovery of radium. Little did it cross my mind that chemistry had touched that watch in a hundred ways.

I stepped from a bed, the brass and springs of which are chemical products of the metallurgist's handiwork, to a rug, whose textile fibers had been chemically treated and dyed with synthetic dyes. I put on a bathrobe of similar origin and stepped into slippers of artificial leather. I passed to a tiled bathroom whose every appointment spoke of chemistry. I drew water in tub and basin which I knew had been purified by chemical processes and carried for many miles through conduits and pipes made under chemical control. The cleansing action of the soap, the softening effect of the shaving lather, the keenness of the razor's edge, the antiseptic dentrifice, the tooth brush of bakelite, the bay rum and face powder, even the materials of the hair brush, the glass of the mirror with its silvered back, and much more afforded chemical luxuries, to all of which I was totally oblivious. I discovered that I had cut my face. I immediately cauterized the cut with a chemically prepared styptic pencil and applied an antiseptic, both of chemical discovery and production. My stomach felt upset and I swallowed a couple bicarbonate of soda tablets. Suffering from an attack of cold, I reached for an atomizer with which to clear the microbes from the air passages of my nose and assist in breathing. From the rubber bulb and tube, the glass and metal parts, to the solution within, this friend of health is chemical throughout. The day had scarcely started, and yet I was indebted to chemistry in a score of ways.

I returned to my room. The paint used in the pictures on the wall, the decorations, the finish of the woodwork, the mirror before which I dressed, the clothes I put on and the shoes I wore told of long centuries of chemical progress. The lenses and the metal in the frames of the glasses I was compelled to adjust preparatory to going down-stairs to read my morning paper should have conjured up a picture of my friend, the chemist. And the paper itself from the wood pulp of the paper-mill to the type metal and ink of the printing-press had been evolved by chemical processes.

I sat down to breakfast. Bacon and eggs, toast and coffee had been prepared over a gas-fired range. The bacon on its journey from farm to packing-house and thence to the retail market tells a wonderful story of chemical triumphs. But about the distant packing-house I did not see in imagination the fertilizer works, glue and gelatin factories, lard refineries, and margarine plants, all under chemical control, for utilizing the by-products incident to the preparation of bacon and other meats. I did not envision the applications of chemistry and bacteriology in the curing of the bacon or the chemically produced ice used in its preservation. The toast from the flour of wheat grown on an immense farm of the Great West should have told me of chemical fertilizers and insecticides, of machinery fabricated under chemically controlled processes going back to the ore of the mine, and of elevators and bakeries employing chemical processes in a score of ways. So too of the coffee from over seas, sweetened with sugar from chemical refineries. Even in the cooking of the eggs chemical changes had taken place. The albumin had changed from a colloidal sol to a gel. But it is the gas range which speaks most eloquently of chemistry. Made of cast-iron or pressed steel, decorated with nickel-plated parts, supplying gas from the destructive distillation of coal in a distant plant through metal pipes and rubber hose to copper gas-jets, this commonplace necessity of the kitchen fairly breathes of chemistry at every point. The table linen, the dishes and the silver, too, could tell fascinating stories of the chemist's art.

I donned coat, hat and gloves, all indebted in innumerable ways to chemical processes, and started for the garage. In a host of points, which we shall not mention, the paint, glass, metal fixtures, and concrete floor of the garage have been dependent upon a working knowledge of chemistry. I opened the garage doors and in my car beheld as big a bundle of chemical triumphs as has ever been evolved. The durable lacquer finish is one of the outstanding achievements of recent years. As we have seen in another chapter, the rubber tires are children of the chemical laboratory. The steel of chassis, body, motor and transmission is likewise. So are the other metal parts, the glass of windows, windshield and lenses, the bakelite of dash and horn, the artificial leather of the seats and much more. In the greases, lubricating oils and gasoline we have the finished products of a long series of chemical processes. Indeed without chemistry this stupendous motor age would be impossible. But I did not pause to reflect upon all this, nor upon the substitutes which chemistry is providing to insure the future of my motor necessities.

I backed my car to the street and drove to my place of business over a pavement of concrete, into the construction of which had gone Portland cement, a chemical product of ancient lineage. I used to define Portland cement in my classes as "an intimate mixture of limestone, clay and sand heated to incipient fusion and ground to an impalpable powder." In that preparation and in the subsequent setting, there is much of chemistry. Presently, I heard the gong and siren of a fire engine. Somewhere a fire, the most fundamental of chemical processes, was raging, and chemical agencies were on their way to fight it. A friend whom I had picked up struck a match to light his cigar, and in so doing let loose a whole arsenal of chemical reactions. Even the flavor of the tobacco may have been improved with furfural, a recent chemical commodity.

Soon I passed a large city gas plant, and I recalled the figures of the American Gas Association showing that approximately fifty-two million people in the United States now use gas, that there are 9,800,000 gas stoves, 3,400,000 water heaters and 4,400,000 space heaters. In this, chemistry was serving millions with an ideal domestic fuel.

In industry, gas is no less important. It touches the lives of millions of workmen daily. Within recent years the number of industrial applications has grown from a thousand to more than twenty-one thousand. And from this process of gas manufacture comes much of the ammonia for fertilizers and refrigeration. I reflected that the artificial ice for industrial and domestic use as well as the ice of skating rinks is made by the ammonia process.

Having parked my car, I entered an office where I was sentenced to spend the greater part of the working day. Immediately, the odor of perfume reached my nostrils, and I knew that the office girl was indebted to chemistry for this synthetic requisite of feminine charm. So, too, as frequently before her mirror she converted the natural bloom of youthful beauty into the sickly whiteness of a painted model. I disposed of my coat and hat on a lacquered rack and sat down to a desk whose metal and woodwork paid tribute to the chemist's art. With chemically prepared ink I began to make black marks upon chemically manufactured paper. With a chemical product the office girl cleaned the type of her machine. I wished to obliterate the evidence of a mistake in writing, and ink removers adapted by my ubiquitous friend, the chemist, were ready at hand. The modern pencil which I used was also a thing of his devising. I stepped to a fire-proof metal file, and once more I was confronted with evidence of his services. An aluminum tray for clips and rubber bands mutely spoke of the masterly research of Hall in developing the electrolytic process for separating the metal from its ore. At various times, I called for paste, glue and shellac without a thought of their chemical histories. I sat by an open window looking out upon what had once been a smoke-begrimed city, and I knew that the clearness of the air was due to the combined services of the chemist and the engineer in providing automatic stokers for the complete combustion of coal. A pocket knife of finest steel with a chemical ancestry of many centuries was in frequent use. The skies darkened and I pressed a button, flooding the room with a wealth of light from gas filled bulbs containing filaments of wrought tungsten developed in the Research Laboratories of the General Electric Company. Time and again, I spoke over the telephone, never thinking that the thousands of parts in the mechanism of this vast system of communication had received the impress of the chemist's thought and effort.

Lunch-time came and an elevator, the steel of which emanated from the chemically controlled open-hearth furnace, safeguarded my descent to the street. The gong of an ambulance and a hurried glance told me that some unfortunate member of society was being hurried to the care of physician or surgeon. There I knew that the chemical discoveries of a century would minister to his needs. I entered a restaurant, where in a multitude of ways the food and service betokened their dependence upon chemistry. At a soda fountain, I quenched my thirst in terms of chemical products. Again at the office, I sat down in the cooling breeze of an electric fan, operated by current transmitted from a distant power-house over wires of purest copper, chemically smelted and electrolytically refined. A box of chocolates on my desk conveyed delicious evidence of the chemist's work in the confectionery industry.

Seated in my car for the home trip, I stepped on the starter and current from a chemical storage battery turned the motor. Current for horn and lights came from the same source. My debt to chemistry was always in the foreground. Having a high-compression motor, I stopped at a filling station selling tetraethyl gas, for I knew that this recent product of chemical research would increase the mileage per gallon of motor fuel. The red and green signals at the cross-streets shone through glass unaffected by the severest weather conditions, a product of war-time chemistry in America.

Arrived at the garage, I looked at my "chemical" watch. I had reached home early. My boy, a born outdoorsman, with binoculars and gun was starting for the woods. Gunsights and lenses, steel of the barrel and powder of the cartridge had in each instance been preceded by a long series of chemical processes. Starting my power-lawnmower, I began to cut the grass. There again in the dry cells for ignition, the steel of the cutting knives and the gasoline and lubricating oils, I was making chemistry my servant. With a flexible rubber hose, fashioned entirely by chemical processes, I sprayed the street and lawn. I entered the garden and in every flower and vegetable, grown in chemically fertilized soil, I beheld a chemical laboratory more wonderful than any of artificial design. The evening meal, chemically speaking, was a repetition of breakfast and lunch. There was not an item on the menu which did not have a chemical origin. And likewise with every article of service in the house. A prominent chemist in making an address offered to speak for twenty minutes on the chemistry of any object in the room which any one might name. This was no task. Indeed, the difficult part would be to keep his discussion within the time limit set. Chemistry is everywhere,—in the air we breathe, the water and other liquids we drink, the food we eat, the clothes we wear, the articles we handle, the processes we employ, the functioning of bodily organs, the healing arts of physician and surgeon, the fundamental bases of peace and war and in the advances of civilization. We encounter chemistry at every turn. It is inescapable. We have made the chemist our bond-servant.

The radio, too, bringing to the dinner hour voices and music from out of the air, was indebted to chemical research for the storage battery, the tungsten filament of the vacuum bulb, the metal of the grid and plate, the copper wire, the "B" battery, the panel of bakelite, the condenser plates, the controlled dance of the electrons and more. The music of the phonograph was probably reproduced from the impression upon a bakelite disk through the medium of a chemically wrought needle and vibrating diaphragm. Even the book with which I beguiled the time between dinner and the moving-picture show was a veritable product of the chemical laboratory. Printed upon chemically manufactured paper with chemically prepared ink, from plates electrolytically deposited from a chemical bath, and bound and stamped with machinery, the materials in the construction of which had been produced by chemical processes, it seemed that little save the thought of the author lacked a chemical origin. And even in that it was chemically digested and assimilated food which supplied the energy for the action of his brain cells.

I do not need to tell you that the transparent cinema film and the art of photography which made possible the moving-picture entertainment of the evening are among the most notable triumphs of chemistry in its modern developments. The aluminum screen also paid tribute to the chemist's art. And in the talking movie which was shown, it was the marvelous photoelectric cell, a product of chemistry and physics combined, which made possible the translation of variable light waves into audible speech and music.

On my way home, time and again I was compelled to jam on the brakes to avoid disaster. Each time chemically wrought linings of asbestos safeguarded my car and its occupants. The electric lights of street, theater and home owed much to chemistry. Conductors, insulators, armatures, commutators, brushes and metal castings would be impossible without their chemically wrought parts.

After a day of business and pleasure, I retired that sleep might "knit up the ravelled sleeve of care" and in so doing destroy the chemically produced poisons in my system which are thought to be the cause of physical weariness and mental fatigue. Even one's dreams doubtless have some relation to the chemical functioning of bodily organs. It was even proposed at the Williamstown Conference of 1926 that a chemical compound be synthesized to eliminate these poisons without the aid of sleep.

In this brief survey of the day's work, we have scarcely scratched the surface of the multitudinous ways in which chemistry touches human life. There is no occupation which is not replete with chemical contacts. In industry they are exceedingly more numerous than they appear to be in this uneventful day's experience. The farmer, artisan, manufacturer and merchant meet with the fruits of chemistry at every turn. The analysis of every situation will reveal the debt. Waking or sleeping, chemistry is the servant of every one from the highest to the lowest.

CHAPTER XIV

RESEARCH THE KEY TO FUTURE PROGRESS

NEED FOR RESEARCH—AN ILLUSTRATION FROM THE PAST—
FARADAY AND RESEARCH—EXAMPLES OF PURE RESEARCH—BE-
GAN WITH COPERNICUS AND GALILEO—IN THE FIELD OF
ELECTRICITY—PURE RESEARCH IN CHEMISTRY—EXAMPLES
FROM THE BORDERLAND OF PHYSICS AND CHEMISTRY—DIS-
COVERY OF A NEW ELEMENT BY AMERICAN CHEMIST—APPLIED
RESEARCH—ILLUSTRATIONS—RESEARCH IN AMERICA—STATE-
MENT BY SECRETARY HOOVER—ACCOMPLISHMENTS IN FIELD
OF APPLIED CHEMISTRY—INSTITUTIONS IN WHICH RESEARCH
IS CARRIED ON—THREE GREAT RESEARCH FUNDS—PREVENTING
FULFILMENT OF MALTHUS' PROPHECY—THE CALL TO RE-
SEARCH.

WE HEAR much these days about research. What does
it mean? Why has Secretary Hoover asserted time and
again that research is indispensable if the industrial and
material progress of America is not to be arrested?
More, that research in *pure science* is equally indispensable to the intellectual and spiritual development of a
great people? Why, under his leadership, is the National
Academy of Sciences endeavoring to raise a fund of
twenty million dollars for the endowment of pure
research? What is pure research? Why, in an age of
unparalleled scientific progress, with new inventions and
applications of science daily coming to the fore, should

461

any one talk of the possible exhaustion of the fountain-heads of such achievement? Is not such an event as improbable as the drying up of the waters of Niagara?

Let us pause a moment on that last question. Whence come the waters of Niagara? Is it not true that, without constant evaporation from the ocean and the abundant rainfall of the Great Lakes region, Niagara would disappear as surely as did the Salton Sink of Arizona in a previous geologic age? From what do these wonderful streams of scientific invention proceed? Where are the eternal springs that give them rise? Why have they not always been here? Why did they not flow forth in the days of the cave man to ameliorate his cruel lot and smooth his pathway? Yes, why not?

The answer is not far to seek. Already, I hear you saying, "Knowledge slowly accumulated throughout the ages by the untiring efforts of many patient investigators is the source of present invention and the foundation of civilization." Without new knowledge, progress ceases. Is there real danger of exhausting the possibilities of our present store as the basis of future advances in the arts and industries? Yes, that is the serious aspect of the situation which confronts the world to-day. In many directions, we are approaching the frontiers of human knowledge. It is true that, despite the brilliant record of present achievement and the vast possibilities of practical application still latent within the great basic discoveries of preceding centuries, we are threshing little new wheat. We are living on capital without making the additions indispensable for future expansion. Applied research, particularly in this country, we have in unprecedented abundance, but the growth of fundamental knowledge is slowing down. The discovery of new principles which may afford fresh starting-points for further lines of advance are not forthcoming.

Let us take an illustration from the past. Suppose the growth of human knowledge had stopped with the cave man; I mean that no new discoveries fundamental to an advance in the culture then existing had been made. The cave man would have acquired great proficiency in the chipping of flints, in the curing and use of furs, in the knowledge of fire then at his command, and in the simple arts in his possession. He would have become a master of applied research. He would have utilized to the utmost his scanty store of knowledge. But he would have remained a cave man always. His seeming progress would have been wholly superficial. He could not have advanced from the Age of Stone to the Age of Metals. To do that would have required that he add to his knowledge of fire its application to the smelting of ores. Weaving, pottery and glass-making, artificial illumination beyond the use of the torch and open fire, the principles of the simple machines, the art of navigation, the mastery of steam and electricity, the conquest of the air and much more would forever have been beyond his ken. Not even the dream of the alchemist could have entered his darkened brain, while the chemistry which has unlocked the treasures of the earth would have forever remained a secret of the gods. With the permanent crystallization of knowledge, the destiny of mankind upon this planet would be achieved.

Although incomparably farther advanced along the pathway of attainment, we of to-day are in a position analogous to that of the cave man fifty thousand years ago. Let us not delude ourselves. Fresh progress means new discovery, that is, the discovery of new truth, not simply a new application of old truth. Without the constant pushing backward of the frontiers of human knowledge, we shall be traveling in a circle. The most important business of the race is this unraveling of the ages-old secrets of the universe and turning them to the account of progressive civilization.

Again, what does pure research mean? Let us borrow an illustration from another field of scientific inquiry. I want you to come with me to the laboratory of the Royal Institution in London. It is nearly a century ago. Before us, we see a patient, quiet, unassuming man of childlike gentleness and simplicity, with no thought of private gain and actuated only by an intense love of truth. He is at work over some clumsy devices, apparatus which we should now consider hardly worthy of a place in the home laboratory of a grammar-school boy. For ten years, he has been seeking to unravel the mystery of the relationship between electricity and magnetism. The Danish physicist Oersted has but recently made the fundamental discovery that an electric current is accompanied by a magnetic field. But what of the law governing this manifestation and how may a magnetic field be made to induce an electric current? That is the big problem, fraught with mighty portent for succeeding generations, to which Michael Faraday is addressing himself. Time and again, he has been compelled to write across his note-book, "No result." And then, within the short space of ten days, we see this patient knocking at the door of eternal truth unlock for him the secrets of electromagnetism. In that moment, the dynamo, the

electric motor, the induction coil, the transformer, the
telephone, the radio art and a host of other potential
applications of the underlying principle there discovered
are born. The Age of Electricity is ushered in. Millions
for centuries yet to come are made the everlasting
debtors of this man whose passionate love for truth has
led him irresistibly, step by step, to the discovery of a
fundamental law of the universe, a law without which by
far the greater part of the progress of the century to
come would be impossible.

That is the meaning of pure research. Content with
the discovery of the law, the unveiling of this bit of truth
essential to the next forward step in the progress of the
race, Faraday turned to other fields. He did not seek to
commercialize his discovery. Its application he left to
lesser brains. In prophetic vision, he saw the immense
amount of applied research which was to give to the
world the marvels of electricity. Fortune was within his
grasp. He rejected it. Huxley has estimated that, had
Faraday chosen to capitalize his incomparable ability as
an investigator, he might easily have amassed an estate
of three-quarters of a million dollars. As a matter of
fact, the total of his private fees did not exceed five
thousand. In his old age, this man whose discoveries
have added more to the wealth of his own and other
countries than have those of any other half-dozen investigators of any time, accepted a pension from his
government, grudgingly given. Knighthood, he had refused. Herbert Hoover asserts that "our banking com-
munity does not do the public service in a year that
Faraday's discoveries do us daily." When the million-
aires who have thrived and grown powerful through the

utilization of the additions to our knowledge made by
Faraday have been utterly forgotten, his name will still
be green in the memories of men. And Faraday worked
in many fields. Some of the most important ground-work
for chemical progress was the product of his brain.

Let us fix in mind that the investigator in the field of
pure research seeks to discover truth for truth's sake
only. His object is to add to the sum total of human
knowledge, without any thought as to the practical application of his discoveries. That is entirely a secondary
consideration. And yet without such research there are
no practical applications. Time and again discoveries
of the most abstract and theoretical character have
proved to be the basis of industrial developments productive of human happiness and vast wealth.

EXAMPLES OF PURE RESEARCH

Until the coming of Copernicus and Galileo there was
little in the achievements of men which might be designated by the term scientific research. All through those
long centuries stretching from the cave man to the dawn
of history, progress had been largely by accident. Accidental discoveries repeatedly made and followed at long
intervals by deliberate attempts at duplication carried
the race forward to the civilizations of ancient Egypt, of
the Valley of the Tigris and the Euphrates, and later to
those of Greece and Rome. True, the ancients studied
the stars and mapped the heavens; they acquired an
empirical knowledge of many arts; great works of architecture and engineering stand to their credit; they became skilful navigators and mighty warriors; but to

them this was a capricious world, a universe of lawless signs and wonders, of miracle and chance. Truth was preconceived. Things were so because men in speculative moods thought them so. Ignorance sat upon the throne. The pursuit of truth for truth's sake was entirely foreign to the intellectual processes of the time. Indeed, men did not know the meaning of the quest.

Then came Copernicus with his new theory of the heavens, dethroning the earth from its exalted position as the central body in this vast universe. Galileo swept the heavens with his telescope and the celestial spheres of the ancients came crashing to the earth, past the possibility of reconstruction. This was the first notable example of pure research in the history of science. Indeed, it marks the beginning of modern science. The practical utility of these discoveries seemed beyond the realm of possibilities. But how they did increase the intellectal stature of men! And Galileo with his discovery of the laws of falling bodies laid the corner-stone of modern physics. Here was an addition to scientific knowledge of the utmost practical value.

Kepler worked out the laws of planetary motion. Newton with his discovery of the universal law of gravitation reduced our solar system to a self-contained unit of perfect law and order. His discovery of the composition of white light anticipated the invention of the spectroscope and its important rôle in practical chemical analysis. Kant and Laplace came forward with the nebular hypothesis for the origin of our solar system. Herschel added a new planet to our solar family and gave to the world wonderful glimpses of this universe, the present known radius of which, as determined by the

Mount Wilson telescope, Dr. Edwin S. Hubble has just told us is one hundred and forty million light years. Here are some of the foremost examples of pure research, research which had no thought of private gain or commercial exploitation. Without them, it is difficult to conceive what the intellectual status of mankind would be. During those formative centuries, the emphasis was upon pure research. Men had not yet discovered the immense practical values to be derived from the applications of scientific discoveries. In fact most of those discoveries had not then been made.

In one important direction, these astronomical researches bore fruit. They became the basis for the practical navigation of ships upon the high seas.

In the field of electricity, we have again many examples of pure research. Little did those early discoverers, making their tiny excursions into an unexplored continent of vast possibilities, know that they were laying the foundations of a science which was to mark an epoch in the affairs of men. The primitive man who rubbed a piece of amber across his furskin coat and in so doing discovered that it would pick up dry bits of wood, though only playing, was taking that first essential step in the conquest of the mightiest force of Nature. The electric machine of Otto Von Guericke was only a toy, and yet it carried forward the knowledge without which future progress would have been impossible. The Dutchman Pieter Van Musschenbroek and the German Von Kleist learned to store electric charges in the Leyden jar and thereby gave to the world the condenser, which has found such wide application in the radio art and in other fields of electrical invention. Franklin drew the lightning from the thunder cloud and established its identity with the electricity of the Leyden jar, thus banishing forever a fertile source of superstitious ignorance and fear. Galvani performed his immortal experiments with the frog's legs and through the genius of Alessandro Volta gave to the world the electric cell. Less than a quarter of a century later, Davy with a battery of these cells decomposed water and discovered six new elements. With a battery of two thousand cells, he produced the first electric arc in history. We have already mentioned Oersted's discovery that a current-bearing conductor possesses a magnetic field. Ampère discovered the law of electric attraction and repulsion. Sturgeon invented the electromagnet. Faraday's work has already been mentioned.

Pure research was this in every instance, and research without which the vast superstructure of modern electricity would have been impossible. Men did not ask of what practical value these discoveries would be. They simply sought to know the truths of Nature. And they worked in the heyday of scientific triumphs. Theirs was virgin territory. But their horizon was narrow, their means of investigation limited, and their appreciation of the possibilities which lay about them in bewildering profusion small. Nevertheless their contribution to fundamental knowledge was immense. Without it the present age would still be but a dream.

But, I hear you asking, "What have these discoveries to do with progress in chemistry?" A great deal. Research is fundamentally the same in whatever field of scientific inquiry it may occur. And furthermore, modern progress in chemistry has been so intimately associated with advances in electricity that one can not be considered independently of the other. As we have seen, chemical action is now known to be largely an electrical phenomenon.

Let us turn to examples of pure research in chemistry. Many of these have already been described. We have traced those great mile-posts of chemical progress stretching from the alchemist to the very beginning of the present century. We are familiar with the work of Cavendish, Priestley, Scheele, Davy, Berzelius, Wöhler, Liebig, Bunsen, Perkin, Mendeleeff, Kekulé, van't Hoff, Arrhenius and others. The initial discoveries in chemistry of the great Pasteur which led to his immortal researches in the field of medicine are discussed elsewhere. All these are examples of pure research. Where would the vast chemical industries of to-day, the children of applied chemistry, be without this rich heritage from the pioneer work in the field of pure research? Had not Davy discovered the potency of the electric current in producing chemical action and Faraday worked out the laws of electrolysis, whence would have come the foundation for that superb group of electrochemical industries which clusters about the brow of Niagara? And did not Arrhenius supplement this with his researches regarding the electrolytic nature of solutions? Let it be emphasized that these works were inspired purely by a desire to add to human knowledge. That millions would be made from the practical applications of this knowledge in developing the resources of the earth was utterly foreign to their thought. Did not the organic synthesis of hosts of dyestuffs, antiseptics, explosives, perfumes, flavors and medicinals grow out of the researches in pure science of Perkin, van't Hoff, Kekulé and their associates? When Kekulé was dreaming of the benzene ring and van't Hoff was creating in his imagination the molecular architecture of carbon compounds, what thought did they give to the possible practical applications of these flashes of genius? The love of knowledge and the supreme joy of discovery were sufficient rewards. No one who has never experienced it can know the depth of satisfaction which arises from the consciousness of having made a great discovery. Who to-day would not gladly exchange all the wealth he possesses or might ever hope to possess for the privilege of adding to human knowledge some great principle which should mark an epoch in the affairs of men?

We can readily see that without this wealth of original work in the field of pure science many present-day achievements would be but iridescent dreams. And we have scarcely more than hinted at but a few of these early discoveries. Priestley's discovery that when electric sparks are passed through air oxides of nitrogen result, coupled with Cavendish's production of nitrate of potash from the gases formed, paved the way for the artificial fixation of atmospheric nitrogen, a process fundamental to the manufacture of fertilizers and explosives and incidentally rendering this and other countries independent of Chile saltpeter. The oxyacetylene torch so widely used in the cutting and welding of metals goes back to the discovery of calcium carbide and acetylene by Wöhler, followed a generation later by the researches of Moissan, Willson, and Le Chatelier. A half-century ago, you might have seen a German chemist bending over a crucible in which flowed white-hot steel at a temperature of 3000 degrees Centigrade. As a result, we have to-day the Goldschmidt Thermit process of welding, which annually saves thousands of dollars and vast quantities of time in the foundries and machine shops of the world,—one of the numberless tangible products of pure research. The commercial separation of potash fertilizer from the Stassfurt deposits or Searles Lake depends upon the researches of van't Hoff in applying Gibbs' phase rule to the laws of solutions and the separation of mixtures of salts. Because the German chemist Kirchoff discovered three-quarters of a century ago how starch might be changed to glucose, a single plant in this country treats fifty thousand bushels of corn a day. The researches of Sabatier on catalytic action have made possible the conversion of cotton, coconut and peanut oils into edible substitutes for lard, thereby bringing vast acreages under profitable cultivation and utilizing much former waste. The researches of Cross and Bevan, two English chemists, in producing a new cellulose compound by treating wood fiber with caustic soda and carbon bisulfide have grown into the rayon industry, which in 1926 produced in the United States alone sixty-one million pounds of artificial silk. Welsbach in carrying out purely theoretical investigations of the elements thorium and cerium blundered on to the gas mantle and thereby saved an industry from threatened annihilation.

And so one might continue. The adequate treatment of the scores of such examples scattered along the royal highway leading from the treasure-houses of pure knowledge to the achievements of practical application would fill many volumes. In another place I have spoken of those researches which led to a knowledge of X-rays, radioactivity and radium. Likewise, in connection with the relation of chemistry to medicine, have been discussed those investigations which have resulted in the isolation of such ductless gland secretions as adrenalin, thyroxin and insulin, so essential to the regulation of the physiological processes upon which life depends as well as governing in a large degree the intellectual and emotional reactions of individuals. These have all had a very direct relation to chemical research.

Let us borrow an illustration from the twilight zone in which chemistry and physics meet. In 1725, DuFay, a French investigator, discovered that the space in the vicinity of a red-hot body is a conductor of electricity. A little more than a century and a half later, Elster and Geitel found that in a vacuum an electric charge might be made to pass between a hot body and another near to it. At about the same time Edison noticed the passage of an electric discharge between the positive and negative ends of the electric filament in an incandescent lamp. Merely isolated and curious observations were these, facts of Nature stumbled on to by gropers in the illimitable storehouse of eternal truth. Of any possible practical significance, there was not the remotest idea. But in 1902 Richardson subjected this phenomenon to critical analysis. He examined the electrical discharge in high vacuum between a heated filament and a surrounding cylinder. Result: the discovery that streams of electrons, one of the two ultimate units of matter both for the physicist and the chemist, boil off from the hot filament.

Still, nothing of practical value. Why did men waste their time by playing with such inconsequential happenings? But, wait. Three years pass, and then Fleming utilizes this "trivial" discovery in the wireless detector for rectifying the exceedingly weak currents received by an antenna. Almost overnight it inaugurated a revolution in the methods of radio reception. And yet, we have not reached the end. In 1907, DeForest by the introduction of a third element, the well-known grid, transformed this detector into the audion bulb, the progenitor of the marvelous vacuum tube amplifier which has made possible the triumphs of modern communication. And DeForest's discovery was the result of pure research, one of those happy accidents which have a way of happening to one who is in search of the underlying secrets of the universe. In present-day telephoning between New York and London, a battery of these amplifiers at Rocky Point, Long Island, magnify the feeble voice currents two billion times and put them upon the ether with a "push" of seventy horse-power.

And more, the researches on the vacuum tube amplifier led directly to the invention of the Coolidge super-X-ray tube, an instrument which has been of the utmost assistance in enabling the chemist to determine with certainty the number of elements, to obtain pictures of molecular architecture, and to fathom the secrets of sub-atomic structure. And the other uses of this invention both in pure and applied science are legion. Can any one measure in terms of human happiness, economic benefits and the growth of human knowledge the values conferred by those simple discoveries concerning the meaning of which the pure scientist paused to wonder and ponder?

Closely associated with the foregoing story is the

purely theoretical discovery by James Clerk-Maxwell of the electromagnetic waves of the ether, followed by their laboratory detection by Hertz and the invention by Marconi of a mechanism which, amplified by himself and his contemporaries, now girdles the earth with the voice of music and intelligible speech. Little did Maxwell and Hertz dream that their researches, undertaken purely for the love of truth, were to annihilate space and inaugurate a new era in the art of communication.

That wealth of research in pure science which has led to our present knowledge of the atom and has literally pushed backward the frontiers of the known universe in a score of directions has been detailed in another chapter. The reader has doubtless noted that in these additions to fundamental knowledge, American investigators have been conspicuous chiefly by their absence. We must not forget, however, that here in far-off America, without the inspiration to be derived from close contact with the centers of scientific investigation, Joseph Henry, independently of Faraday and indeed prior to his work, had discovered the laws of electromagnetism. And during the year 1926 America forged into the forefront of pure research with a chemical discovery which will forever rank with any made by European masters.

Out in the University of Illinois stands a laboratory which will always remain a hallowed spot in the annals of American chemistry. There Professor B. Smith Hopkins, as the result of five years of patient investigation, discovered the only element ever to have been isolated by an American chemist. Were you to visit his laboratory, you would see less than half an ounce of a pinkish-yellow substance, all that is left from four hundred pounds of rare earth materials with which he started. And even that is not the element in pure form. How, then, does he know that he has discovered a new element? The answer is the spectroscope, an instrument with which we are already familiar. The telltale spectrum of bright lines produced by every element in the state of incandescent vapor reveals the discovery. No two elements give the same lines, and the spectroscope has never been known to tell a lie. Written, as it were, in letters of living light, its messages are always true. And the spectrum of this pinkish-yellow substance unmistakably tells Professor Hopkins that he has found a new element, for it must be remembered that the spectroscope will detect an element even in the presence of others. He has named this new member of the family of primordial building blocks *illinium* in honor of the institution in which he labors.

How did Professor Hopkins happen to make this discovery? The answer is the chance information received from the spectroscopic examination of elements 60 and 62, neodymium and samarium. Very faint lines belonging neither to the one nor the other appeared in the spectrum. The conclusion was inevitable. A hitherto unknown element was in the offing and search began. The result was element 61.

You ask, "Of what use will this element be?" No one knows. When Sir Norman Lockyer, in 1867, discovered helium in vast quantities in the atmosphere of the sun ninety-three millions of miles away, he did not know that to-day we should be filling our air-ships with it. The value of radium, at first only a scientific curiosity, is measured in terms of the preciousness of human

Courtesy, Prof. B. Smith Hopkins

Prof. B. Smith Hopkins (standing), of the University of Illinois, and two assistants in the laboratory in which, in 1926, he isolated illinium, the only element ever discovered by an American chemist

Courtesy, General Electric Company

The new Coolidge cathode-ray tube

Madame Curie in her laboratory

Joseph Henry, America's first great research scientist

life. As small a quantity as two-tenths of one per cent. of vanadium increases the elastic limit of steel fifty per cent. One per cent. of the oxide of the rare earth metal cerium in a gas mantle multiplies many times its light-giving properties. Every element has its niche of usefulness, and some time, some where the ingenuity of the scientist will find it.

And so we see that these discoveries of the secrets of Nature, made in almost every instance without any thought of their material value, have been the stepping-stones upon which the race has risen from the primitive life of the cave man to its present command of power and dominance of the earth. It is in these additions to fundamental knowledge that the world is slacking just now. America has never made her full contribution in this field, and Europe burdened with the aftermath of war and the economic necessity for reconstruction is for the time at least unable to carry on research as in former years. But without the continual tapping of these springs of eternal truth progress ceases and even the intellectual and spiritual life of a people withers and decays. Research is the price men pay for material advancement and that economic independence and leisure essential to the life of the spirit. Neglect it for a hundred years and the uncivilized hordes among mankind may once more dominate the earth.

APPLIED RESEARCH

When we come to applied research, we have another story to tell. The worker in these fertile fields garners the golden grain which has sprung from the seed sowed by the pure research scientist. Here we have that multitude of practical applications which have transformed the earth from a howling wilderness or desert waste into vast industrial areas peopled and directed by highly organized groups of society. But in every instance these triumphs of modern civilization are products of pure research. There is nowhere a single exception. Directly or indirectly, they strike their roots deep into the subsoil of original scientific discovery. The truth of this we have already seen. Without pure research there could be no knowledge of the great fundamental principles which men have applied and adapted to human needs. To smite the rock of Nature's resources and bring forth these never-failing streams of truth requires genius of a high order. To apply this truth in masterly inventions for the control of the earth and the advancement of men also requires genius, but the achievement is a vastly simpler one. Without the pure researcher, this latter task would forever remain but a dream of unfulfilled accomplishment.

Already we have had many examples of applied research. In every direction, we come upon them. Volumes might be filled with these fascinating stories of achievement, and still the tale would be only begun. For to be complete it must portray the record of human progress from earliest times to the present moment. All the arts of peaceful industry, the terribleness of war, the conquest of disease, and the advances in education, morals and religion are the outgrowth of this perpetual application of eternal truth to the needs and desires of men.

Let us take some concrete examples from the recent past. We have seen that because German and French chemists, through the utilization of the fundamental principle of catalysis, have succeeded in perfecting a synthetic process for the production of methanol, wood alcohol, from carbon monoxide and hydrogen, President Coolidge has been compelled to increase the import duty on this essential material of chemical manufacture from twelve to eighteen cents a gallon. This was necessary to protect from financial ruin the wood distillation industry of our country. That is the price which one country often pays to another for lack of research by its own men of science.

Professor Friedrich Bergius, of Germany, who is just completing his monumental researches on the liquefaction of coal, but recently announced a process for the manufacture of sugar from wood. The process is already passing from the laboratory to that of practical production. A factory is being erected for this purpose near Geneva, Switzerland. It is a continuous process, carried out entirely by machinery and without the necessity for manual labor. An acre of forest land, it is estimated, will produce as much sugar as an acre of sugar beets. It is unlikely that it ever will be profitable to convert good timber into sugar, but sawdust and waste lumber, of which we have in this country a prodigious quantity, may be used for this purpose. The product is not cane sugar but glucose, the sugar which is produced from corn starch. That this synthetic sugar may affect the prices of stocks in the money markets of the world is entirely within the realm of probabilities.

In the autumn of 1926, Dr. William D. Coolidge, of the Research Laboratory of the General Electric Company, announced the perfection of a new cathode-ray tube, which shoots streams of electrons with a velocity of one hundred and fifty thousand miles a second into the outside air. It produces as many electrons per second as a ton of radium, worth at present prices a hundred billion dollars. The bombardment by these missiles produces many remarkable physical and chemical changes in matter. Minerals are caused to glow with brilliant colors. Crystals of rock salt become brown. Acetylene gas is changed to a powder. Castor oil becomes a solid. Bacteria are instantly killed. Exposed for a tenth of a second to these rays, the skin of a rabbit develops first a scab and then a new type of long snow-white hair.

Of course, we ask, "Of what use is this invention?" That remains to be seen. However, if Doctor Coolidge, with the super-tube which he plans to build, can speed up these electrons to a velocity close to that of light, it may be possible to substitute this powerful source of energy for radium in the treatment of cancer. With such a prodigious command of radioactive rays, this dread scourge of the race may at last be brought under scientific control. And when we can measure the value of a great discovery in terms of human life, the most precious thing in the world, it becomes a priceless boon.

Again, Dr. S. C. Lind, head of the Chemistry Department of the University of Minnesota, not long ago succeeded with the use of radium in changing methane, the chief constituent of natural gas, into a petroleum-like liquid suitable for motor fuel. Since the world possesses in the free state considerably less than a pound of radium, all told, this transformation seemed likely to remain a scientific curiosity. In speaking of this discovery, Dr. James F. Norris, in addressing the American Chemical Society, on September 6, 1926, said: "But radium is not necessary. The work of Doctor Coolidge shows that we can get this kind of energy from an X-ray tube." At the time, he knew nothing of the cathode-ray tube just described. With the prodigious quantities of electronic energy now available, particularly if the more powerful tube in contemplation is perfected, may it not be possible to place this process upon a commercial basis and thereby provide another route to substitutes for gasoline? Time will tell. It is a rash thing these days to assert that any project is impossible.

In the laboratories of the American Telephone and Telegraph Company, there has recently been made a new alloy of iron and nickel, called permalloy, which permits the sending of cablegrams five times as fast as formerly. It possesses remarkable magnetic properties, being more easily magnetized and demagnetized than any other metal or alloy now known. That these properties can be utilized for increasing the strength and ease of control of huge electromagnets for lifting purposes, there can be no doubt. This alloy will make possible much more sensitive magnets for all sorts of purposes. A product of applied research was this, of immense practical importance.

Who has not benefited by the cracking of petroleum and the consequent enormous increase in the gasoline output? And from what a hideous nightmare have the recent developments of applied research in the liquefaction and processing of coal and the synthesis of motor fuels relieved the world!

As a result of pure and applied research, Dr. Irving Langmuir, of the Research Laboratory of the General Electric Company, has just announced a new method of welding metals, employing a newly-developed source of high temperatures, which he calls "flames of atomic hydrogen." Into an electric arc between tungsten electrodes and all about the metal which is being welded, he shoots streams of hydrogen gas. Now the hydrogen as it enters the intensely hot arc is in the form of molecules, but, as it emerges on the opposite side, these molecules have been broken down into atoms. The heat of the arc has accomplished this. Immediately, in the outer zone of the arc, the atoms recombine to form molecules again. In doing so they liberate an enormous amount of energy in the form of heat, producing a temperature of about 4000 degrees Centigrade. This is the hottest *flame* known to science, being more than twice as hot as the oxyhydrogen flame, for many decades the highest temperature possible to produce. Already, this discovery foreshadows new methods in the welding and working of metals. One important advantage is the prevention of oxidation by surrounding the metal with an atmosphere of hydrogen as it is being worked. When we remember that man's first great conquest of Nature came with his mastery of fire and that his progress in metallurgy and in many of the useful arts has been coincident with the attainment of constantly higher temperatures, such an achievement as this takes on a deep significance.

In these days, applied research is often carried out to order. Let me quote a statement by Dr. Charles M. A. Stine, Chemical Director of E. I. Du Pont de Nemours and Company, regarding specifications handed to him for the production of a new finish for automobiles and furniture. He says, "In effect, we were told that what was wanted was a finish that would protect cars, furniture

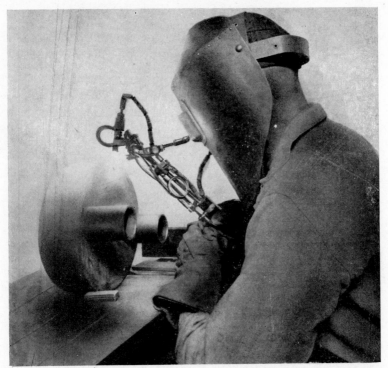

Flames of atomic hydrogen being used in the new process of arc welding

Invented by Dr. Irving Langmuir

Largest and smallest Coolidge X-ray tubes

Courtesy, Dry Ice Corporation of America

"Dry ice," solid carbon dioxide, a new refrigerant

It is being used here in a shipment of frozen fish going from New York to St. Louis. No re-icing will be required in transit

Courtesy, Goldschmidt Thermit Company

Welding street-car rails by the thermit process

Molten steel is flowing into the mold and between the ends of the rails. This process was a by-product of pure research

and other finely finished objects. The paint, or lacquer, or enamel, or what-not, that we were to develop must be as handsome when it was applied as is the finest finish ordinarily used. Yet it must be capable of much more rapid application. It must be capable of carrying color pigments or other coloring matter, so that various shades might be readily obtainable, and these colors must not fade. When dry, the desired product must be hard, so that it would not scratch, must—in this particular—be similar to glass. Yet it must not have the other properties of glass, lest it crack too easily. Therefore with its hardness it must be tough. Furthermore, it must be proof against the action of water, against oil, against grease, and against the action of such acids as might come in contact with it. It must not deteriorate under the action of heat or cold. Ice and snow, sunlight, dust, sandstorms or mud, must leave, if possible, no mark at all. And of course, the product must be able to compete in price with the finishing compounds in ordinary use.

"What this new finish was to be made of, no one cared. But of certain things we were sure. It must be made of such mixtures as would not eat their way through tin cans, for example, for tin containers would be necessary for its shipment and storage, and the paint would be worse than useless if it ate through the tins and trickled all over the shelves. Neither must it undergo any chemical changes after it was prepared, for that might change the final result. Then, too, it must have good 'covering power.' That is, it must not be transparent, except when used as a varnish, for part of its job is to hide the color and texture of the material over which it is to be spread. And there were many other qualities that it must or must not have. And with these specifications we set to work.''

Surely, this was a large contract. Indeed, it would have seemed easier to prepare the Philosopher's Stone. And it proved to be a baffling problem. For a long time but little progress was made. The solution of nitrated cotton with which experiments were being made would not remain thin. It became thick like jelly and would not spread. Then one day a happy accident occurred. As an experiment, into a new batch of the stuff, some caustic soda had been put. But just at this point the mixing machine broke down. For several days, the mixture stood in the heat of midsummer while repairs could be made. Then, lo, as the lid was removed from the containing vat, to the astonishment of every one, the thick pasty mass had changed to a clear liquid, almost as thin as water. Unwittingly, a step in the right direction had been taken. Caustic soda together with a moderate degree of heat had wrought a highly desirable molecular transformation. Still, the problem was a long way from being solved. Many difficulties must be ironed out. In drying, the new finish condensed moisture from the air and discolored the paint. Not nearly all of the desired properties had been attained. A host of experiments were yet required. However, chemists do not work singly these days. A small army of them, if necessary, attack a problem from many angles. At one point in the program, Doctor Stine and his assistants worked evenings, Saturdays, Sundays and holidays for four weeks to untangle a difficult knot. At length, every one had been straightened out.

And what of the results? Where formerly it required three hundred and thirty-six hours to paint the body of an automobile, it now takes but thirteen and one-half, for the new finish is administered with a spray gun instead of by hand. The floor space required in the finishing room of an automobile plant has been reduced by seventy-five per cent. Because of this triumph of applied chemistry, time and labor costs have shrunk. And who benefits by these gains? Obviously, every one who directly or indirectly uses a car, and that is the whole public.

Because of applied research directed against solid carbon dioxide, a product long known to the chemistry lecture-hall, a revolution in methods of long-distance transportation looms to-day. The frozen snow of this waste gas of industry, produced in ton-lots, is becoming a tremendously important factor in artificial refrigeration. So efficient is it that ice-cream has been shipped from New York to Havana in such quantities as to bring an embargo from the Cuban Government. Fish may be shipped by rail on a five days' journey without re-icing. Solid carbon dioxide can be manufactured to compete with ice at a half-cent a pound. As it evaporates in the refrigerator, no water is produced. The solid passes directly into a gas, and, as it does so, it produces nearly twice the cooling effect that ordinary ice does. The carbon dioxide gas which results, by preventing oxidation, actually has a preservative effect on foodstuffs.

The preparation of liquid carbon dioxide is the essential first stage in the manufacture of the solid. That being the case, let us connect this achievement with its precedent in pure chemistry. A little more than a century ago, Faraday and Davy, working in the laboratory of the Royal Institution, liquefied the first gas and later succeeded in liquefying all of the known gases but six. Toward the close of the century, these six were reduced to liquid form in the same laboratory. Because Faraday liquefied chlorine, in one instance receiving thirteen pieces of glass in his eye from an explosion of the stuff, we now manufacture the liquid in tank-car lots for the bleaching of fabrics and paper and for the purification of water. Thus do these practical applications go back to the work of the original seeker after truth.

Vast strides are being made, as we have seen in another chapter, in the fixation of atmospheric nitrogen, absolutely indispensable for agricultural and peace-time uses as well as for the manufacture of explosives in time of war. So important is this work that the government maintains a research laboratory devoting its entire efforts in this direction.

When industry or science needs a new compound for a specific purpose, the chemist goes into his laboratory and builds it. Like an architect, he draws the plan of the molecule and then puts together the individual atoms and atomic groups accordingly. If the product is lacking in any particular property, he alters the architecture to produce the desired result. Witness, procaine and other harmless anesthetics; hexyl-resorcinal, an antiseptic fifty times as powerful as carbolic acid; salvarsan for syphilis; Bayer's "205" for sleeping sickness; and plasmochin, a synthetic drug much more efficacious than quinine in the treatment of malaria.

A field which offers large opportunities for industrial research in the immediate future is that involved in the utilization of cellulose, the woody fiber of trees, cotton and many other varieties of vegetation. An editorial in the July, 1927, issue of *Industrial and Engineering Chemistry* says, "Through the achievements of chemistry the products of cellulose have figured largely in the new competition between industries for the privilege of serving a consuming public. Cellulose has been designated as the field in which the next great chemical discoveries will be made, just as coal-tar has provided the raw material par excellence of the present generation. After all, we know very little about cellulose, and thus far in none of the great universities or other research centers of the United States have there been provided adequate equipment and generous endowment for the prosecution of that basic research without which processes in many industries depending upon cellulose must continue their empirical way."

The editorial suggests the use of other woods than those now demanded for wood pulp in paper manufacture, new methods in the handling of cotton as a source of cellulose, and in particular the diversion of cornstalks to the cellulose industry. Already much investigation has been done and a ten-ton pilot plant for purposes of experiment and demonstration is in process of erection. Before this is in print, it will probably be in operation.

An interesting practical development in this field is a process resulting from the researches of Arthur D. Little, Inc., for the manufacture of newsprint paper from gumwood and southern pine, two of the most rapidly growing and abundant of southern woods.

The examples of applied research are legion. The pages of this book are full of them. But, as we view these achievements in retrospect or behold them as they almost daily come to pass, let us ask, "What chance of success would these prolific workers have had without that great body of original truth which the pure scientists have been accumulating for three hundred years and more?" That is the capital without which applied research could pay no dividends. These many triumphs, of which we boast so proudly, are the blossoms from the tree of knowledge, a tree which has required ages for its growth. If we cut its roots or cease to tend and fertilize it, there will be no more harvests. Perpetual discovery of new truth is the price men must pay for the satisfaction of plucking the golden fruit of progress.

RESEARCH IN AMERICA

It is in the field of applied research that America looms large. In speaking of this situation, Secretary Hoover, in a recent address, said:

"As a nation we have not been remiss in our support of applied science. We have contributed our full measure of invention and improvement in the application of physics, in mechanics, in biology and chemistry and we have made contributions to the world in applied economics and sociology.

"Business and industry have realized the vivid values of the application of scientific discoveries. To further it in twelve years our individual industries have increased their research laboratories from less than one hundred to over five hundred. They are bringing such values that they are increasing monthly. Our federal and state governments to-day support great laboratories, research departments and experimental stations, all devoted to applications of science to the many problems of industry and agriculture. They are one of the main elements in our gigantic strides in national efficiency. The results are magnificent. The new inventions, labor saving devices, improvements of all sorts in machines and processes in developing agriculture and promoting health are steadily cheapening cost of production; increasing standards of living, stabilizing industrial output, enabling us to hold our own in foreign trade; and lengthening human life and decreasing suffering. But all these laboratories and experiment stations are devoted to the application of science, not to fundamental research. Yet the raw material for these laboratories comes alone from the ranks of our men of pure science whose efforts are supported almost wholly in our universities, colleges and a few scientific institutions.

"We are spending in industry, in government, national and local, probably $200,000,000 a year in search for applications of scientific knowledge—with perhaps 30,000 men engaged in the work. . . . Yet the whole sum which we have available to support pure science research is less than $10,000,000 a year, with probably less than 4,000 men engaged in it, most of them dividing their time between it and teaching."

That tells the story. America has profited more than any other nation from the discoveries of pure scientists and has contributed the least to the common storehouse of fundamental truth. Had it not been for the accumulated wealth of the European masters of pure research, ready to hand for American exploitation, the conquest of this continent, the mass production of to-day, and the marvelous facility with which new processes thrive and come to fruition on our farms and in our mines and factories, would be painted in different colors. The highlights which fascinate the eye and charm the spirit would all be lacking. Where would our automobile industry, which boasts twenty million cars and trucks, be to-day, without the internal combustion engine of Otto and Langen, the storage battery of Planté, the induction coil and generator going back to the researches of Faraday, and the principles of mechanics dating from Galileo? And our chemical industry, which bids fair to outstrip its older rivals across the water, is built almost entirely upon those monumental researches of the European chemists of the last century. In electricity, we have accomplished much. Still, it has been chiefly the product of applied research and not that of original discovery. The great discoveries in medicine have been largely of foreign origin.

In the brilliancy of her adaptation of fundamental principles to practical invention, America has done herself proud. She stands without a peer. Were we to call the roll of such achievement, it would be a long one. It is a just source of national pride. We can not forget that it was the experiments of Hall, while still a student at Oberlin College, which gave to the world cheap aluminum, a metal which may some day attach its name to a new age of industrial progress. Bakelite is a triumph of synthetic research of the first magnitude. Bradley and Lovejoy blazed the way to the artificial fixation of atmospheric nitrogen, but American capitalists allowed the development of the industry to drift to foreign shores. Carborundum and other products of the electric furnace are shining examples of American ingenuity. The development of ductile tungsten in the Research Laboratory of the General Electric Company annually reduces the nation's electric light bill by a billion and a half dollars over what it would be with the old carbon filament lamp. The gas-filled bulb with its large increase in electric lighting efficiency was a by-product of research in the same laboratory. The work of Le Sueur at the Massa-

chusetts Institute of Technology resulted in the first
commercial electrolytic cell for the production of chlorine
and caustic soda from common salt. And we must mention the atomic weight researches of Professor Theodore
Richards of Harvard, work of the utmost significance
both for theoretical and applied chemistry. In the field
of metallurgy, America takes first rank. American
genius is conspicuous in every phase of industrial chemistry. It would be wearisome to prolong the record of
practical achievement.

Let us enumerate the classes of institutions in this
country devoting money and brains to the work of research. First we have the universities, the original
homes of research. But in these days of enormously
swollen student enrollments with the resultant increasing
burdens of education, university faculties are finding it
constantly more difficult to maintain the former output of
research, much less to expand it. After the universities,
come such organizations as the Smithsonian Institution,
the Carnegie Institution, the Rockefeller Institute and
the Mellon Institute. Aside from the first, work in these
institutions is largely that of applied research. The
Rockefeller Institute, which annually spends millions in
the promotion of world health, is content to make use of
known facts regarding disease and does nothing to
increase knowledge in this field. Then, we have the
government laboratories, both state and national. The
Federal Government is the largest employer of scientists
in the world. But its efforts, varied and important as
they are, are directed entirely toward tangible, concrete
ends. Lastly, we may name the private research laboratories of industrial organizations. Chief among these

are the laboratories of the General Electric Company and of the American Telephone and Telegraph Company. The accomplishments of these large groups of research workers are among the chief fruits of science in America. The immense expansion of the industries for which they labor is proof eternal of the commercial benefits of applied science, that is, of the practical application of great fundamental principles to definite ends. But before the applications can be made the principles must be discovered. That is the goal of pure research.

In a paper read before the Institute of Chemistry at Pennsylvania State College in the summer of 1927, Dr. Charles H. Herty voiced a supreme need of the hour when he expressed a fear for a slackening in the forward march of research because "the demand for qualified men outstrips the ability of our universities to furnish them." Doctor Jewett, of the American Telephone and Telegraph Company, has asserted that many problems in that organization await solution, not because of a lack of funds to prosecute the investigations, but because men of the requisite ability and training are not to be had.

In the summer of 1927, another of our large industrial organizations, the United States Steel Corporation, turned to science as an aid to further expansion. Judge Gary announced the creation of a Department of Research and Technology under the direction of Dr. John Johnston, of Yale. After all, it is not the physical properties of a great corporation which constitute its most valuable assets. Essential as these are, they would be useless without the discoveries of science, upon which their operation depends. No more eloquent tribute to the immense value of fundamental research could be had than the establishment of research laboratories by our eminently practical boards of directors, who are credited with thinking chiefly in terms of mass production and dividend-paying stocks. But the spirit of money-making can not be allowed to infect these laboratories. Untrammeled with the rampant commercialism of the present age, these workers must be free to pursue the trail of truth wherever it may lead. And yet out of these discoveries in pure science has grown every industry of any era. The wealth of the ages has been evoked by the men of science.

Three great research funds have been recently initiated. The first of these is a fund of a half-million dollars, contributed in equal proportions by John D. Rockefeller and the Universal Oil Products Company for pure research in the chemistry of petroleum. It is only just beginning to be realized that petroleum affords a store-house of valuable chemical products, rivaling in variety and number those of coal-tar. It is already known that petroleum will yield alcohols of various kinds, and, in the prophetic vision of Dr. James F. Norris, we shall soon see emerging from it brilliant lacquers, artificial rubber, imitation leather, ebony-like plastics, soaps, drugs, medicinals, anesthetics and much more. It will be the work of the researchers employed under this fund to explore this new realm of chemical possibilities. Though our petroleum wells go dry, the oil shales will provide this raw material of chemical manufacture for several centuries to come.

The second fund, already mentioned, is that of twenty million dollars being raised by the National Academy of Sciences under the direction of Secretary

Hoover as an endowment for pure science. It will be expended largely through the universities and existing institutions. Its purpose will be to release a potential Newton or Faraday from routine work and enable him to pursue in peace and leisure those investigations which are fundamental to future progress. There is no price so great that the nation could not afford to pay it for the services of such men. As Huxley said, a Faraday at a million dollars a year would be dirt cheap.

The third endowment fund, still in a state of incubation, hinges upon the successful passage of a bill introduced into the United States Senate by Senator Ransdell, of Louisiana, providing twenty million dollars for the establishment of a National Institute of Health for research in medicine and the treatment of disease. Regarding the need of such work, Dr. Alexis Carrel recently said: "If physiology were studied as a pure science far from hospitals and medical schools, by men possessing the creative imagination and the spirit of the discoverers of the fundamental principles of physics and chemistry, the secrets of the functions of the body that we still lack would be brought to light. These discoveries would indirectly lead the physician to understand the nature of the diseases of the organs whose functions are incompletely known to-day and to prevent them. This institute of pure science, where physiologists, physicists and chemists could devote themselves to the investigation of fundamental problems, would also create the proper conditions for the building up of the science which will occupy the summit of the hierarchy of human knowledge, the science of thinking matter and energy." Who knows but that the creation of the institution contemplated by

Senator Ransdell may bring the vision of Doctor Carrel to pass? It is in such great research centers as this may be, where many scientists gather, that the hope of the future lies. The picturesque figure of the poverty-stricken inventor in the attic has become a thing of the past. He no longer works alone. In well-equipped laboratories, surrounded with all that money can provide, he collaborates with his fellows. Problems are solved by team-work and by flank and frontal attacks from many directions. Cooperation is the keynote of scientific progress.

This nation has more than ninety billion dollars invested in industries directly or indirectly dependent upon chemical products for their success. The annual output of commodities of all industries is valued at fifty billions. A tenth of one per cent. of this huge total devoted to pure research would provide fifty million dollars a year, a very modest sum to put back into the capital fundamental to future progress, and yet one which would pay larger dividends than any other investment the nation could make.

Malthus, an English economist, warned statesmen a century ago of the dangers impending from constantly increasing populations. He held that while population increased in a geometrical ratio, the food supply grew only in an arithmetical ratio. The result would be constantly lower standards of living until eventually lack of subsistence would limit by starvation the number of people which the earth could support. That this prophesied catastrophe is not on the highway to fulfilment is due wholly to the discoveries of science and their application in industry. Instead, we have seen a growth of population far in excess of anything Malthus imagined possible and at the same time a constantly increasing standard of living. Should the world slack in its work of pure and applied research, the prediction of this foreboder of dire calamity may yet engulf the earth. In other words, the goblins will really get this planet, if its inhabitants don't watch out.

For successful research two things are needful,—money and men. Money to provide the sinews of war and men of brains and vision who can sail into the vast ocean of unexplored truth and discover new continents. Let no one deceive himself with the thought that practically all the discoveries in science have been made. Discoveries as far-reaching in their significance as any that adorn the annals of preceding centuries but await the coming of the genii who can unveil them. Without this new knowledge, the glittering accomplishments of applied research must ultimately come to an end. We may continue for a long period to make recombinations, readjustments, and new applications of existing knowledge, thereby cherishing the delusion that all is well, but the life-blood of future progress will have been sapped. This call to research is the greatest challenge to the American people in half a century, not even excepting the Great War. The way in which it is met will determine their capacity to become the masters of their own destiny.

THE END

BIBLIOGRAPHY

BIBLIOGRAPHY

The following list of references is by no means complete. After the first two chapters, these references have to do chiefly with articles in recent publications, the material of which has not yet been put into book form. Numerous references to news despatches in the current press have had to be omitted.

CHAPTER I

"Ancient and Modern Alchemy," Paneth, *Science,* 64: 409, 1926.
"The Alchemist," Foote, *Scientific Monthly,* 19: 239.
"The Story of Chemistry," Darrow, *The Mentor,* May, 1920.
The Story of Alchemy, Muir, Appleton.
History of Chemistry, Von Meyer, Macmillan.
A History of Chemistry, Moore, McGraw-Hill.

CHAPTER II

History of Chemistry, Von Meyer, Macmillan.
A History of Chemistry, Moore, McGraw-Hill.
Essays in Historical Chemistry, Thorpe, Macmillan.
New Era in Chemistry, Jones, D. Van Nostrand.
Modern Chemistry and Its Wonders, Martin, D. Van Nostrand.
Eminent Chemists of Our Time, Harrow, D. Van Nostrand.
"Chemistry," Herty, *Scientific Monthly,* April, 1927.

CHAPTER III

The New Knowledge, Duncan, Laidlow Brothers.
New Era in Chemistry, Jones, D. Van Nostrand.

"The Alchemist," Foote, *Scientific Monthly,* 19: 239.

"The New World of the Atom," W. L. Bragg, *Yale Review,* 12: 755.

Free, *Forum,* 72: 505.

Millikan, *Scientific Monthly,* 18: 665.

Dushman, *Scientific American,* 126: 372.

Aston, *Scientific American,* 128: 233.

Rutherford, *Scientific Monthly,* 18: 337.

Millikan, *Science,* 59: 473.

Menzies, *Scientific Monthly,* 15: 364.

Brace, *Scientific Monthly,* 17: 168.

Foote, *Scientific Monthly,* 21: 449.

Aston, *Scientific Monthly,* 20: 128.

Rutherford, *Scientific Monthly,* 20: 121.

Russell, *Nineteenth Century,* 97: 393.

MacMillan, *Scientific American,* May, 1926.

Slosson, *Scientific Monthly,* 20: 108.

"Millikan Rays," *Scientific Monthly,* 21: 661.

Millikan, *Scribner,* 77: 75.

Rutherford, *Scientific Monthly,* 19: 561.

Compton, *Scientific American,* 133: 246.

Harrow, *Harper's,* 149: 251.

Foundations of the Universe, Luckiesh, D. Van Nostrand.

Eminent Chemists of Our Time, Harrow, D. Van Nostrand.

"Ancient and Modern Alchemy," Paneth, *Science,* 64: 409.

Science News Letter, 10: 21.

Romance of the Atom, Harrow, Boni and Liveright.

CHAPTER IV

"Giant Power," Cooke, *Atlantic Monthly,* 138: 813.

"Power Resources of the United States," **Panton,** *Scientific Monthly,* October, 1926.

"An Engineer's Viewpoint," Ely, *Scientific Monthly,* November, 1926.

"A Look Ahead," Norris, *Ind. & Eng. Chem.*, 18: 994.

"Hydroelectric Power in Industry," Davis, *Ind. & Eng. Chem.*, 18: 1058.

"Cheap Power," McBride, *Chem. & Met. Eng.*, 33: 724.

"Oil Production," Phelan, *New York Times*, August 1, 1926.

"Oil Supply," *New York Times*, September 6, 1926.

"Relation of Chemistry to the Development of Power," Haslam, *Ind. & Eng. Chem.*, 18: 1047.

"Relation of By-Product Coke Ovens to Superpower Development," Newell, *Ind. & Eng. Chem.*, 18: 1052.

"Trends in Power Development," Fieldner, *Ind. & Eng. Chem.*, 18: 1054.

"Our Future Sources of Energy," Doherty, *Ind. & Eng. Chem.*, 18: 1062.

"Future Trends in Automotive Fuels," Fieldner and Brown, *Ind. & Eng. Chem.*, 18: 1009.

"Future Trends in Low-Temperature Carbonization," Parr, *Ind. & Eng. Chem.*, 18: 1015.

"Processing Bituminous Coal," *Chem. & Met. Eng.*, 33: 736.

"A Brief Résumé of the Fuel Field," Parr, *Ind. & Eng. Chem.*, 19: 7.

"The Screw as a Carbonizing Machine," Laucks, *Ind. & Eng. Chem.*, 19: 8.

"Low-Temperature Semi-Coke in Briquetted Form," McIntire and Thomson, *Ind. & Eng. Chem.*, 19: 12.

"Low-Temperature Carbonization," Brownlie, *Ind. & Eng. Chem.*, 19: 39.

"Many Changes in Gasoline of Future," Egloff, *Oil & Gas Journal*, October 7, 1926.

"Anti-Knock Properties of Cracked Gasoline," Egloff, *Oil & Gas Journal*, April 29, 1926.

The Tragedy of Waste, Chase, Macmillan.

Proceedings of the International Conference on Bituminous Coal, Carnegie Institute of Technology.

Numerous articles in the current press during the summer and autumn of 1926, relating respectively to the Williamstown Conference and the International Conference on Bituminous Coal.

CHAPTER V

History of Chemistry, Von Meyer, Macmillan.

A Popular History of American Invention, edited by Waldemar Kaempffert, Scribner's.

Chemistry in Industry, Vol. I, Chemical Foundation, Inc.

Everyday Science, Vol. VI, Williams, Goodhue.

"Fifty Years of Gas Chemistry," Fulweiler, *Ind. & Eng. Chem.,* 18: 945.

"Growth of Industry," Editorial, *Ind. & Eng. Chem.,* 18: 552.

"Gases in Commerce and Industry," Wilson, *Ind. & Eng. Chem.,* 18: 1273.

"Fifty Years of Developments of Compressed Gases," Carter, *Ind. & Eng. Chem.,* 18: 954.

"Developments of Twenty-five Years in Coal Processing," Porter, *Chem. & Met. Eng.,* 34: 245.

CHAPTER VI

"Plowshares from Chemistry's Swords," Killeffer, *Ind. & Eng. Chem.,* 18: 253.

Creative Chemistry, Slosson, Century.

Chemistry in Agriculture, Chemical Foundation, Inc.

Nitrogen Fixation, Fixed Nitrogen Research Laboratory, Government Printing Office.

"Nitrogen as a Plant Food," Allison, *Journal of Chemical Education,* 3: 50.

"Fertilizers from the Air," Cottrell, *Scientific Monthly,* 21: 245.

"The Fixed Nitrogen Research Laboratory," Lind, *Scientific Monthly,* 22: 166.

"Fixation of Atmospheric Nitrogen," Hetherington, *Journal of Chemical Education,* 3: 170.

"Catalytic Synthesis at High Pressures," Almquist, *Journal of Chemical Education*, 3: 385.

"The World's Inorganic Nitrogen Industry," Ernst and Sherman, *Ind. & Eng. Chem.*, 19: 1927.

Potash, Turrentine, Wiley and Sons.

"Chemistry's Contributions to the Fertilizer Industry," Breckenridge, *Ind. & Eng. Chem.*, 18: 941.

"Expansion or Growth," Teeple, *Ind. & Eng. Chem.*, 19: 318.

"Manganese Deficiency in Soils and Fertilizers," Schreiner and Dawson, *Ind. & Eng. Chem.*, 19: 400.

"Are Armies Needed Any Longer?" H. G. Wells, *New York Times*, 1927.

CHAPTER VII

Everyday Science, Vol. 4, Williams, Goodhue.

Life of Pasteur, Vallery-Radot, Doubleday, Page and Co.

The Future Independence and Progress of American Medicine in the Age of Chemistry, The Chemical Foundation.

Chemistry and Recent Progress in Medicine, Stieglitz, Williams and Wilkins.

Microbe Hunters, de Kruif, Harcourt, Brace and Co.

The Glands Regulating Personality, Berman, Macmillan.

How We Become Personalities, Williams, Bobbs-Merrill.

Why We Behave Like Human Beings, Dorsey, Harper's.

"The Future Progress of Medicine," Carrel, *Scientific Monthly*, July, 1925.

"Chromosomes, Endocrines and Heredity," Davenport, *Scientific Monthly*, May, 1925.

"The Prevention and Cure of Rickets," Craig and Belkin, *Scientific Monthly*, May, 1925.

"Modern Cardiology," d'Irsay, *Scientific Monthly*, May, 1926.

"The Discovery of Anaesthesia," Smith, *Scientific Monthly*, January, 1927.

Chemistry in Agriculture, Ch. 12, Dutcher, Chemical Foundation, Inc.

Popular Research Narratives, Vol. II, Ethylene, Williams and Wilkins.

"Medicinals and Dyes," Volwiler, *Ind. & Eng. Chem.*, 18: 1336.

"Aniline Dyes in the Treatment of Infection," Churchman, *Ind. & Eng. Chem.*, 18: 1337.

"Future Chemotherapy," Loevenhart, *Ind. & Eng. Chem.*, 18: 1268.

"The Relation of Light to Life and Health," Price, *Ind. & Eng. Chem.*, 18: 679.

Numerous articles in the current press and scientific publications.

Chapter VIII

"Plantation Rubber, Its Source and Acquisition," Lloyd, *Scientific Monthly*, September, 1926.

"Synthetic Rubber," Howe, *Scientific Monthly*, September, 1926.

"New Methods in the Manufacture of Rubber," *Science*, November 26, 1926.

"Synthetic Rubber, Is there Anything in It?" Ingalls, *Scientific American*, July, 1926.

"What of Synthetic Rubber," Killeffer, *Scientific American*, January, 1927.

"Raw Rubber Symposium: Twenty papers read before the Division of Rubber Chemistry at the 72nd Meeting of the American Chemical Society," September 5 to 11, 1926; *Ind. & Eng. Chem.*, 18: 1104-1177.

"Rubber Industry," Geer, *Chem. & Met. Eng.*, 34: 227.

Creative Chemistry, Slosson, Century.

Thinkers and Doers, Darrow, Silver, Burdett and Company.

"Twenty-five Years of Rubber Chemistry," Geer, *Ind. & Eng. Chem.*, 17: 1024.

"Revival of Synthetic Rubber," Editorial, *Ind. & Eng. Chem.*, 17: 992.

"Changes in the Rubber Industry in the Last Fifty Years," Oenslager, *Ind. & Eng. Chem.*, 18: 902.

"Is Commercial Synthetic Rubber Probable?" Weber, *Ind. & Eng. Chem.*, 18: 404.

"The Economical Use of Reclaimed Rubber as a Substitute for New Rubber," Bierer and Davis, *Ind. & Eng. Chem.*, 18: 348.

"Crisis in Rubber," Marcosson, *Saturday Evening Post*, June 5, 1926.

CHAPTER IX

Colloid Chemistry, Alexander, D. Van Nostrand.

Applied Colloid Chemistry, Bancroft, McGraw-Hill.

"The Twilight Zone of Matter," Findlay, *Ind. & Eng. Chem.*, 17: 891.

CHAPTER X

A Popular History of American Invention, Vol. II, Scribner's.

Iron and Steel, Hearson, Spon and Chamberlain.

"Future Demand for Metals," Bain, *Mining and Metallurgy*, October, 1926.

Popular Research Narratives, Vols. I and II, Williams and Wilkins.

Mineral Resources of Future Populations, Tyron and Mann.

The Strategy of Minerals, Smith.

"American Creator of the Aluminum Age," Oskison, *World's Work*, 28: 438.

"Future Developments in the Light Metals," Frary, *Ind. & Eng. Chem.*, 18: 1016.

Profitable Science in Industry, Farnham, Hall, Howe and King, Macmillan.

What Price Progress?, Farrell, Putnam.

"Fifty Years' Progress in Aluminum," Edwards, *Ind. & Eng. Chem.*, 18: 922.

"The Steel Age—1876 to 1926," Mathews, *Ind. & Eng. Chem.*, 18: 913.

"Metallurgy Fifty Years Ago and Now," Corse, *Ind. & Eng. Chem.*, 18: 892.

"The Problem of Secondary Metals in World Affairs," Willard, *Ind. & Eng. Chem.*, 18: 1178.

"Catalysis," Taylor, *Ind. & Eng. Chem.*, 18: 958.

Chemistry in Industry, Vols. I and II, Chemical Foundation, Inc.

"Future Trends in Electrochemistry," Blum, *Ind. & Eng. Chem.*, 18: 1028.

"Industry Finds a New Tool," Killeffer, *Ind. & Eng. Chem.*, 18: 577.

"Some Technical Uses of X-rays, St. John, *Ind. & Eng. Chem.*, 19: 339.

"New X-ray Studies of the Ultimate Structures of Commercial Metals," Clark, Brugmann and Heath, *Ind & Eng. Chem.*, 17: 1142.

Creative Chemistry, Slosson, Century Company.

Chemistry in Modern Life, Arrhenius, D. Van Nostrand.

Chemistry in the World's Work, Howe, D. Van Nostrand.

Story of Iron, Smith, Appleton.

Combating Corrosion in Industry, (booklet) Chem. & Met. Eng.

CHAPTER XI

"Germany Regains a Place in the Economic Sun," Dennis, *New York Times*, May 1, 1927.

Profitable Science in Industry, Farnham, Hall, Howe and King, Macmillan.

Press Reports of Williamstown Conference, 1926.

Sir James C. Irvine in *New York Times,* August 29, 1926.

Creative Chemistry, Slosson, Century Company.

"Future Trends of Synthetic Organic Chemistry," Herty, *Ind. & Eng. Chem.,* 18: 1025.

"Evolution of Synthetic Medicinal Chemicals," Arny, *Ind. & Eng. Chem.,* 18: 949.

Modern Chemistry and Its Wonders, Martin D. Van Nostrand.

Silk and Civilization, Crawford, Program International Silk Show, 1921.

Chemistry in Industry, Vols. I and II, Chemical Foundation, Inc.

"Advance of Rayon," Wilson, *Ind. & Eng. Chem.,* 18: 829.

"Artificial Silk," Luft, *Ind. & Eng. Chem.,* 17: 1037.

The Story of Bakelite, Mumford, Robert L. Stillson Company.

"Development of the Aromatic Chemical Industry," Szamatolski, *Ind. & Eng. Chem.,* 18: 933.

CHAPTER XII

"Chronological Table," Browne, *Ind. & Eng. Chem.,* 18: 884.

"The Training of Men for the Profession of Chemistry," Johnson, *Science,* 64: 74.

Journal of the American Chemical Society, Jubilee Number, August, 1926.

"Charles Frederick Chandler," Hendrick, *Ind. & Eng. Chem.,* 17: 1090.

"Charles W. Eliot," Newell, *Ind. & Eng. Chem.,* 18: 1207.

"Dr. Remsen," Munroe, *Chem. & Met. Eng.,* 34: 192.

"American Chemical Industries," Reese, *Ind. & Eng. Chem.,* 17: 1093.

"William H. Nichols," Norris, *Ind. & Eng. Chem.,* 18: 317.

"The Technical Chemistry of Vanadium," Saklatwalla, *Ind. & Eng. Chem.*, 14: 968.

"The Vanadium Corporation of America," Saklatwalla, *Ind. & Eng. Chem.*, 17: 321.

Popular Research Narratives, Vols. I and II, Williams and Wilkins.

Profitable Science in Industry, Farnham, Hall, Howe and King, Macmillan.

Creative Chemistry, Slosson, The Century Company.

Chemistry in Industry, Vols. I and II, Chemical Foundation, Inc.

"Progress in the Domestic Manufacture of Dyes and Other Synthetic Organic Chemicals during 1924," Watson, *Ind. & Eng. Chem.*, 17: 1018.

"Ten Years of Progress in the Dye and Intermediate Industry," Crossley, *Ind. & Eng. Chem.*, 18: 1322.

"Importance of Research in the Dye Industry," Derick, *Ind. & Eng. Chem.* 18: 1324.

"The Development of Synthetic Anthraquinone," Klipstein, *Ind. & Eng. Chem.*, 18: 1326.

"Progress in the Development and Manufacture of Vat Colors in America," Bishop and Sachs, *Ind. & Eng. Chem.*, 18: 1331.

"Fur-Dyeing and Fur Dyes in America," Austin, *Ind. & Eng. Chem.*, 18: 1342.

"The Contribution of the Dyestuff Industry in the Development of the Rubber Industry," Powers, *Ind. & Eng. Chem.*, 18: 1344.

"Dyestuffs Industry, Forerunner of What?" Irénée du Pont, *Ind. & Eng. Chem.*, 18: 1002.

"Indigo and the World's Dye Trade," Watson and Penning, *Ind. & Eng. Chem.*, 18: 1309.

"Twenty-five Years of the American Dye Industry," Derick, *Chem. & Met. Eng.*, 34: 248.

"Sheet and Plate Glass Industry," Cruikshank, *Chem. & Met. Eng.*, 34: 233.

"Developments in Glass Technology During Recent Years," Morey, *Chem. & Met. Eng.*, 34: 230.

"Half Century of Progress in Glass Industry," Morey, *Ind. & Eng. Chem.*, 18: 943.

"Fifty Years of Glass-Making," Silverman, *Ind. & Eng. Chem.*, 18: 896.

"Progress in Chemical Equipment," *Ind. & Eng. Chem.*, 17: 1002.

What Price Progress?, Farrell, Putnam.

The Preparation of Synthetic Organic Chemicals at Rochester, Eastman Kodak Company.

"Our Foreign Trade in Chemicals in 1925," Wilson, *Ind. & Eng. Chem.*, 18: 267.

"Chemical Production Establishes Record," *Chem. & Met. Eng.*, 34: 52.

"Our Trade in Perfumery and Toilet Articles," Wilson, *Ind. & Eng. Chem.*, 19: 346.

"Our Foreign Trade in Chemicals and Allied Products in 1926," Wilson, *Ind. & Eng. Chem.*, 19: 469.

Alcohol for Industrial Purposes, American Solvents & Chemical Corporation.

Alcohol Chemistry, U. S. Industrial Alcohol Company.

"Chemistry," Herty, *Scientific Monthly*, April, 1927.

"Butanol and Acetone from Corn," Killeffer, *Ind. & Eng. Chem.*, 19: 46.

"Solvents and Automobile Lacquers," Keyes, *Ind. & Eng. Chem.*, 17: 558.

"Lacquers as Protective Coatings," Orr, *Journal of Chemical Education*, April, 1926.

Modern Lacquer for Architectural Use, Orr, Commercial Solvents Corporation.

Modern Lacquer for Railroad Use, Orr, Commercial Solvents Corporation.

"Paint and Varnish, Yesterday and To-day," Toch, *Ind. & Eng. Chem.*, 18: 948.

"Business Has Wings," *Atlantic Monthly*, March, 1927.

"Furfural Steps into Industry," Killeffer, *Ind. & Eng. Chem.*, 18: 1217.

Chemistry in the World's Work, Howe, D. Van Nosstrand.

CHAPTER XIII

Chemistry and Modern Life, Arrhenius, D. Van Nostrand.

Chemistry in the World's Work, Howe, D. Van Nosstrand.

Chemistry and the Home, Howe and Turner, Scribner's.

CHAPTER XIV

National Research Endowment, (Bulletin), The National Academy of Sciences.

The Fifth Estate, Little, The Chemical Foundation, Inc.

"Chemistry," Herty, *Scientific Monthly*, April, 1927.

Chemistry as an Investment, Little, Arthur D. Little, Inc.

The Vital Need for Greater Financial Support of Pure Science Research, Hoover, The National Research Council.

The Rôle of Research in Medicine, Jackson, The National Research Council.

Science and the Industries, Carty, The National Research Council.

"Applied Chemistry," Baekeland, *Ind. & Eng. Chem.*, 7: 978.

"Industrial Research at the Mellon Institute," Savage, *Chem. & Met. Eng.*, February, 1920.

"The Administration of Industrial Research," Weidlein, *Ind. & Eng. Chem.*, 18: 98.

"Some Present-Day Problems of Chemical Industry," Bacon and Hamor, *Ind. & Eng. Chem.*, 11: 470.

Chemistry Extending Its Frontier, Harvard University.

Chemistry in the Service of Medicine, Harvard University.

Chemistry in the Service of the State, University of Wisconsin.

Popular Research Narratives, Vols. I and II, Williams and Wilkins.

What Price Progress?, Farrell, Putnam.

"Building Blocks of the Universe," Hopkins, *Scientific American*, February, 1927.

"A Romantic Achievement in Industrial Chemistry," *Scientific American*, July, 1926.

"Solid Carbon Dioxide," A New Commercial Refrigerant, Killeffer, *Ind. & Eng. Chem.*, 19: 192.

Profitable Science in Industry, Farnham, Hall, Howe and King, Macmillan.

"Research under Government Auspices," Editorial, *Ind. & Eng. Chem.*, 18: 331.

"The Practical Aspects of Research," Fink, *Ind. & Eng. Chem.*, 18: 752.

"The Nation and Science," Hoover, *Science*, 65: 26.

"Science for Humanity's Sake," Blum, *Science*, 64: 76.

"Progress of a Year—A Chemical Review," Killeffer, *Ind. & Eng. Chem.*, 18: 1041.

"Future Progress of Medicine," Carrel, *Scientific Monthly*, 31: 54.

INDEX

INDEX

515